# A FIGHTING CAUSE

### Edited by

### Zoë Rock

First published in Great Britain in 2000 by
*POETRY NOW*
Remus House,
Coltsfoot Drive,
Peterborough, PE2 9JX
Telephone  (01733) 898101
Fax (01733) 313524

*Copyright Contributors 2000*

HB ISBN 0 75432 443 5
SB ISBN 0 75432 444 3

# FOREWORD

Although we are a nation of poets we are accused of not reading poetry, or buying poetry books. After many years of listening to the incessant gripes of poetry publishers, I can only assume that the books they publish, in general, are books that most people do not want to read.

Poetry should not be obscure, introverted, and as cryptic as a crossword puzzle: it is the poet's duty to reach out and embrace the world.

The world owes the poet nothing and we should not be expected to dig and delve into a rambling discourse searching for some inner meaning.

The reason we write poetry (and almost all of us do) is because we want to communicate: an ideal; an idea; or a specific feeling. Poetry is as essential in communication, as a letter; a radio; a telephone, and the main criterion for selecting the poems in this anthology is very simple: they communicate.

# CONTENTS

# In Perpetuity

All is war
Ceaseless struggle against
Invaders, the opposition
Inside us: Man against
Woman. Woman against child. Child
Against nature. Nature against man. Master
Or servant of machine?
That tears up the land
And evicts beasts. Car creature
Devourer of roads
Progeny of capital, oil and gas
Ignorant of beauty except in
Sex, violence and the thin line
'Twixt ecstasy and death
We are consumers
And creators of war
Ceaseless struggle against
The unknown, unknowable
By kindness the opposition
Inside us against
Man against woman against child against nature against man

(where is the God in this - I can see only Satan)

Light and dark war and peace murderers and victims rapist and innocent
prophets and lost tribes profit and loss the antagonism between us ever
to be reconciled where is the God in this I can see only Satan let's guess
the God in each of us of not we are forsaken.

*Paul Thompson*

# THE STATELY HOME

Displaying an example of excess,
With beautiful tables, chairs
Mirrors, beds, curtains and ornate stairs
The huge mansion opened to the crowds,
Opened to the offspring of the
Once-exploited workers
Whose backs had built the fine building
To house the few
Who kept the key
And chained neighbours to their tyrannical will.

This many-roomed building had a history,
Entwined the threads of good and evil.
Heartless pseudo-powers plundered
The crafts and skills of the simple
To gain the material wonder
That fades, and frayed around the edges
Moves the haves and have-nots to ponder.

Today, we view this mansion of great splendour
And feel the mixed emotion in our blood.
Anger at the sacrifices.
Sad, that hearts could stand
Stone-like in the chill of separativity
And de-rail the good with greedy hands,
Install the illusion of conquering time
Frenetic to preserve a life
That death claims,
And in the change, the unstoppable change
We all march on.

*Marion Elvera*

## ATTITUDES - BEATITUDES

From off the potter's wheel we come:
The Semite, the Aryan, the black, the gay,
And white with 'lick of the tar-brush' grey.

With Shylock's words we challenge detractors,
'Are we not as human as they?
Are we not fearful, tearful, gay?

They would slot us in pigeon-holes:
The Pakis, the micks, the nigs, the queers,
Closed minds and ignorance breeding fears.

Can we not be poor in spirit?
Can our hearts not be pure?
Blessed are they who trials endure.

*John Jenkin*

# FLAMES OF THE WORLD

Destruction of the soul
Is all that we have left in today's society
Fear and hate consume the heart
And pain in visions aspects of the mind
We fear what is different
And so kill to make it the same
Death is part of life
And pain is brought on by society
Blood of victims
Run as rivers to oceans of deceit
Leaving only the guilty to gloat
We have no means to prevent this despair
And like a disease it spreads with consumption
War creates poverty and famine
And if they don't succeed then guns will
Killing masses for nothing but pleasure
Leaving Earth empty of people
Heaven full to the brim with lost souls
And the Devil sits waiting in Hell
For those who began all these wars.

*Kim Darwell*

## JUST BORN . . . FOR THIS?

A lovely little toddler girl
bewildered by Western lenses
here to film her swollen tummy
bulging, not through greed, nor overeating
swollen, but empty, except for hunger pangs
and parasitic worms; but Mama cannot feed her
and lies in pain, upon the rocky sand
her outstretched hand, for baby.
Too hot in the day, too cold by night
too sick to eat donated grain
too weak to join the hopeless fight
does she have no right . . . to live?
And baby, with her swollen tummy
and flies that linger upon her brow
is dying now.
Her big brown eyes, shining with tears
reflecting the fears within her.
Never to see another day
she fades away
forever.
The Red Cross nurse
emotion etched upon her face
covers the toddler's withered form
and hears the cry of a babe, new-born
wailing from amidst a sea
of swollen tummies;
just born for this
just born for this
just born . . .
for this?

*Elizabeth Wilson*

## PLAYING AT TOY SOLDIERS

Advancing,
I see the men of war,
In their mighty armoured tanks,
Playing at toy soldiers,

Their mighty guns,
Blast into the air,
Thunderous sound, deafening,
Playing at toy soldiers,

We see these men,
Run for cover,
Falling to the ground,
Playing at toy soldiers,

Buildings fall,
And amongst the ruins,
Bodies, scattered lie,
Playing at toy soldiers,

A little boy stood,
Just looking on,
Shot he fell down,
Playing at toy soldiers,

A game he thought,
Red on the ground,
This was reality,
Playing at toy soldiers,

Boxes wooden, cardboard,
Lie, side by side,
He in his, just,
Playing at toy soldiers,

Senseless war,
Scars never heal,
Whose is the battlefield,
Playing at toy soldiers.

*Ann G Wallace*

# HOMELESS TONIGHT

Spare a thought for those of us
In cardboard homes tonight
A piece of this a bit of that
Will maybe shield the light
In my 'des res' tonight.

Today the sky was pink and blue
And then I knew the snow was due
Us homeless dread this time of year
It brings with it another fear
Of desperateness tonight.

It's two o'clock I cannot sleep
The Earth is quiet and still
My boots have sprung another leak
Oh God I'm feeling ill
In my paper tomb tonight.

I coughed a lot more blood just now
It gave me such a fright
I've wiped my eyes and mopped my brow
I hope I'll be all right
On this godforsaken night.

The snow is falling thicker but
I think I can see a little hut
With windows lit and roaring fire
Calling me come o'er, come o'er
On this brilliant night tonight.

I stagger on but now it's gone
I want to get there soon
Fight the good fight is a joke all right
Please take me God from this plight
On this wondrous, wondrous night . . .

*J Henry*

## WITHDRAWAL

Cold clammy skin,
The dead chill from freezing sweat
Slithers down her back like a slug.
Stomach pains,
Rip relentlessly inside like a blunted knife.
Veins that once pumped healthy blood
Are now shrivelled fragments of life.
She used to be pretty,
Blue eyes so bright and a face alive with smiles.
Her laughter once drifted through the house
Like a scented breeze,
But now she lays in her own vomit,
Drowning on the dreams of her first high.

*Paul Willis*

## LITTLE PEOPLE, BIG WORLD

Given to us at birth,
The way we live on Earth,
In our colour, race and faith,
Always some who are born taught to hate.

Their adversaries are the same!

Bombs against faith go flying,
While the young innocent ones lay dying,
Boys who have grown into men,
Tortured by their beliefs and fighting again.

They are all the same!

Both breathe the same air,
Have the same thoughts,
Both want the same
Peace of some sort!

We are all the same!

Our globe is so big
But their thoughts so small
They can't or won't see,
It's big enough for all!

Are we all the same?

*Kez*

## SHAME

When nightly on my TV screen I see
Long straggling lines - so very long -
Of figures, persons once as you and me,
Shuffling and shambling wearily along,
I weep

For children in this piteous band,
Who uncomprehendingly, innocently, cling
So trustingly to a mother's hand
And are quite bereft of any childish thing,
I weep

For dead dark eyes in skeletal sockets deep
And the hopelessness so eloquently shown
In ravaged faces, too exhausted e'en to weep;
For tired frail women, menfolk stolen, all alone,
I weep

Such men as can in this grim mass be seen
Are old, infirm, rejected as not worth the kill.
The women thus are left, not just to keen
But the brunt to bear, the menfolk's places fill.
I weep

If some omnipotent great God there be
Who coolly contemplates this dreadful throng,
Implacably permits this evil tragedy,
No censure I can make could be too strong.
I weep

Yet from this rumination, revelation came:
Such callousness lies beneath the reach of any single heart,
So there can be no God, all-powerful, to bear the shame.
This lies with humankind alone - of which I am a part.
So I weep.

*G F Pash*

## AUTUMN'S CHILL

The autumn winds blow golden leaves for playful fox cubs to jump
and catch.
And butterflies flit everywhere to find a safe sheltered place to sleep.
A robin sings upon the blackberry bush and all is peace
And beautiful . . . the hill in mist where mushrooms grow for people
to pick as a breakfast treat.
The pheasant in colours of a stained glass window walks upon the
ploughed field.
Timid deer stand by the wood and old man's beard grows on hedges
and rabbit and hare run for fun in the meadow.
The peace of it all is torn by a distant horn and hounds baying and
the cry 'Tally Ho!' of man.
And mindless men and women come on horses made to chase their
fellow creatures, these horses would not hurt, but man makes them
help to kill as hounds bay for blood, unfed, untamed.
The fox cubs stop their fun . . . and watch with fear,
As their mother the vixen runs towards this screaming noise.
They watch . . . and do not understand . . . 'Surely we should hide?'
But she is wise . . . and leads the hunt astray from her young.
Then torn apart and all for fun . . . her brush cut off and blooded
on the face of man . . . ! Their eyes are mad and wild
They lick the blood upon their face . . . as if it were red wine and smile!
Her cubs together in their earth they hide . . . no mother comes to bring
them food . . . or cuddle snug and warm in winter's cold.
She lies in her own blood as golden autumn leaves fall on her
sacrificial form.
. . . And magpies peck the fear out of her orange eyes . . . !

*Jennifer M Trodd*

# A Thought For The Third World

How is it to live in the dark shadows.
To not know what the morning could bring.
To dig many a grave so shallow.
To hold onto each breath suffering.

Why is the reality of third world life so wicked?
So many dying, neglected, each day for them a fight.
To not know whether you will get to morning.
That death may collect all you have in the night.

To struggle to find food for your starving children.
Where famine strikes, it never seems to stop.
The ground baked hard from the sun, the long droughts,
As it yields you no worthy crops.

This world a demon seems evil.
Full of cruel intent.
That's why some receive in abundance.
Others lack medicines, food, water.
Helpful aids for their immune system's defence.

Their poorly, weak, tired, bloated bodies,
Fighting to live on less than a crust of bread.
Unfair that they should be barely surviving,
Whilst we sleep, fed well, in the warmth of our cosy beds.

*Natasha Faiers*

## PURPLE POLICIES

Red is in, blue is out.
Benefits of the doubt make us see purple.
We whisper. We shout, mainly lie about.
Doing everything and nothing.
Money hesitates the voice.
Comfort cocoons apathy.

The social student sits on its ass.
The fees policy is passed. 'Let's have a laugh.'
Debts left to repay later on and on.
Decisions are made. Reasons are given.
Education is put to the Victorian task.
'Where has Socialism gone?' is asked.

Jobs are given to the young.
The old are forgotten.
Low taxes pacify eight in ten.
The new deal is sweetly rotten.
Companies are given money to train. No assurances.
Cash is a good incentive for silence.

The economy is stable.
Able to pay for all this employment.
The pound is high for investment.
Will a red letter be sent?
At the expense of services.
More state, public services to rent.

Spin Doctors are given clout.
MPs say they will, they won't.
Single mothers are singled out.
Family values are in a 28 rout.
With all the turnabouts it's a wonder
they don't disappear up their own policy.

Whatever the men in grey suits propose.
Watch for the thorns in the Red Rose.
When substance is nothing. Image is everything.
Cool Britannia is ruled by Panto Kings.
The politic has the power to devour the rights of the people.
Not the human spirit.

*Stewart Tunnicliff*

## WORLD IN FOCUS

*Hype*

Your inner cities are no metaphor
For what life may be like
Once you've changed the words
And turned up the lights
You may induce the hype
But cannot maintain it
Or sustain the grandeur you gave it
In the fools' parade
We'll see how it's made
And the masses will unite.

**Kate Williams**

## JUSTIFIED CYNICISM

I know disgust at my own kind, they come
from every affluent race,
Schooled in words, they cut their avaricious
swathes with confidence,
Feel no remorse, or self-contempt, or deep disgrace:
Man's greed and cruelty goes unabated, in vain
some cry 'Stop!' but they cannot be sated.

How think you that these powerful ones, these
so-called upper classes,
Became so confident, powerful rich, deceiving
the simple masses?
They looted and claimed the riches of Earth,
dismissing the natives as savages,
And have always the means to silence those
objecting to their ravages.

This Earth was blessed with wealth for all, no
need for misery or hunger,
But as we see, it's paradise lost, to those who
live for plunder.

'Be sure the next millennium will be a time to smile . . . '
Beware, beware, you trusting souls, their guns are primed with guile.

*Rita Dawson*

## WARNING

Things are a-changing. Global warming
is on its way bringing rapid weather changes.
Temperature rises, ice caps melt, rivers run high.
Today birds face more rapid changes, can they adapt.
What can we do to help? First we must slow down the
gasses which are destroying our Earth. Then create wetlands.

Man in his infinite greed has caused such harmful effects.
Little did we realise what harm we were doing with $CO_2$.
Our climate can take no more. What then for the outlook?
Left in our hands man must get together to solve his mistakes
but please no more pie in the sky.

*Kate Davies*

# I'M HAVING THE WORLD FOR LUNCH

I'm having the world for lunch tonight.
The recipe you see is oh so simple,
It goes like this:
Take one of the Earth's creatures,
Stub out her life.
Rip out some undergrowth
Well-sprayed of course.
Tear the fruit from Mrs Tree
Only the biggest mind,
Cut her down, pulp her.
Send her off to the cardboard factory,
Boil together, let the gasses escape,
Wash away the grime from nature's stream,
Toss out the scraps to slowly sink into the spoil,
Smile gently and go for a relaxing drive in the countryside.

*P Benton*

## THE SPOILERS

Lauded by poets, Shakespeare, Clare
The England that we knew
Her quiet ways in other days
Now alas too few

Past nesting time the young birds flew
From copse or thick hedgerow
Unhampered by the grubbers-out
With noisy gear in tow

Cowslips in abundance grow
Still in meadows today
Too soon our search will be forlorn
If planners have their way

On village green the sturdy oak
Spreads welcome shade around
Oh why should they the land grabbers
Usurp this time-worn ground?

What joy upon a summers day
The exquisite skylark brings
Rising from his secret bed
On swiftly soaring wings

Little unnamed woodland walks
A seasonal delight
In danger of banishment now
Forever from our sight

Surely solutions can be found
Alternate ways, other schemes?
Destroying all these in your wake
You trample on my dreams.

***Doris A Birke***

## WHY?

What sort of world are we living in
When someone thinks it's fun to fight?
What sort of life are we leading
When everything wrong, feels so right?
What is the meaning of unity
When people are tearing the world apart?
Why do we teach children manners
When we probably don't know where to start?
What makes this world worth living in
When there's violence and war every day?
How can we explain, in the future
Why people are abused for being coloured, or gay?
So we're not all the same creed or colour
We're not all perfectly formed or made
It's not a crime to be different
But it's a price that so many have paid.
Everyone has the right to be happy
The world may be a cruel place,
But everyone, everywhere, has the right to be here
To compete, and to be a part of the race.

*Margaret Ann Scott*

## THE LITTLE FOXES

Bye Baby Bunting,
Daddy's gone a-hunting,
To hunt for little foxes,
To cut off all their lockses,
To make fashion for ladies frockses,
The animal liberators,
Are seen as perpetrators,
But they're only fighting a cause that is just,
Don't you wish the huntsman,
Could be confined in little wooden boxes,
And be returned to dust.

*Alan Pow*

# THE HOUNDING

I've run so far my lungs are bursting
I hear the horseman's bugle cursing,
My legs are weak my mouth is dry my body's racked with fear
The dogs are getting closer now I sense my end is near,
The hounds will tear me limb from limb
Not much hope left I'm giving in.

My partner's lost her soul-mate, my young I'll never see
I know that within minutes, in pieces I will be,
The lead dog sinks his teeth in me, no guilt remorse or strife
They've worn away my will to live, last seconds of my life,
They're tearing me to pieces, my ginger furry locks
The curtain of life closes, why was I born a fox?

*N W Pomfret*

## ELEMENTAL

Wind air, sea and water,
throughout the globe they scatter.
Air to breathe, the cruel sea,
essential water, things that matter.

Take thought of our needs,
The wind to scatter many seeds,
Pure air is the air we need.
The sea and tides defy man's learning,
turning water to its many uses.

Mountains to climb where air gets thin.
Seas to sail and swim and dive.
Clear water in which we thrive.
Cold air, warm air, air obscured,
tainted by what must be cured.

Polluting plains, traffic and the planes.
Drains unclean into the sea.
Wind whistling through the trees,
a breeze, a storm, a tornado,
causing havoc to the home and land.

Peaceful skies, dark skies,
red skies, heavy clouds,
giving warning of the rain and
the thunder loud.

*J Merrifield*

## NO SIMPLE SOLUTION

Is the progression of technology hastening devastation?
Reducing man's inheritance, despite deploring castigation.
Has our evolution overturned the purpose of our existence?
Whilst mutely, we stand by, inactive, offering little resistance.

Half the world is starving,
The other half carving.
Out the earth and clay,
Creating ribbons grey,
Scarring the countryside,
We no longer walk, we ride.

How many of us can now survive without our annual holiday?
As we converge like swarming wasps on airports, all ready to convey
Us to our exotic destinations, soaring high into the sky,
Thousands of feet above the ground, and I wonder, was man meant
to fly?

Villages turning into towns,
Houses built upon the downs,
Empty churches, mobile phones,
Mortgages and huge bank loans,
Working mums and latch-key kids,
Child abuse and porno vids.

Space travel, future exploration, is the entire world computerised?
Swiftly connected to every nation, brains expanding, oversized.
The consequences of greed and power have not yet been realised,
What generation will bear the brunt of what this one has devised?

Concrete jungles, hardship, war,
Floods, disasters, rich or poor,
With the experience of years,
Strange, but it appears,
We still don't know,
The way to go.

*Helen Mitchelhill*

## PROPER VENALITY

Painting brushstrokes of truth on the canvas of falsehood,
Eluding detection, the antithesis of good,
Armoured in arrogance creeps the iconoclast,
Stalking the heroic and noble myths of the past,
Betrayal and stealth subsumed in subtle sabotage,
Obsolescent deities risen in hubris to charge,
But fall to the harsh harvest scythe of the media,
Forelornly prostrated with the sordid, the seedier.

Mocking in ice tone, some cackling hyena,
Besmirches legends like sacred Athena,
Honesty obscured, a curtain of lies
Closing fast, its masters, it satisfies,
Waving mediocrity's banal standards,
Splintering greatness in scintillating shards,
The real, strained through a polemical sieve,
Adorned in a cloak of hateful invective,
Making us base we become jaded and less,
Casualties of political correctness.

*Peter Walton*

# NEWS FLASH

Huge blast! - Bus eliminated;
Passengers disintegrated
By cowardly men
Attacking those not at war.

Slogan-filled feuders,
People abusers
Bitter against the world
Destruction unfurled.

What is the point of it?
Who gets the benefit?
What is the meaning
Of all this anger.

The snarled bus wreckage - Unforgettable.
The tangled wrecks of lives - Unforgivable.
Therefore war will continue - Inevitable.
Where will it end? - Inconceivable!

*Marie McKenzie*

## VIEWPOINT

Hello Mr Scientist,
What have you done today?
Is it work on saving lives
or blowing them away?
Are you hiding within whitewashed walls
where all the nasties lurk?
Are you creating anything new
or, just copywriting some of God's work?
Do you ever stop to think
what good you ever do?
For all your good intentions
do you really have a clue?
We all know you can do so much,
no-one's denying your success,
but the flipside you're also proud of
is causing some distress.
We don't feel the need for bigger bombs
with an ever-smaller mass,
Why don't you irrigate the deserts
instead of making toxic gas?
What's wrong with curing cancer?
Wouldn't that achievement thrill you?
Or how about inventing a cigarette
you could smoke but wouldn't kill you?
Why don't you stop doing what you can
and instead ask if you should?
Or does blame wash out of white coats
along with death and blood?

*M Morris*

# IN MY VIEW

I look around with wondrous eyes
And catch a glimpse of countryside
I see the hills - vast expanses of green;
This land, my home - in harmony.

As time goes on I live and learn
I realise conservation is my concern.
It is up to us all to try and preserve
Give children the views that they deserve.

As I get older I realise
That my region has become industrialised;
No longer have we hills to climb
But growing towns - the world in decline.

The young children - they won't know
What it is to watch clean waters flow
Through unlimited and beautiful countryside -
To walk the downs with heartfelt pride.

We take out province too much for granted,
No thought for trees and flowers planted
Years and decades before our time
When the south-east region was in its prime.

I want to take the time to think
Before parts of my world become extinct.
I'd like my children to see my world
Wild, boundless, majestic and undisturbed.

*Chrissi*

## THE DAY

What carnage caused this?
A land cut and polished.
Smooth: life slips down shiny sides
To red seas of extinction.

Clammy people-skin,
Cling to ugly steps of perfection,
Loose with vermin's footfall.
Pray someday they falter!

Blow a land of stone and glass,
See this course unfold.
Through windows we shall watch
Wingless birds try and flee their raped-up land.

*Nicholas Daniels*

## YOUNG GERMAN WAR WIDOW AT BAYEUX 1946

Transposed to the land of irresponsibility,
Finger on the catch that obliterates,
Eye on the aim that measures sin,
Mindless to the point of the barrel,
Release the missile into carelessness,
Close one's eyes unto consequence,
Pourquoi?

My blessed Rolfe your Mr Browning,
Upon such fateful Norman soil,
Lose their lives, their one chance, each other -
Son of Frankfurt, Lad from Oxford, so dead in France -
From Mother, from Father, from Sister, from me, and the
                                        unborn - severed!
Slaughtered in the way of slaughtering!
Pourquoi?

At Bayeux they stay in rows like the straight-line threads in worsted:
Who dares to stake a cross-stitch upon every human heart?
Who dares?
(In history perhaps one long linen strip enwraps) -
But they all sleep too silently -
Quand je dors, je cris,
Pourquoi, oh Pourquoi . . . ? *Pour-quoi?*

*John M Reeve*

## DOLPHINS OF THE SEA

Swim wild and free my beauties
of the sea
Of sailors bold as it was told
May their spirits now be free
Dolphins of the sea.

See them jump so high
in and out of the waves
As the boats go by
So why o why don't we try
To save their lives?
May their spirits now
be free
Dolphins of the sea

They can't tell us what
they want
To live in peace and harmony
It's time for the killings
to stop
So their spirits can now be free
Dolphins of the sea.

*Leeane Shires*

# Kosovo

The happenings in Kosovo
are causing so much grief
And the way some people
treat people is way beyond belief
Old ladies wrapped in their shawls
With tears falling down old faces
People who have lost their all
Even pride in their races
Patriots should be proud of their land
But to treat folk like this is beyond.
NATO and we have all tried
Indeed help has been offered worldwide.
Refugees have been offered a place
Until it's safe to go back to home base
The children their eyes wide and sad
Wondering just where is their dad
And mothers, well how do they cope?
With many husbands shot, where is hope?
O Lord, up in heaven above
Be with them and give them your love
Help us to do what we can
And sort out the mind of that man
And bless them Lord . . .

*A Clark*

## TIME TO STOP

The raging bull speared in the back
And taunted till the sword brings peace;
The noble stag collapsed, but alone,
With bulging eyes; but breath won't cease
Till blood-crazed hounds of huntsmen's pack
Tear living flesh and skin from bone.

To satisfy a female whim
For fur, the baby seals must die
In spring: that's all their lives are for;
The blood-soaked ice will testify.
The screaming hare, torn limb from limb,
A plaything in dogs' tug of war.

The trusting whales on Faroes shore
Mindlessly butchered in the name
Of blind tradition. Red the sea
Whilst mankind weeps and shares the shame
In prayer, to beg there'll be no more
Of this debased atrocity.

The hapless fish on angler's line,
Plucked from the depths to suffocate
At water's edge. The badger gassed
Below the ground; that is its fate;
Or dug out, dogs and spades combine,
And bludgeoned till sweet life has passed.

The flailing cockerel, razor-spurred,
Will either win and strut with pride
Or lie with crumpled feathers, still.
The wily fox will try to hide
From country gents who, undeterred,
Urge packs of hounds their own to kill.

New season's pheasants, plump in girth,
From sky are blasted; few are saved:
Take no more life! It's time to give.
Or is man really so depraved?
Spare all God's creatures on this Earth;
Stop now you cowards; let them live.

*Graham P Manuell*

## CASUALTIES

He lifted up his weary head
From where he lay in his hospital bed,
To watch his comrade cross the ward
Bandaged up all around his head,
Arms outstretched to find his way -
His eyes sightless, in his plight.
Whilst others dragged themselves around,
Crutches propping up empty pyjama legs.
Agonised screams rent the ward
From tortured lungs through want of air.

Yet these were the innocents
Of the atrocities of war.
All of them children
Who had got in the way
Of the bombers, and the raiders -
Of men with their guns,
In a war zone created
By the greed of man.

*Margaret M France*

# A Modern Cry From The Heart

Surely someone once loved and cared for me
Before I finished up here.
Sleeping in rags and cardboard, among
Drunks and their foul-smelling beer.
Was I really so wayward that I would not
Heed what they said.
Or didn't they care, and so gave me 'my head'.
Perhaps if they had been kind, patient but firm;
I would, eventually, have had the sense to learn,
And not maybe, have been left penniless
And with no real hope.
Old before my time. Dead. Full of soul-destroying dope.

*M Poole*

## WHAT PRICE FUN?

For one set of God's creatures, to gamble is such fun -
A day out at the races! How much will I have won?
For others in their paddock, to gambol is preferred,
And being gently sociable with man or equine herd.
A pity they must break their necks in jumping fences tall
To satisfy man's wish to win with no deserts at all!

For one set of God's creatures, to hunt is oh, such fun -
To seal one's group-awareness, and hoi polloi to shun.
For others chasing rodents is just the stuff of life -
The pleasantest diversion, to play with cubs and wife.
A pity handsome foxes must be torn apart by hounds
In acts of sheer barbarity whose thoughtlessness astounds!

For one set of God's creatures, to paint oneself is fun -
To change one's basic features, to spray oneself to stun.
For others, loss of anguish is but a hopeless dream -
A home with loving family who'd hold them in esteem.
A pity cats and rabbits, too, must suffer injury
To satisfy some selfish woman's idle vanity!

Maybe in medical research we need to ask their aid,
But let us weigh quite carefully the price that must be paid.

*Anne Sanderson*

## MEMORY

Shuttered our vision
Lost to view, distances
Farswept in new derision
As if in a trance:
Yet the outline clear
Defined and definitive
The answer here
Where we could live!

The question not all in
Our soul searching
The brighter truth
A song to sing
Knowledge or revelation
Yet with us here
Sorrow in elation
That we might hear

So yet to speak in basic
Numbers before death
In life can trick
The image that in stealth
Is so witheld.
A reminder of what is live
And in its killing spelt
A hope for all. In this contrive.

*John Amsden*

## BOTTLED BEAUTY

Beauty in a bottle,
bought at any price
face cream, hairspray,
elixir of life.

Trapped inside a bubble,
corked into a glass
told exactly how to look,
attraction made to last

Lipstick, shampoo,
anti-wrinkle lotion
distorted face, unreal vision
vial of magic potion

Socially acceptable,
appearance made a duty
to shut out any ugliness,
and buy the bottled beauty

*Elizabeth Read*

## WAR GAMES

Peace is an unknown quantity in this world in which we live.
A word that becomes seldom used with the help of weapons, we enlist.
With many technical achievements,
And brains that must create more,
We play a chess game of stalemate, hoping each side to ultimately lure.

Humanity feels really quite clever, a pat on the back it awaits,
The terrible chaos that will happen as we sit and leave it to fate.
What a world we've created to live in a universe of destruction
and dread,
A world full of power-mad mortals
Who would kill us all in a hair's breadth!

It's all down to just pressing a button and a touch of man's ingenuity,
A slight disagreement between neighbours and an untimely end
we shall see.
To those who are grabbing that power it's really just one large
board game,
But how will we feel when it's over?
With the boundless humanity it will inevitably maim.

Won't we then want to disclaim the technology
That brings nothing but trouble and strife
When our families are dying around us, sisters, husbands and wife?
When will the forgetting world remember?
Peace though a very small world may be,
Is a word that could alter our universe
If only common sense and pure logic we could see!

*Valerie Wilhelm*

## JUNKIE

Hate the junkie,
Beauty lies within.
Not just a junkie
Behind a glazed grin.
Not just a junkie,
Someone suffering in pain.
We're nothing without friendship,
Is her searching in vain?

Needle in vein
Drawing back blood.
Not just a junkie,
A human being with love.
With personality, feelings,
With a heart of such worth.
Not just a junkie,
Not the scum of the Earth.

She dreams of the future,
Desperate for hope.
Turned to heroin to escape
At the end of her rope.
Lost down a dead end,
Soul longs to be free.
Don't hate the junkie,
She is you, she is me.
Not just a junkie.

*Jez Scott*

## No Escape

We can only imagine what it must be like
To live through fire, floods and quakes when they strike.
Be near all the danger zones living in constant fear,
Of what could be blown into the atmosphere.
The fire that boils in the centre of the Earth,
Spurting out harmful substances - for all its worth.
Always taking lives, how can people escape?
Without sufficient warning - even when they are awake.
The trembling and rumbling that comes from below,
Where can they run? There's nowhere to go.
The Earth opens up disclosing bottomless pits,
For endless miles, the world seems to have split.
There's not just one catastrophe to cope with at any one time,
Because one will lead to others in succession - a vivid line -
A quake destroys the buildings, causes explosions which lead to fire,
Amenities are gone - disease can set in - for these people I can
                                              only admire,
Their guts and determination with which they carry on,
A closeness with tragedy between them - their loved ones gone -
I don't know how they cope, their problems are so immense.
How do they restart their lives? How do they commence?
There's special aid from countries all around - afar and near -
Plus medicines, food and support, their dilemma is stark and clear.
Having to live in tents for shelter - surviving appalling conditions,
Surrounding them - their livelihoods - in total demolition.
With such courage we see people pulling together, to start all over again
Their lives they have to carry on - while enduring extreme
                                              loss and pain.
The destruction they face - while feeling such utter devastation,
They build again - with safety in mind - thinking ahead for
                                              the next generation.

*Beverley Diana Burcham*

# FOCUS ON LOVE

We can't help but focus on the big things
That are happening around us today
Disasters - wars - man's inhumanity to man,
'But what can I do?' we say.
If we focus for a while on things nearer home
We can more clearly see
The deep rooted reason for the big things
In situations all around me.
Children living in misery,
Parents afraid of their sons,
Life becomes alarming,
The indiscriminate use of guns.
There is one word the whole world over
That has lost its meaning today.
*Love* for one another
*Love* in a caring, sharing way.
Children are brought up on monsters and fiends
Games - set them up to - destroy
Caring for life all around you
Is definitely out - if you're a boy
But love in your heart for everyone
No matter their colour or creed
Can lead this poor world
Back to peace once again
Focus on love
It's the world's greatest need.

***Irene Spencer***

## NATURE'S RUIN

There's more to life than meets the eye,
so much to admire as it passes by.
What can compare to the setting sun
going down slowly after its daily run?

Springtime leaves on lush green trees,
or the feel of a gentle bracing breeze.
Gaze in wonder at beautiful flowers,
lifting their faces to April showers.

Waves crashing in on a sandy shore,
the peace and serenity of an English moor.
We walk for miles over rocks and hills,
admiring birds with their colourful bills.

On some beach, the children will play,
blissfully unaware of the time of day.
Faces covered in vanilla ice-cream,
all magic moments, of which we dream.

But some seek to spoil this grand ideal,
to them, wondrous things have no appeal.
See and destroy, is their cruel tirade,
when setting out on a mindless crusade.

Nature's beauty is wasted on them,
everything nice they will always condemn.
Pulling up flowers and scattering trash,
too many windows do they want to smash.

They gather in mobs to smoke and drink,
with limited brain power, they do not think.
Nature itself creates all this wonder,
it takes but a few . . . to pull it asunder.

*John Topham*

## AT THIS POINT IN TIME

*'Get back to basics'* the wise politician said.
'Just stop and think what lies ahead . . .'
The world is moving oh so fast . . .
What will be left when the balloon bursts?
Take it steady, one day at a time.
Computers, internet, technology are all very fine.
All these things for one and all . . .
Even send pensioners back to school!
'Tis nice to have these wonderful things,
Don't be blind to the hazards they bring.
People will never be *all one class*
Some are *go ahead,* some just sit on their *ass!*
Internet opens so many doors,
Some are best left closed, I am sure!
Don't generalise about children's potential
Each one is different, like chalk and cheese.
They will each become expert in their own field . . .
You will never make silk purses out of sow's ears!
So *get back to basics.* Three hearty cheers!

*M L Hensman*

## ZIMBABWE UNREST

The sins of one's fathers have reared their heads.
Sadly many have been injured and some are dead.
There's many a reason for the recent outbreak.
The main one appears to be how much land to take.
Mugabe has ruled Zimbabwe for years.
It has not been easy, there have been many fears.
Man against man is always a bad sign.
The country's divided, will it heal with time?
Many years ago the white man took land.
Africans driven from their homeland,
Prosperity came as the farms successfully grew.
Life appeared to improve for all old and new.
A new generation of white farmers in place.
Many had bought the land, not took as their base.
Memories go deep and never forgot.
War veterans who'd fought wanted a plot.
Unrest was rife, Mugabe at a loss.
Rival political party gaining strength, who'd be boss?
Mugabe decided that the white man was bad.
White Zimbabweans were ever so sad.
They had worked and with candour.
Now alienated overnight, by their country's leader.
Unsure of their future many fled for their lives.
Their farms plundered and sadly set alight.
Much land had been reclaimed.
It made no difference all the same.
Years ago the white man did do wrong.
White Zimbabweans now wonder where they belong.
What for the future? Who really knows?
Unity a must, Zimbabweans must not be foes.

*Anne Sackey*

## WAR AND SUFFERING

The world today is in a sorry state
War, famine,
starving people, starving children,
no country to call home,
being shunted from one camp to another.
No shelter, only a tent,
no medical supplies, no hospitals,
nowhere to lay dying weary people.
Soldiers killing innocents
who have done no wrong.
Why do they do it?
The world was not built by Jesus for that.
People try to help,
but help sometimes comes too late
to save the severe suffering.
Get your heads together
to try to bring peace to the world,
no longer suffering and war,
which does not help the human race.
War is not the answer.

*N A Callear*

## GOOD VERSUS EVIL

Men walk on the moon, thinking they're so great
While landmines seal a small child's fate!
Satellites bring pictures onto TV
People copy the murders they see!

Apartments with luxuries from the start
The families in them torn apart!
They split the atom to give great power
But the bomb makes people cower!

Planes quickly take us where we have to go
While others wreak havoc on their foe!
A struggling mother rears her child with strife
While yet another takes its life!

Into lush gardens tourists want to steer
While the rainforests disappear!
Children throw their lunches into the street
While starving bodies crave for meat!

Water running down the gutter wastes away
Others don't have a cup a day!
Palaces with royalty living within!
Poor people's homes are bits of tin!

Tell me when balance will come to it all
Who will hear the suffering call?
Who will end selfishness and cruelty?
Who will set the human race free?

*V Spall*

# DUNBLANE

Skipping and dancing down the lane.
Smiling children from the city Dunblane.
Unaware of the horror lying ahead.
In half an hour some would be dead.

PE began in the gym having fun,
Then evil burst in, firing a gun.
That monsters' evil deed was done.
In a couple of minutes, out went the sun.

Children lay injured, some lay dead.
Cradled in the arms of the horrified head.
Sixteen children and teacher lay slain,
Others dying, or writhing in pain.

The news when it came, was sombre and brief.
But the whole of the nation united in grief.
Carpets of flowers from far and wide.
The city of Dunblane, everyone cried.

Weeks go by, and memories fade,
Other news the headlines made.
Dunblane itself was left in peace
To come to terms with the horror, and grief.

Sixteen new stars are shining bright.
All of them angels, dressed in white.
Rainbows, flowers, in sunshine or wet
The people of Dunblane will never forget.

*Lesley Charters*

## POLLUTED RIVERS

Have you seen the state of our rivers today,
Where once children paddled and played,
On the river beds, lay pieces of bottles smashed,
Cattle and Sheep walk in and get their feet slashed,
Old tins are opened and thrown in,
Polluting our rivers, where we once would swim,
Road signs, traffic cones, lay on the river beds,
But to the culprit very little is said,
People throw in anything, and don't give a care,
Even an odd supermarket trolley here and there.
Companies have polluted our rivers where once fish swam,
They know what they are doing, but don't give a damn.
Oil, diesel, chemicals, into our rivers are pumped,
It's a crime, criminal, disgraceful, and that's being blunt.
People don't think of the pleasures they have lost,
When it comes to it, they don't really give a toss,
Why don't people stand back and take a good look,
Then take a leaf out of mother natures book,
Stop polluting our rivers and streams,
And make them once more, a beautiful sight to be seen.

*Allan J Young*

## MOTHER

So, she sat
Child laid across her lap.
Death was close,
A final breath,
Then silence.
She shed no tears,
Just sat looking
White faced into distance,
Eyes turned inward.

*T M Webster*

## THE TIME OF OUR LIVES

I woke up late, I went to work.
I threw away the key.
These shackles could drive me berserk,
So I pretend, I'm free
Same routine but still no rhythm,
Spending life to earn a living.
Places to go and people to see,
Caught in a rush there seems to be,
So little time for poetry.

Thousands of planes fill up the skies.
Commercial plans unfold.
The world  is full of adjusting ties
And thoughts are left untold.
As power struggles fill the Earth
And hatred kills the hope of birth.
This current phase of history,
Attacks our sensitivity.
So little time for poetry.

And all these things which cost us dear,
And cause us so much strife.
Persist with us from year to year
And occupy our life.
Before we reason days have passed
And there's no rhyme to make it last,
The gift of life fades presently.
So take your opportunity
And make some time for poetry.

*Steve Woollard*

## FOCUS

Who is to blame
for the state we are in?
This world of unrest
surrounded by sin.

Is it something we've done
or neglected to do?
An answer we need
the question is who?

Is it money or greed
that has caused this despair?
If so. Let us heed
think and beware.

To the environment
damage is clear.
To late to lament.
Retribution is near.

God giveth and taketh away
the earth is not ours.
Why? can't the children play
safely every hour.

Who is to blame
we can only guess?
Always the same
they will not confess.

We cannot put the world to right
that is what we say.
We'd better try with all our might
before it fades away.

***Thora Carpenter.***

## BUILT TO LAST

The bulldozer came, knocked it down.
The school where I spent my youth.
Left a space full of rubble.
Builders came, cleared the land.
An old school yard, where I spent my youth.
Diggers made big holes.
Filled them with bricks and mortar.
A playground where I spent my youth.
Construction teams came, assembled homes.
Ten, twenty, thirty or more.
On land once full of children, playing,
    learning developing.
Now it displays signs that say,
'Newly developed dwellings for sale.'
The school where I spent my youth.

*Susan Mary Gardham*

# REALITY OF LIFE

Whilst those who enjoy themselves
Frolic in a den of fun,
Drink till they droop like dead flowers,
Smoke till they cough their last,
Gamble no end and win
Lie in the sun on holiday
At their own holiday villa.
Others cry and scream, pity themselves,
Have no fun,
Cannot afford to make a gamble.
Whilst some eat until their stomachs burst,
Others starve, they wither and die.
Whilst some spend on what they do not need.
Others can only afford to look at what they do need.
Whilst the guilty man can get away with murder.
The innocent could well be sitting in the stench
Of overcrowded cells in a cramped prison system.
Whilst workers demand rewards and more payment.
There are those who would appreciate work and payment.

*P Edwards*

# You Me And The World

You and me have brought this magnificent world
Almost to the brink of disaster.
Destroying trees in the wild,
Are we not a ferocious monster.

You and me think of nothing but pleasure,
When we are not seeking money advancement.
The internet has almost taken control,
A treasure, yet not so if it takes it's toll.

You and me have destroyed the world's good nature
Fighting battles, torturing, innocent people.
For no good end and laying bear a future
That children will hate and despair, a nasty principle.

You and me have taken the liberty
Building homes on grassland,
Whilst houses in cities are empty
Of a family, use them first then use other land.

You and me must start afresh
Be kinder to the world and favour
The thought of love and kindness
Brush away forever Mother Earth's constant labour.

You and me can do a good turn,
Try and love one another and tune
Our hearts to give and not spurn
Each other; in every way, to wickedness be immune.

You and me and the world will be much happier,
If the world is no more polluted.
Animals, fish, birds and insects will feel freer
Yes, give the world a chance, then you and me
    will benefit not be sullen and muted.

*Alma Montgomery Frank*

## THINGS MUST GET BETTER

Today we live in a world, too big for it's own boots.
Changes happening, does anyone give a hoots.
people unhappy, searching for happiness, but to never find
A stressful time, never in history, known too mankind.
Money makes the world go round, now is this all? . .
Kids on the line, struggling, driving ourselves up the wall.
Be better, than everyone, got to be the best
And the not so brilliant are thought of less . . .
For we must believe in something
If it's your faith, that keeps you on going
Will asteroids, quakes, wipe out our human race.
Always living in fear, unhappiness written on our faces . . .
I know the spirit of god, shall keep me moving on.
And I will believe, whether they think I'm right or wrong . . .
Today we live in a forever, changing, dark universe,
That needs the love, too repair and bring us, back to us . .

*D Riches*

## CEAUSESCU'S LEGACY

The saddest face I have ever seen
Shall haunt me 'til I die;
And all because of one bad man.
The dreadful Nicolae.

Romania is a hell on earth.
No *ifs,* or *buts,* or *maybes.*
How can we soothe the heartache
For Ceausescu's loveless babies?

If my own kids had flown the nest
And I was on my own.
I'd pack my bags and give those tots
The love they've never known.

Romania's orphans have no choice.
They cannot make decisions.
For Nicolae took hope from them
With surgeon-like precision.

***Linda Zulaica***

## ELEPHANT SONG

India and Africa
Racked by poverty
Riven by greed
Spirit of the grasslands
Brought down to bleed
My humbled majesty
On blood drowned dust
Brave mouse you are forgiven
Human you are cursed

*Brendan O'Neill*

## As Time Goes On

As time goes on and on and on, I hear a young child's cries
his morning of sorrows and sad, sad tomorrow's
  learning to live through the lies.

As time goes on and on and on, I see in the young man's smile,
The hope of joy, pleasure and love
  that will be his in a short short while.

As time goes on and on and on, I see in the old man's face,
The pain and the tears, the anguish and fears,
  nearing the end of the race.

As the world spins on and on and on, and day turns into night,
In the air nothing but despair, corruption, destruction and plight.

As the world spins on and on and on, and countries go to war,
Life accelerates at a greater, greater pace,
  increasing productivity for all.

And as the world spins on and on and on, and before the ball
  starts burning bright,
I look in the eyes of every man here and I ask him to seek out the light.

For the light will burn away the darkness of the night and the light will
  show him the way,
Preparing him for a man who will come to show him the wrong and
  the right.

*P Loudon*

## MILLENNIUM TIME

'Time is of the essence,'
a saying that's well known
we *see* time in the faces
of our children who have grown.
We *hear* time strike the hours
of the clock's face on the church.
We *feel* time sadly wasted
when a friend leaves us in the lurch.
A *taste* of time can have us
in mouth-watering expectation
as a banquet is prepared
for our delectation.
A *scent* of time is arriving
on New Year's Eve ninety nine
a second past midnight heralds
Two thousand years of Time
How then will mankind see,
Scent, hear, taste, or touch
those coming precious moments
that in time will mean so much?

***Zoë Ford***

## THE QUESTION IS?

A taste of blood for our young warriors,
Hiding behind their rose-coloured glasses.
Into the range of fire they leap, smiling.
They who sought revenge, die laughing, not.

The resentful jungle plays hide and seek
And our brave, fearless warriors sweat
Cradling precious weapons in their arms.
They who longed to be hero's, die quickly, not.

Snipers so inconsiderate for human life,
Our brave young warriors, social victims,
Belly crawling, into hush-hush ambush.
Errand boys, for political conformity, not.

Discontented tunnel rats huddle below,
Waiting for the armoured ferrets to find.
Blowing them away like leaves in the wind.
Our trained boys loving their missions, not

So many deaths, no freedom of speech.
Friendships incomplete and repressed,
Witness every colour and creed violated
And all we wanted was to say we won, but did we?

*Amanda Thompson*

# A THOUGHT

It's very late and my head does ache,
and I have been watching the TV.
If you've just seen what I have seen,
you'd feel exactly just like me.

It was about pollution in our world,
and it wasn't good at all.
They talk of mankind and how he is going to take a fall.
You see it is in front of us! But nobody wants to here,
there are very few that really know that judgement day is near.

To all of our trees and woods,
a future is not very good.
We are felling so many trees today,
the ozone layer is being eaten away.
The fish in the sea are getting diseased,
and the poles are melting down fast.
It makes you wander if you give it a thought,
how long our earth will last.

*David Cook*

## 'TILL THE END

Deep rooted and highly strung,
So wise for someone so young.
Deep in thought yet shallow beneath,
The hidden aura of mixed love and pain.

Words, words with meanings so slight and delicate,
To touch the minds eye,
Like a piece of lead on your leg,
So cold.

A glance that goes nowhere but seeps through you.
Fires glowing strengthened by the wind of love.
As he takes his last breath and mutters,
'Till the end!'

*Gemma Keyte*

# ROAD BUILDERS
(A vision of the future)

What will our children's children say
To the things their forbears planned.
What happened to this island,
Once a green and pleasant land?

Meadows, fields and forests gone,
As houses and more roads appear,
All that are left are memories
Of all we once held dear.

Where are the birds and animals,
The things of nature we could feel.
All gone, to make more room
For miles of concrete and of steel!

What will you tell our children,
of the vista they will see
*This*, is your *'Blessed Heritage,'*
A concrete cow and painted tree!

***Marlene Meilak***

## DREAM OR VISION

I saw a vision in the sky,
Or was it just a dream?
A voice cried out in anguish,
Of things that might have been.

I saw a vision in the sky,
It told me to believe.
If I did success would come,
Of all the dreams we weave.

I saw a vision in the sky,
It begged me to have grace.
It told me one day rich and poor,
Would surely then embrace.

I saw a vision in the sky,
It said world peace would reign,
Wars, poverty and disease,
Would never come again.

But then the vision vanished,
I thought what might have been.
And told myself of sadly,
It had only been a dream.

***John Hopkins***

## THE GATHERING

All is safely gathered in.
The reapers have their day,
The fields are wet with diamond dew,
Contented, filled, we go away.

But what of harvests torn apart
By floods or lack of rain?
Sorrow and hardship, pain and grief,
Some lives will never be the same.

Our trust seems thwarted by these acts,
A helplessness in what to do,
We've ploughed the fields
And harvested while others muddle through.

There is no easy answer,
We all must play our part
To help in time of trouble,
A gesture from the heart.

So as we gather through the years
And glean what life can bring,
We'll trust and pray with each new day
And find the time to sing.

*Jean Humphris*

# WAR FOR THOSE SIERRA LEONE BOYS

Their beauty's hidden in a thousand
Hungry faces, defies
The dearth beneath plenteous skies.
Not famine starves, but lies,
Rain's vain
Waters where dust has lain
Cries, dies,
All boys must love weapons,
Slash with their machetes, blood their land,
Become thus worthy sons.

Drugged visions in the young, enrage, cheat
Compassion's valid plea.
Diamonds will pay for this cruelty.
Their years too few to see
Hate's gate
Opens to terror's spate,
Territory
Poisoned and out of reach.
Childhood has suffered a great defeat.
That is what war will teach.

### *John Bate*

## DIFFERENT BELIEF

I remember the floor
With a knock to my head
Such feelings of life
But I know that I'm dead.

I'm watching the pain
Of their mindless intent
The anger they show
With no way to vent.

It's finished, it's done
They can all step away
Now peaceful and quiet
They don't know what to say.

Look at this body
All battered and red
Killed in cold blood
It believed what it said.

*James L Wood*

# A Fox's Life

I'm running, I'm running,
I can hear the clip clop.
With a swish of my tail,
I dart through the bush.
I can hear the gun man coming,
So I must run at high speed.

The horn sounding high,
And the hunts man, he shouts!
Bang! Bang!
I hear the gun,
But my luck it's in,
And I'm off home, without a doubt.

Safe at last,
But for how long?
Just till the next time,
When that shrill horn sounds.

*Charlotte Stace*

# I Wonder Who

When the war is over
When the fighting's done
I wonder who is better off?
I wonder who has won?
Who has gained the victory?
Who was it had no loss?
I wonder, which one suffered most?
I wonder what the cost?
Where did it lose its way?
How can life piece together?
How did it break away?
Why are still the bugles calling
Why the silent drums still beat,
While guns no more are firing
When there's no more marching feet
Now the war is over
Now the fighting's done,
I wonder who is better off,
I wonder! Who has won?

*A Lawson*

## YOU DID NOT KNOW ME

What does it take to reach into your world?
How loud do I have to shout before I'm heard?
Reaching down into your cosy little dream
Is that what you think I am? Is that how I seem?
Am I just another body lying in the mud
You see on your telly? Don't you think you should
Sit up and notice my child crying there
It's real, it's not made up, why don't you care?
She's an orphan now that I can only trust to
People like you hoping for pities sake that you
Won't let her starve or to sickness fall
Will you answer the need in her sad eyes call?
Sorry I've intruded and your evening spoiled
I wouldn't want your nice clean delusions to soil
I realise you're busy in your cosseted fat life
You don't want to hear about my child's strife
But if you ever should remember the Lord's words
Think twice about just whose voice it is you've heard.

*Dave White*

## WORKING WITH KIDNEY MACHINES

When the late shift comes to a close
   and makes all daily noises dim
a mood of twilight spreads to the ward
   then I pause for a minute's dream . . .

It may be about the future
   of what the coming years could mean,
how will kidney machines be built
   say in two thousand fifteen . . .?

They already have brains
   of electronic kind
that think and test and analyse
   as much as a human mind.

They may even speak a language
   made by new technology
so as to give not just treatment
   but also a close company.

What will contacts then be like
   between men and machines
I might think too far ahead
   still with last century's dreams.

The future's distant . . . yet so close
   borders of ages are thin
More than ten years a step in time
   to two thousand fifteen . . .

***Anthony Gyimes***

## WORLD IN FOCUS

A man who doesn't believe in himself
believes in war.
Hidden by the reeking camouflage called power
some people actually believe he is strong.
I believe everything he does is wrong.
I look at the news.
I read the newspapers.
I believe we are much better than war.
I believe we are much better than we think we are.
There's so much beauty in this world.
If only everybody could see or feel it.

*John Beals*

# LOWRY'S PEOPLE

These are not Lowry's people,
For they walk on matchstalk legs
Not in industrial Manchester,
But across sun-parched plains
In a country ravaged by war
And famine.

And yet, although skeletal ribs
Show through black skin
Above malnourished pot bellies,
Still, unprompted,
They find something to sing about
And a smile for the camera.

*Joyce Walker*

## GENERAL

How fearless men of all shapes and sizes
Are goaded to fight for tokens and prizes.
It's part of the psyche we load on the guilty,
Like sides of a weakling who drinks of the mighty.

Suppose you or I were the bringers of death,
To abandon the hopeful and snap off their breath,
We would not be useful in spite of our fame,
But sharing with vanity to harbour that shame.

Consider the plentiful, the fat, and the sham.
No sponging of their juice, but lick of the scam.
I wonder if Generals are generally fit,
Possessing of compassion instead of true grit.

*S Pete Robson*

# REVOLUTION

Turbulent! Terrible! Inevitable! Disillusionment! Indignity!
Determination! Revolutionary! Chaos! Willingness! Power!
Bleeding! Struggling! Liberty! Aristocracy overthrown!
                                                    Anarchy!
Monarchu, serfdom, antiquity. Visions, idealism, knowledge, utility.
Theorist, scientists, scholars, uniformity.
                        Meetings advising the future pathway.
Theorists moulding other's minds. Rebellion scattering
                                                feelings of hope.
Masses in hordes raised to rioting. Nobles and Kings
                                banned and slaughtered!
People, president, rules, uniformity! Society disillusioned and
miserable.
Changing to hope through delirium and false gaiety.
                                Stupid artistic creeds abounding.
Inevitable overthrow of past antiquity. Production of ideals
                                based on whims of society.
Arising mountain of vast uncertainty producing a
                                purposeless period of insanity.
Falling in with the new societies' ideals. Pushing out the
                                old fashioned method of power.
Using the force of the moment to change. Adapting people
                                        Unused to liberty.
Into a false feeling of safety. Redeveloping the ways of a nation.
Using music to move the media to hysterical heights at
                                        revolutionary ravings.
Promising youth its finest hour released to all the trappings of royalty.
To begin in its wake a new power, conditioning, creating
                                        an artistic barrier.
Believing ideals to bemass and production, social and military,
                                        formidable and base.
Losing the desires of a lifetime of servitude to a military
                                regime of power and oblivion.
Believing that all that was royal was wrong. Replacing it
                                with a power more strong -

Putting in place of monarchs and kings dictators,
        manipulators, presidents and things.
Redeveloping the minds of lambs from the fold responsively
Learning to do what they're told.
No more kings crowned! No more slaves of the Czar!
Now only workers following a star!

*Joan Blissett*

# A Nation's Problem

Now coming to terms with life today
Is not as easy as some folks say
Everything moves at a faster pace
Older generations cannot join the race.

The millennium year has brought many changes
Some for the better and some rearranges,
What with the Government, finance, and health
It seems there is never enough ready wealth.

There is always a cry for desperate need
From countries, who's people, beg and plead.
For a safe asylum, and a fair deal.
It takes time to assess, the genuine and real.

Our own population are left high and dry
Trying to help others who continue to apply
In the old days, charity began at home
Now it seems, we are helping those who roam.

Our hearts go out to the young and oppressed
Not forgetting, the old, alone, and distressed,
We seem to have lost our true British nation
A problem to tackle with grim determination.

*C King*

## SEEDS OF EVIL

Mines have been outlawed, but are still underground,
How many hidden, no one can tell,
By innocents, these are always found,
Thousands of victims, living in hell.

Be alert, where you place your feet,
These often explode, at a touch,
Protrusions, can cause pain, death or defeat,
Most through life, must use a crutch.

Long forgotten wars, but still casualties rise,
Their leaders, exiled or dead,
Mine fields, does anyone know where or the size,
Still causing terror, and dread.

Countries and nations, anonymous show no remorse,
No compensation, for those who are maimed,
Nobody admits to the blame, of course,
So, how can they ever be ashamed.

Just for the sake, of a drink of water,
Shocked by terror, and mind numbing pain,
Innocents, led to the slaughter,
Life, never the same again.

From a hospital bed, those wild staring eyes,
This was never, ever their war,
Stumps bandaged, from ankles to thighs,
And then I ask myself, God, how many more?

**Robert Thompson**

# THE PLIGHT OF THE DANCING BEAR

Is there anybody out there? Does anybody care?
Can anyone help the plight of the poor dancing bear?
They are snatched from their mothers when they are small
To endure a lifetime that is so wicked and cruel.

A ring is pierced through their nose to attach a rope
These poor frightened creatures, they have no hope
With a tug of the rope, hurting the bear's sensitive skin
They learn to shuffle their feet as the music begins.

The bears are dressed in clothing to make them look cute
If they don't dance to the music, they get to feel his boot
They stand waiting for hours in the scorching hot sun
For tourists to see them perform, they think it's such fun.

Many watch and take photographs of the poor dancing bear
Not realising the cruelty the creature is suffering there
Often deprived of water, the animals could dehydrate
As they walk the long journey back when it is late.

The pads on their paws become so sore, cut and bleed
Their diet is poor, not of what they would normally feed
They are kept on short leashes or in a confined cage
Their lifetime is shortened, they don't live a great age.

Many countries now ban this but in India it still goes on
These people must learn that this cruelty is wrong
We must fight to protect these animals, they have rights too
For them to live in their own habitat or a well managed zoo.

*Linda Brown*

## MEMORIES

They shall not grow old as we will do
They gave their lives for me and you
Some died in battle, others on our streets
But no matter where there was no need
For though they thought, they died for peace
It was a lie they died for greed.
The greed of others who hoped to rule
Over this world by being cruel.
Yes they fought and died that we might live
Together as one, learn to forgive
Though they shall not grow old as we do
We must remember them and their families too.

*Maureen E Smith*

## CHILDREN

Tall, small, big and little.
Girls, boys making noise.
Happy, sad little lads
Laughing, crying,
Can be trying
Often make their parents mad
And even sometimes glad.
All the world over
Children are the same
They delight in fun and games.
Some are starving hungry
Let us set them free
From the atrocities and famine
In their country.
Sending food and parcels far across the sea
And ease their pain and sorrow of feeling hungry.
Help the children
Set them free.

*Patricia Farbrother*

## Kosovo

Like a sighing wind
the line trods on
man . . . woman . . . child
beast and creaking wheel,
over wild mountain
snow capped trails.
The weak . . . the crippled
falling exhausted there
when life could
give no more.
The world looked on
gave a sigh and said
'Poor things why is
this happening now?'
Barbarians are gone
humanity is free,
what new monster
is born, its fangs
running red in
angry blood on
destruction's manic highway.
Should we not kill it
or force it back
to its lair lest,
all suffer this endless
wrath in a frenzy
of barbaric deeds.

*H A Brawn-Meek*

# A HARLEQUIN OF NEWS

At eventide the newscasters
their faces woven from emotive stories
bring us the happiness and rubble of the world
broken into small fragments
so we can strive to ingest and empathise
how it must be on location
where floods surge their frothy heads
breaking forth to riot through all in their path
destroying people and buildings and leaving cumulative grief.
Twisted metal, misshapen wood piled in large heaps
among sprawls of mud.
World leaders dialogue inside great buildings
making pronouncements, trying to orchestrate a nation's grief.
Turmoil, disaster, heroism
hope, reunion, happiness
all woven into the face of the newscaster
as their emotions are daily torn apart.

*Wendy Dedicott*

## WHY?

Why don't they educate people, not to have children to
                              bring up in this sort of life,
help them to cope first, with only themselves and combat
                                        their personnel strife.
teach them the way to live without children, at least for a few years
until they, themselves, grow stronger and learn to conquer their fears.
Give them the tools to work on their lands, for they need
independence as well as a helping hand.
Britain is small, but has a big heart, it likes to help,
it likes to take part but self help is needed, more than before,
so why bear babies into a starving war?

*Dorothy Howell*

# THE OAK TREE

A tiny acorn observes the world from a worm's eye view
then struggles to get noticed as inch by inch it grew,
reaching for the stars and spreading roots wide,
now to make its mark on a changing countryside.
Every year, each season it put on a display
for an audience too busy to notice, and who look away.

They are clearing a forest for profit and greed,
leaving future generations with famine and need.
The Earth is being blown away by soil erosion,
poisoned by acid rain, pollution and explosion
and by dumping toxic waste and contaminating the sea,
this self-destruction by mankind is destroying humanity.

Ever changing fashions in an immediate, disposable society,
no time to wait for an oak, plant an instant growing variety.
Now at last, realisation, as the century has passed,
that to secure the future, we must safeguard the past,
by helping mankind with inventions, discoveries and cures,
and putting an end to poverty, extinction and wars.

In the safety of your branches, birds and squirrels abound,
ivy clings to your trunk, your roots established underground.
Media coverage treats you like a star, giving you centre stage
a preservation order saves your life, because of your great age
with a lifetime achievement accolade for still being around,
the motorway planned here will be scrapped and a new location found.

*Pamela Eldridge*

# GOD'S CHILDREN

Don't shrug your shoulders and walk away
Look at the face of my little lass
Cut to ribbons by flying glass.

Don't turn your back on me
Because of *you* my child can't see
God only knows when there will be peace
And when the evil bombing will cease.

Don't say what do I expect you to do
Everyone knows the rumours are true
We have all heard them say
You're a member of the IRA.

Don't tell me your cause wasn't wrong
It was evil to plant that bomb
So close to where children played
And so near the church where youngsters prayed.

One day my little lass said to me
'Mam - in that church a bride I'll be
And dad will walk by my side
And you will cry, eyes filled with pride.'

She saw it all in her dreams
Now dreams are all she will see, it seems
Yes that's right just walk away
But you will answer to God some day.

Try telling him your cause was just
Then look at the children - in God they trust
Everyone there with God because of a bomb
Now tell him you were right
And the rest of the world was wrong.

*Joe Bell*

# Two News Items

This small Roman,
A dead star in Londinium,
Had her tombstone cracked open,
Her lead coffin prised apart.
They found her bones -
One arm across her heart.
Under her ancient spine
Lay specks of wreaths.

Since Planet Earth
Took her last breath
Two millennia have slid away.
It's not so long ago,
For she was no Andromeda
'Forty-four light years away,'
But a human of recent history,
With a constellation of mind
That also gazed upon the Milky Way.

*June Benn*

# THE FOX HUNTERS

I walked through the trees and the meadows,
And drank in the peace of the day.
I gloried at the beauty of nature
Feeling refreshed, as I went on my way.

Then suddenly I heard a commotion
The raucous shouting of men
The loud baying of hounds - and hoof beats -
Horns blasting and men shouting again.

The air had become frenzied and fearful
The peace and tranquillity gone
A whole sense of evil pervaded
As the strange lust to kill drove them on.

I returned home, with the sounds in my ears
And the tears still wet on my face
I felt so deeply ashamed that day
That I belonged to the human race.

*Phyllis Hall*

## MANDOVA ORPHANAGE

Who left these darling babes acrying
Who left them all day in their cots alying
Poor little darlings in their cradles lay
Not knowing if it was night or day.
Frozen cold no heating at all,
Their little world's torn apart
Where are these people with a heart?
Bruises all over in a terrible dismay
Poor babes at this orphanage hidden away.
Some crawling never walked on the ground
Little mouths open, but no sound.
Dearest Lord I thank you, for they were found.
These poor little babes cry out to all, you and me.
A little help off all, each they need,
A little love isn't much to ask indeed.
Poor babies, little children don't know how to play
Locked up forever out of ones way.
Never a love, a hold, a touch,
Poor babes left mostly alone.
In a cellar they called their home.
Darling ones with this poem I hope I can help
People to stop thinking, only of their self.

*J Hardy-Pierce*

# Kosovo

Save me from tomorrow,
It'll just be another day of sorrow,
Take a look at a TV screen
And you'll see people and the horror they have seen.
It's not just a war about politicians and dictators,
It's about people like us,
But we're just spectators
Bombs keep on falling,
So people keep on dying,
They walk in their thousands to escape the carnage,
Carrying all they can manage,
Walking to safety,
But, what cost do they pay?
Broken families, death and destruction all around,
And when it's all over, they'll go homeland bound,
To pick up the pieces and to rebuild.
How long before they're back to the office,
Or work a field?
So please save me from tomorrow
And the terrible suffering in Kosovo.

*Mark Leaver*

## NEWS

The bones of Middle Africa sheened in overlapping
blued, winged, thick coverings;
flies after putrefaction that is still live,
and when it reluctant moves to suck in vain
at that tattered flattened bag that was a breast -
God! Give them rest!

    Black gathered blood matts the face-hair
    of farmers beaten from their homes
    in Zimbabwe. Ian Smith and U.D.I.;
    whatever did you start, and why?

        Shrieking shrill females, Muslim since The Wall came down
        or Catholic in Derry Town -
        widowed, orphaned, clasping at the hand
        remnants battered by a rabid band:
        We do not *know;* from what is told,
        there may be right on both your sides, just as there may be
        wrong.

            And nowadays all-seeing eyes
            urgently go to probe where reason dies.
            There is a great revulsion
            not only of fanaticism that wreaks and reeks;
            but of you, televisual perpetrator.
            We have no want to witness
            the loathings of Man's bitterness.
            Turn your lens the other way,
            leave us watch some fools at play.
            There's nothing we can say to shift
            or alter mobs; no moneyed gift
            can get them where they want to be.
            Our guilt smothers. There is no want to see.

*Seán Jackson*

## MOTORWAY MADNESS

And standing still I blinked again,
while meadows green with fronds of camomile
stood proudly where now, no grasses even grow,
and skies of thunder gloomy in their wrath,
watch over fields where farmers never sow.

And harvesters and working men
have disappeared into the depths of time.
While in their place a tarmac blanket rolls.
And creatures long ago gave up the fight.
They now succumb to cars and motorways and tolls.

The land once filled with tree and wood
and flowering shrub to please the mind,
has disappeared into the misty paths of fate
and never looked behind,
or ever cried out once in hate.

Remember then, and weep for yesterday.
For nature's sweet revenge will surely dawn.
And those who dare defy her laws today,
may never ever come to be re-born,
or witness once again, a child at play.

*Pamela Phillips*

## ROBES OF ANGUISH

People of the plain,
People of the bush,
What must you think of us,
When you have so very little,
And we have so very much,
When again you flee the drought and war,
Walking with your belongings,
Across your barren land,
To a far off haven of hope,
Columns of people scramble over rough terrain,
Older children with smaller children in hand,
With the graves of those gone before,
Sign-posting the route,
On reaching the station,
You find thousands and thousands,
Of your countrymen just the same at you,
All with aching hearts and starving bodies,
And you lay down to cry, because you cannot go on,
As the whitemen in charge prepare to fly,
After singing you, their old song,
Why is it you wonder?
Do the black people always wear the robes of anguish,
And always but always own faces drawn, gaunt and hollow,
While well made sturdy whitemen in arrogance and self
importance wallow,
So we lay down beaten and ready to die,
While they in their helicopters up and fly,
The rumour going around here is that,
Somewhere in Europe food mountains reside,
We can only dream of those mountains of plenty,
As slowly we slip beyond.

*P J Littlefield*

## TRICHINA

The one exiled casts a flitting greyness
As he lashes out a corrugation
Upon the eyes plan,
With isolated bands of what is
And what has always been,
While all rebellious upon his salients
leer upon the higher plane and smile,
Experienced with a dribbling pout
heeled over by anoxia
The higher drag ladders
But once it climbs too far, it is lost.
They smile and furrow more into
The depths that would not have
Been dug had the passage not been defined
So as to follow detriments progress.

They rear and gaze impudently
when one dares to resuscitate the protest
by clawing away the dead dust
which incubates the uprising unliving;
No shadow would chase overhead
None would have been lost
Had he not initiated a darkened way.

*Lisa Watt*

## CRUEL

Passion's not the fashion,
Being beaten is a treat.
Love 'n' compassion are on ration,
Screaming fills the street.

Hysterical lives are carving in,
Going under with the pressure,
Torturous melodies they sing,
Not the kind that bring you pleasure.

Pleasure and coinage - a passing phase,
Smuggling them up for a while.
So they won't cope with tougher days,
As the debts strike the mat in style.

'Mustn't grumble - so they say,
There's always someone else worse off.'
Another repetition as one lay
Dying - through his spittle and cough.

*Tanya Shaw*

## ODE TO THE CONFLICT

Don't they understand
In handing in of guns
The foodstuff of the peace
With Ireland's long lost sons
So you use that for the deal?
Do you sound the gong?
The London song
Oh give you peace
After Easter Days judged long
If that they say is real
Don't they understand?
The beck and call of blood free land
The rocking orange
Blood red green
Protégé battle
For the reborn Queen
The mince of many
The beef of a few
The gristle of the bullets
And rocket's carcass flying true
Why not give up your arms?
Why not your Sodom glow?
For peace belongs not just for playing
Traitors in the courts of Death You Know.

*Anora Kay*

# MAY GOD BLESS THEIR STEPS

I have heard on the news today
Some refugees are on their way
Back to their country, back to what?
All they carry is all they've got.

I pray to God they'll be alright
With no repeats of their awful plight
Give them strength to meet the tasks
And still find time for what He asks.

Religious barriers must disappear
As they did when they were over here
Have faith in God for all your needs
And may your crops outgrow the weeds.

Give free in the name of our Lord
Build your nation with one accord
Let Him come in and help you start
He'll give strength to those weak in heart.

God will help if you pull your weight
And this inner warmth will make you great
Then fight the rigours of the day
As to Jesus Christ we pray.

**Stanley Swann**

## UNPREDICTABLY CRUEL

O death you're all around us
Unpredictable and cruel
O death you just surround us
As water in a pool.

Quietly you sneak upon us
Suddenly you strike
Caring not whose going to miss us
King, beggar-man and the like.

The living you seem to scorn
So not waiting till the morrow
You take over, old, newly-born
Leaving us all in sorrow.

But death we shall remember you
And your cruel deeds
Oh how could we forget you
And your merciless seed.

*Barbara Sherlow*

## DEMOCRACY DISTRAIT

I'd like to think politics honest,
All members of Parliament true,
But slanging and recent betrayals
Gives vent to the opposite view;
So little achieved while they barrack,
Most speeches decidedly poor,
The lack of sincerity angers.
Time wasting a trait we deplore!
Bone-dry are the crusts such are chewing
Who try to outscore for applause,
Worse still is their nonsense debating
When sitting all night without cause!

I'd like to think politics useful,
Fulfilling, objective, once more.
And sacrosanct in jurisdiction,
The passing of logical law;
Without interference from others
Who wish to control us outside,
If we have elected our members,
Let *these* govern Britain with pride;
Applying themselves in real earnest,
So earning their generous wage,
Revealing as generous a purpose
Which soon would forebodings assuage.

I'd like to think politics noble,
Which ethics must not be defamed,
Or else is staid Whitehall a shambles
With former great statesmanship shamed;
Let other folk practice their folly
In novel demeaning pursuits,
We are a more glorious nation,
And stronger and deeper our roots!

Our need in the modern is simple,
Good men and good women with flair
To hold to our richer traditions . . .
God help the old Country to care . . . !

*R Gaveston-Knight*

# A MESSAGE FOR YOU

How can you ignore the child who cries?
How can you turn away from the pain in their eyes?
How can you refuse to hear what they need you to know?
How can you fail to see all the signs that show?
The child who needs you cannot reach you
Children are neglected and abused,
They'd love to walk away from it too
To believe it does not happen but it has repeatedly to them
They spent childhood wishing, hoping, praying it would end
Not to talk or think about it, won't make it go away
It is our problem - yours and mine
For thousands of children need our help today.

*Karen Reader*

## CARE HOME

Nature has been kind to us, our brains are *hunky dory*
but sadly there are others who could tell a different story,
sometimes there are special ones who don't behave the same
but they still deserve respect, we cannot pass the blame.
When they are in loving homes with care and kindness plenty,
they may be tiny little ones or going on for twenty.
They are safe and sound within, their happy family ties
but inside some *care* homes another story lies.
Wicked people shout and push and pinch and threaten too
the children do not understand what they are meant to do,
they should be showing understanding not using pain and fear
don't they see the frightened faces, don't they see the tears?
Why is it allowed to be? I just do not comprehend.
My son is a *special one* you see, he'll be with me till the end.
God forbid I have to leave him and into their path he lands
my heart fills up with dread to think of him in their hands.
These children deserve respect and love and if we turn away
we are as bad as those that hurt, we all must have our say.
So take up pen and paper now and tell the world the truth
we want to know what's going on, we should demand the proof.
Look at your children and be glad they do not suffer so,
but don't forget the ones that do, it still goes on you know.

*Cheryl Mann*

# THE SAME SONG

An exhibition shows of Auschwitz
In a London museum where,
Folk whisper of humans in cattle trucks
But don't let your compassion stop there.
Let your minds wander now to trucks
Holding cows and the lambs of God,
For slaughter goes on behind closed doors
Just as it always has.
At harvest festivals Christians give praise
Altars bearing our food of life,
As they sing *All Things Bright and Beautiful*
Why do cattle trucks still roll at night?

***Patricia Gargan Spencer***

# INFINITE END

Disaster, after disaster
And still there is war
Do we listen to our master
Nothing but gore
The world is disintegrating faster
Than ever before
What more can we bore
There's global warming
War, war, war
Horrible things are happening like never before
Is the end getting nearer?
Is God showing us the door?
There's so much wickedness
And breaking God's law
Has God had enough?
This I emplore.
We're ruining his world
The bad and evil just want more
They've wrecked this world
And that's for sure!

*Theresa Hartley*

# VICTIMS

Protective arms enfold the younger child
whose tear-stained face, just level with
his sister's chest, is buried in her coarse
blue cardigan which, with her calf-length skirt
of sombre hue, endows her with a strange
maturity her years deny: for she can be
no more than ten, and he but still
an infant: both too young to know a friend from foe.
Her eyes, half fearful, half in hope,
now upward gaze to seek some reassurance in
a stranger's face, the U.N. quite beyond
her ken, but not, alas, brutality in men.
The homeless flotsam of wars lethal tide,
too young to understand the reason why
their parents had to die because of creed
or ethnic cleansing's growth that thrives
there from Germanic seed, where once again
the dormant Phoenix will arise, and these
sad children's homeland still continue long to bleed.

*T C Hudson*

## STARBURST

Suddenly the stardust skies
Burst the seams of existence,
Like a ripe fruit splitting open
Scattering the seeds of time

Travelling aeons of circling jets
Spinning round solar orbits
Elipsing towards the source,
Retracting to the end.

Here, landed, grounded, but
Floating in the middle of neon
Electric strands twining around
The interconnected galactic

The paradox is compounded,
Conforming one myriad
From the chaos, eclectic,
We smile at the sun, confounded.

*Louise Shirley*

## PEACE - IN A TEACUP

When peace broke out
My mother said to me
'Eee, lud, this call for celebrations -
Let's have a cup of tea'
For cups of tea
And what the British have
At cause to celebrate
No troops
No guns
No blood
No tears
No tanks
No wounds
No hate.

This is what was started
When Berlin Wall fell down
And release of Mid-East hostages
Followed by Mandela's frown
The fall of Russian Communists
And Ulster - Dublin pact
It all calls for a cup of tea
And cream bun -
That's a fact.

And now, in 2031
The thought of war has gone
Their reverberating circuits are severed
Every one.
Future must be created from the *now*
And not the past
You see
This calls for celebration . . .
And another cup of tea!

***John Crowe***

# KILL

Kill
Is it
easier to kill after you have murdered the time
does a gun take away your conscience and soul
does hatred
make you kill with clinical ease
do children
old men and women became a threat to kill
is it
easier to kill after you have murdered the first time
do you
discard and dispose of humanity with ease
do differences
in race religion and people make you take sides
does the
absence of love instil anger to kill
is it
easier to kill after you have murdered the first time
murder

*Roman Suchyj*

## OUR WORLD

We live in a world of wonder
With scenery of breathtaking splendour;
Mountains and valleys that change with the seasons
Like the trees and rivers and streams.
The birds, with their perfect plumage;
The sun, the moon and stars;
So much to enjoy and cherish
In this wonderful world of ours.

This same world holds so much that is chilling;
The mindless destruction of life.
Wars just for the pleasure of killing,
Giving childhood no time to unfold.
Living becomes an existence
Comprising terror, hunger and cold.
What happened to change the purpose
Of this wonderful world of ours?

The will of Almighty God will surmount
The onrushing tide of decay.
He will not always stay His hand
Whatever men think or say.
One day, when least expected,
The whole Earth will be shaken by powers
So long by mankind rejected
To restore this wonderful world of ours.

*Joan Picton*

## GRAPPLE

The wretched, blinded birds
The X-ray of my finger bones
The odour of fluorescing air
My hands no shade
From what shone there
I crouched, prostrate as prayer
The conscript of a hate and fear.

The tannoy counted down
They'd told us:
'No danger here
This station's clear.'
Closer they lie
Behind the bund
In buildings, trenches
Shielded, underground
But it's you who waits
Open and damned
Etched in glare
Sintered by Medusa's stare
To hear the voice -
The tearing shroud -
To feel the pulse
Of Megatonne.

As faint a heart that beats
In womb
Reborn, wedded, shaking
I turned
Fumbled, removed
Extreme-smoked glass
The colossal cloud, full flower
Rising, then

A toppling breakdown
In writhing flumes of gas
In vents of steam and of dust
And molten artefacts left by man
High cataracts, coral debris and . . .

Telemetry ran riot
Then went dead
Even electromagnetics
Can be bled.

Seized by cancer
In these years
Swigged 'Old Tom'
Confused
Like alcoholic
Tears
Remembered when
The aircraft climbed the sky
That 'Christmas' day
In peaceful ocean's
Innocent eye
I thought the fusion
Conceived the split
Cell by cell,
In cannibal flesh,
And wondered what
The bomb had done.

'Think on my lads,'
The sarge had said
'We've had our backsides
Roasted red
Tonight we'll just
Slope off to bed
And then, tomorrow
We'll wake up dead
Just like our effing mothers
Dread.'

***Bill Simpson***

# A GLIMPSE OF HELL

With eyes as big as saucers as brown as they could be,
Looking sweet and innocent he took a peep at me,
When he saw me watching him his lips formed a leer,
And for the longest moment my heart was filled with fear.
His stare was kind of crafty, his movements full of stealth,
So when he stood before me I fretted for my health.
'Cough up all yer money then' a falsetto voice commanded,
'Before I bash yer brains in' this imp from hell demanded . . .
I stood my ground defying him . . . while tine refused to pass,
Then from the deep dark shadows came his cohorts . . . all . . .en masse.
All of them were children, but their age I could not tell,
I only know that standing there I caught a glimpse of hell . . .
They found me in the gutter, my ribs all bruised and sore,
But my handbag and the children had vanished . . . evermore.

*Valerie McKinley*

## CONFESSION

We strived to make every little thing fit
Like hand in glove or hand in pocket.
No gold or purple notes in our jeans
No reminders or letters or brass for our means.
Food was scarce, we ate humble pie,
That fear of starvation, that fear that we may die.
A hand was placed on our possession -
Took from the wage of sin,
Never revealed through confession.

Then we all bend the rules -
Well, it's the only way around some obstacles.
Or, then again, straight through them,
Through concrete walls and a barrage of a thousand men.
And the great artist, the sculptor supreme,
Makes what is physical and what is not seen.
He sows the seed for conception -
Make of his way what you will,
Choose your own direction.

Friends are not as thick as blood,
But would they be, if they could?
And all confessed could slightly
Blow our marrow minds, not let us see,
That, residing within the confines of false sensuality
Is a place more absurd, where we all want to be.
Channel your mind's extension -
Believe in your faith, though
Charged corkage for redemption.

*Paul Magson*

# HOPE

Oh little child with faltering steps still innocent in mind
Within whose future growth and path the vagaries of life will find
Confusion from the acts of groups, though loud, who do not truly
represent mankind

The message from God's books on shelves unopened gather dust
One wife with family base disdained and drowned in seas of lust
Those people no less ill though fashion now dictates that being straight
is not a must

The beauty of the spoken word sullied with doubt
When being gay instead of full of joy means sex about
And politics, which should promote the moral high, means nothing
more than clout

The greed of man not knowing bounds will take from you whilst
saying friend
And the law may deal you down because truth is a game and not its end
Yet I kindle hope for the hills are high and with the trees and lakes
they blend

*Robert Lumley*

## WHY?

Why are so many people dying in care?
To make it hardly seems fair
Why spend millions on the Millennium Dome?
Then they get given their request for another loan.
Why do footballers earn millions a year?
It's surgeons, doctors and nurses with brains under their hair.
Why does the government not seem to mind?
Catering for the rich, it's not to them they should be so kind.
Why are so many charities in need?
Some people just need some food to feed.
Why don't the government give more money to the sick?
I would say they are taking the mick
It's on the news every day, in hospital there are not enough beds
I think it makes everyone wonder what goes on in their heads.

*Bianca Fairless*

# IT TAKES ONE TO KNOW ONE (BLESSING IN DISGUISE)

Twenty years ago this week
saw the tragic scene.
How she thought she'd never speak
of it's happening.
Today she runs the busy centre
of the rape crisis.
An offering to all who enter,
who've experienced like this.

It was ten years ago today,
he was the tragic case.
How he thought he'd never say
how alcohol defaced.
Today he lectures everywhere
on the drink crisis.
An offering to all who care,
who experience like this.

It takes one to know one,
and sometimes misfortune
can be of help to grow one
out of their mess too.
At the time, their tragedy.
At present, their motive.
Taken then to agony
for a destiny to give.

*Debra C Rufini*

# LOOK - AND YOU WILL SEE!

If you look at the world through rose-coloured glasses,
you won't see the death and destruction that passes,
the distended bellies of young children, crying
for food, as they cling to their mothers, now dying
from famine and drought, nor the flies ever swarming
and crawling in nostrils and eyes, or the mourning
of heartbroken widows, lives viciously shattered
by war, they have lost the one person that mattered,
you won't see the limbless, the crippled, the maimed,
the blinded, the mass graves that can't be explained,
you won't see the children that can't even cry,
they are shocked beyond measure, but you won't ask why.
You'll carry on seeing a rose-tinted hue,
on all that surrounds you, the cosseted you.

*Jim Sargant*

# FRRREEEDOMMM!

Freedom? Just what is it?
William Wallace yelled for it loud
And Jesus promised to bring it
On his return from the clouds

To the young lad in Ireland,
Freedom comes in peace
'Twould make his father's army death
Worth something at least

Then to the single mother
With all her kids to feed
'Twould be to work to give them
Everything they need

For the depressed, there's freedom
In understanding, peace of mind;
For the lonely person
In that true friend they find

Freedom is for ev'ryone
A very different thing
But, all told, it's something
We each could help to bring

*S J Robinson*

## OF HANGING MEN (A SONNET FINISHED)

And as they found their exits from the cell
All countenance composed - gone guilt, gone grace -
The silence snaps the story how they fell
Despatching men dropped them to lower place;
But though these two are both inclined to hell
One won't go yet, he's going home - for tea . . .

. . .

. . .

To sip the stillness from an empty cup.

*Kenneth Campbell*

## CRY FREEDOM

Vietnam. Napalm
A screaming child runs down a barren road
trapped in an inferno. Engulfed in flames of hell.

What price innocence? The slaughter of the innocent.

Biafra.
Extended bellies of starvation.
Foul flies explore, lay eggs in cracks and crannies of mutilated flesh,
swarm round the large dulled liquid eyes of children
mewling newborn kitten tears.
Too weak to wipe away running mucus
Too weary to protect pus infected weeping open sores.
Suffer little children. Victims of senseless tribal wars.

There will always be wars and rumours of war. Why?
Do we learn nothing? Inhumanity knows no bounds.

Scratch the surface, the surface of civilised Man
The beast emerges, jaws slavering, sneering in vicious triumph.

The church, self-satisfied, self-righteous, preaches it's panacea.

The State, self-absorbed, abdicates responsibility; spews forth
unfulfilled prophecies of peace.

Politicians perverted by greed make fortunes. Easy pickings of
conflict and war.

In the never changing world is God on the side of the mercenary?

Bitter pictures of my adulthood remain.

Nightmares impregnated on my brain. Forever part of maturity.
Nothing changes.

The summer's gone.

*Barbara Radcliffe Davies*

## HOUNDS OF DEATH

Frantic attempt to outrun baying hounds
anxious for his blood
panting with exhaustion, desperately seeking escape
filled earth denies salvation
spent form faltering on weakened legs

Snapping at his mud-sodden heels
beautiful rust fur sweat-stained
once striking brush dragging the ground
wild creature begging for his life
his pleas hang in the still air
rent by raucous yelps from excited hounds
chasing full pelt impending triumph

Tails of excitement rob the stillness
persecution of the target is theirs
death claims victory
razors tear the helpless victim
no longer shines his russet coat
shredded in haste as carnage pervades the air
bright eyes dulled within mask of mortality

Gleaming blood spills from his limp form
painting the surrounding earth
with the stain of life
stolen from a wild spirit

*Sandra Bond*

## MARKET STREET

Young people throng the pavements
And shops
Of Market Street.

They bring their dreams
Of university
Starting school
Apprenticeship
Changing school
The weekend's fun
And starting work.

But the cruel, skeletal hands
Of men dead
Three hundred years
Reach out from their graves
(As they've done
All too often
In the past thirty years)
And operate the strings
Of their mindless puppets.

The young people
And their dreams
Lie shattered
Amongst the wreckage
Of Market Street.

*Brian Edwards*

## JUDGEMENT DAY WILL COME

Many people are so greedy in this world today
Stepping on anyone who gets in their way
Never feeling satisfied with what they've got
Always wanting to add more money to the pot

Their greed completely takes over all their thinking
And they'd rob their loved ones without even blinking
A bigger house - a faster car they seem to need
And no one else's feelings do they ever heed

Then there are the gentle souls who plod along the way
Trying to do their best as they struggle day to day
Doing a good deed whenever they can
Trying to make life easier for their fellow man

Taking time to give a smile to someone on their own
It makes such a difference to those who live alone
So remember when the judgement day finally arrives
We all have to look back on how we lived our lives

*Mary Lunn*

## PENNINES SMALL FARM, 2000

The blight is there to see,
insidious as peeling paint
on grimy windowsills;
as rusting implements
litter the slimy yard
and hens pathetically
cease to eke out ready cash;
as broken gates and thick stone walls
collapse for want of skills;
as fleeces raggedly attest
to lack of tender husbandry
and once proud faces
seared in desperation
see sons with little hope
retreat to distant streets.

And all this while
on Friday shopping trips
(grab this, grab that
from bright-lit temple shelves)
*we* pay the profits
from the bleeding fields
and never see the hanging rope
in some dark corner of the barn.

***Michael Nelson***

## OUR BROKEN WORLD

So many people are born to poverty, living a life of misery,
in squalor, starving and homeless,
And they die without anyone caring or even acknowledging
that they ever existed.

Money is spent on weapons, wars, rockets to the moon,
people are more important than these things, rich countries
could be doing a lot more to help those worse off in the world,
Wealth needs to be distributed so it is more equal,
famines and disasters are often a result of greed and folly,
what we do affects others not just ourselves.

The whole creation has been spoiled by humans going against God,
there is no love thy neighbour, the attitude is take rather than give,
people are self centred and selfish.
Money and possessions blind our hearts and eyes to the needs of others,
it's 'I'm all right' whilst we watch the poor suffer,
being uncaring, unfeeling, we fail to demonstrate God's likeness.

Our self interest has gone on far too long, we need to learn
how to feel the hurt and pain of others' suffering,
to see people going hungry, struggling, deprived, is so very sad,
We need to recognise our broken world, to have concern for others,
helping every way we can, loving each other the way God loves us,
showing love and compassion, this we must have.

We live in a love starved world, love and kindness
brings happiness to others, so love all people as yourself,
By doing this we will be reaping what we sow, when we give out love
we grow richer in love, that will be our wealth.

*Linda Roberts*

# MUSE ON A SYDNEY TOMBSTONE

Here I lie beneath a flagstone
In this cool and sacred spot,
Church of England vicars intone
Psalms and hymns and tommyrot.

Came I to this place a soldier,
Founder, planner, builder too.
But this land became my gaoler
When I finished dead with flu.

I was full of expectation
That this was the promised land,
Till the bugs and infestation
Showed that they had upper hand.

Buried in this soil I lie spent,
Listening, watching, waiting for
Time to end, the day of judgement
And reunion with my corps.

Meantime, tourists snapping photos
Sucking drinks and chomping food
Pass on by towards Kyoto
Leaving me in solitude.

*Brian MacDonald*

# REGRET

Oh God! What have I done?
It seemed the best thing at the time.
Another child into the world
Fatherless, just can't be kind.

The shame, rejection, hard to bear.
Poverty won't ease the hurts
I'd have to work. No mother there,
And that just only makes it worse.

Fostered out to other places,
Never knowing family life.
Another of those latchkey cases
Full of anger, pain and strife.

But here I am, my inside's empty,
They tore you out in little bits.
Then out the door to home they sent me,
And now I have to deal with it.

*I caused you pain, rejected you.*
You never had a chance to try.
I wish I could go back and choose
To let you have a go at life.

It might be hard, it could get rough,
But that's what life is all about,
And all you'd really need is love
I surely could have given that.

I'll never know what might have been
Or what you may have done
I'm truly sorry for my sin,
Please, forgive me little one.

***Ginny***

## CHANGE THE WORLD

How can I change the world without
The world changing me
Because everything about me
Is not the same as when I was a child
I am sure you see.

How can I change the world without
Changing the few good things
Like having a bit more money
And the good songs that we can sing.

How can I change the world without
Going too far back in time
I do not want some of the old things to happen
Like my children working down a mine.

*Keith L Powell*

## SAVE THYSELF SOLDIER . . .

Save thyself soldier
Turn not back into the fray.
What unplanned valour
On this dire day
Will take you, unthinking,
Again, into enemy fire?
To pluck from oblivion
A comrade riven
With mud and mire
And enemy fire.

In this brave deed
You took no heed
Of saving your own precious skin.
Felled. Lost to pain
Before your own life could begin
Now, of you young man,
Barely a man,
No earthly remnants remain.

In the ensuing years
Silence has descended
On an earth
Carefully tended,
Where scars have grown over
And nothing shows through
Of the hell
Of the horror
Of the fear of those
Who lie
In ordered rows
'Neath a foreign sky.

*Jill Ward*

## FAIRYLAND (THE ALTERNATIVE VIEW)

The world is just ideas thought of by a higher mind,
making it quite difficult for all our humankind.

And when we get it wrong,
we suffer on for centuries long.

It's like a nuclear power house churning out the power,
the only way to stop it would mean having man's last hour.

So much for his free will it only amounts to this,
Will he live or will he die, the supreme optimist?

Everything has been thought out and planned,
that's why man thinks that God's holding his hand.

Science is just finding out what is already there,
as we stumble like blind mice along life's thoroughfare.

We are flying around in space just waiting for the crunch,
still helpless children Mother Nature calls for not a bunch.

Someday we may learn to use our minds and try to help ourselves,
but, now we're just in Fairyland, we might as well be elves.

*Jean Paisley*

## HUNTING

In days gone by at the dog track
There were live hares to chase
Now they use mechanical toys,
so no one's in disgrace.
Hunters can still hunt if its only for the thrill,
They don't need live animals to satisfy at will.
They say that dogs will be shot
if they cannot hunt again
They kill them anyway if they're old
or fail the men.
We peasants have moved on
To a more civilised way of life
The rich are still bored children
So hunting feeds the strife
We are better educated
No longer fooled by talk
We've been in fields where foxes are
We didn't see them stalk
Sunning themselves in the early morn
Sheep nearby with new lambs born
Undisturbed by the evil fox
They think we are ignorant
We are not.

*Christa Fisher*

## OPPOSING THE BIGOTS

Sparks dance upon the ground
Where unarmed crowds, defiant, stand
And death waits at the corner,
Blood to spring at his command

Streets awash with anger
Through which danger cares to splash
And feel the city hold its breath
Just moments from the clash

Brutality in uniforms
That proudly boast the crown
Keep hatred's waters flowing
In which generations drown

And hear the flutes of Orangemen
Their bigotry the tune
But on the road before them
Opposition's nails are strewn.

*Kim Montia*

## OUR EARTH

Oh help us save this special land,
United we all must lend a hand,
Rubbish will grow and pollution increase,
Everything will die and our world will cease,
All around things are dying,
Really we should all be trying,
Take the time to lend a hand,
Help to save the special land.

*Sandy Grebby*

## PADDY

Paddy my friend what is life?
To let alcohol cut into you like a knife,
Paddy my friend forgive when I stare,
When you say the most beautiful place is Nowhere,
In your seventy years what have you done?
What came to pass below your stars and your sun?
When you met your wife Gerty did you love her more?
More than the bottles that heave you to the floor?
An elegant Irishman you were,
With an enjoyment of society and fashion flair,
But something inside led you to drink,
Something had broken in your life link,
I wish I could heal you and make you well,
Setting you free from this torment and hell.

*L Petherwick*

# IS IT TOO LATE?

The acid rain has killed the trees
No sound is heard from the rustle of leaves
The birds are silent and all at rest
We have ravaged the Earth to our very best.

The seas are angry in retaliation
Their beauty poisoned by every nation
Crystal water's no longer pure
The crime is ours that's for sure.

No winters of old in breathtaking white
No sparkle of ice in a ray of light
Our world unbalanced and out of tune
We have altered the tides. - Don't blame the moon.

The Earth is our power providing all we need
Black or white, we all still bleed.
Envy and greed are worth the price of life
Money rules t he world by gun and by knife.

*A Harrison*

## THIS IS PROGRESS

Poor little rabbit lying dead on the road
How could you know a motorway now traversed your home
Cutting its way through the fields of green
Where once wildflowers or small animals had been
Too late if in much later years
We wish to retrieve what we once held dear
The flowers and rabbits will all long be gone
Just a memory, as a pleasant swansong.

*Melanie M Burgess*

## SOME MEN

Some men grow in stature
Some men grow in size
Some men grow no more
The size of their tiny eyes.

Some men travel their lives
Seeing nought at all
Some men travel their lives
Seeing pleasure in plain walls.

Some men look with open minds
All happiness they find
Some men's other points of view
Most men they'll see are kind.

*Ron Marland*

## EXODUS FROM KOSOVO, APRIL 1999

As far as the eye can see
An endless sea of humanity
Forced from the land of their birth
By the hand of tyranny
Into a world of uncertainty
With heads hung low in utter despair
Onward they trek to who knows where
Cold and hungry, tired and worn
With aching hearts and eyes forlorn
Struggling on through wind and rain
Will they ever see their homeland again?

*Don Wilkinson*

## THE NEVER BORN

Murdered before they even see the day;
Begotten not of love, nor any light,
But only pleasure of a passing night,
Into death's rising dark tide cast away:
Young lives they are, whatever men may say.
No pity for them in their helpless plight,
Unfriended and unarmed, the crushing might
Of human cruelty they cannot stay.
Unwanted on the world's receding shore,
Without a name, without a home, they know
No sunshine round them, only night complete,
Yet the same way all souls must go, they go.
They, the unloved, the God of love will meet,
Home in that love for evermore secure.

*Diana Momber*

# TIME TO GIVE

November seventeen out there in Greece
Time to turn it around. Think on peace.
The Russian booming in Uzbekistan.
Ethnic cleansing down to a man.
Mighty China and little Taiwan,
Use your own teaching, live as one.
India and Pakistan you're killing too
Live in harmony, what's wrong with you?
ETA with your grievances in Spain,
Valencian or Catalonian, Spanish you remain.
Iraq and Iran what of your spoils?
Politics, religion or the price of oils?
The people that persecuted the Jew,
Those with prejudice you, you and you.
The Irish are trying, so follow their lead.
Killing and fighting, we no longer need.
Nature itself kills enough every year.
Thousands in Turkish earthquakes we hear.
Volcanoes pumping out their lava streams,
Wiping out homes, crops and dreams.
Drought, famine, flood and disease,
If you stop fighting, we can all tackle these.
Make the world a better place to live,
For all you have taken, it's now time to give.

*G Rossiter*

## FRONT PAGE

War in Yugoslavia, starvation in Iraq,
Race discrimination, white against the black,
Woman murders husband puts body in a sack,
Increase in drug addiction, youth goes mad on 'crack'.
Government says inflation is surely going down,
Houses being re-possessed all over every town.
AIDS are on the increase, physicians wear a frown.
Should the Queen pay income tax? That's all up to the crown.
Divorce is causing broken homes, children sleeping rough.
Joy riders stealing cars, police are getting tough,
Villains robbing pensioners, wages not enough,
Common Market ministers call each others' bluff . . .
Front page! Outrage!

*Evelyn Balmain*

## PROGRESS

I watch the rising, unrelenting tide
Of 'progress' creep in ever-widening waves
Up inlet after inlet of life's shore,
Insidiously flooding with white foam
And sinister dark water, one by one,
Each dwindling spit of land, till all in sight
Is fatally awash, save here and there
A grassy tussock that seems to be
Not as yet engulfed. Though perilously small
And ever threatened by the lapping flood,
These quaking, shrinking islets are to me
As holy places where I still can find
Some relics of a vanished way of life,
Some faint reminders of departed joy,
Of beauty, peace and dignity, before
Destructive man took it upon himself
For greedy aims to ravage all the earth.

*Evelyn Scott Brown*

## ONE WOMAN'S HERO IS ANOTHER WOMAN'S VILLAIN

We lived in peace with our neighbours and friends
In a beautiful part of the country
Some were Muslims but it did not offend
They fitted in like the flowers or a tree

He came to tell us they should not be there
They were stealing our homeland and our home
They must go back south, it was only fair
To their own homeland and leave us alone

We owed them nothing, we had let them stay
For a while but it was now time to go
Leave more land for us when they go away
He was so right and would always be so

We lived in peace with our neighbours and friends
In a beautiful part of the country
Some were Christians but it did not offend
We fitted in like the flowers or a tree

He came to rouse them, it caused us alarm
We only wanted to be left alone
When they took our jobs, young men took up arms
He sent soldiers to destroy my home

They raped my daughter and then shot my son
I am made to feel my life is over
As I sit alone in this transit camp
Far away from my beloved Kosovo

*John M Spiers*

# SOMEONE I DON'T KNOW

Another shell flies through the air
From someone I don't know over there
Now he longs for my defeat
This stranger I could pass in the street

I glance to see his face
But a body lies in his place
Killed by someone he never knew
In the street he was passing through

Another plane flies overhead
Another soldier boy is lying dead
Another stranger starts another fight
Surely this cannot be right

He doesn't even know my name
A bomb falls from another plane
A moment later he is lying dead
A soldier's bullet fired through his head

Another shell flies through the air
From a stranger somewhere over there
My friend gives out a sudden cry
I turn to watch him slowly die

Another stranger tries look my way
A moment later he is blown away
I turn to ask why another stranger has to die
But you only get an answer in the form of a lie

*J C Walters*

## WHY

Weary, starved, each day no rest
Outside, inside, still try your best
Raw life for all, for all infest
Laying, lying, each body pressed
Dying, is not world impressed?

In home, on land, each view is sparse
Neighbour too, all lost, but hearts

Failing through our love of greed
Outstretched not hand to those who bleed
Cannot, for life, now runs at speed
Unto ourselves, we want, we need
Souls lost, they are another breed

***Geof Farrar***

## CONCLUSION OF THE CURSE (HOPEFULLY)

The young boy saw his father shot dead,
an assassin's bullet right through the head.
A world-wide vision of that final salute,
everyone said, 'Aah, isn't that cute.'

Tragedy dogged that young boy's heels,
at times it must have felt so surreal.
Father, uncles, even cousins couldn't escape,
murder, drowning, death and even rape.

Next to die was good old uncle Bob,
killed by another assassin, just another job.
Then uncle Ted went with Mary-Jo for a drive,
the car went off the bridge, only one survived.

Through it all he suffered but grew strong and tall,
with a passion for action sports and even football.
Everyone thought politics would be his thing,
he decided the Stock Market had a nicer ring.

The story ended with a terrible mistake,
a plane crash in water, turned a wedding into a wake.
Let's just hope the curse is over at last,
and pray the others can put it all in the past.

*David Ian Muncaster*

## APATHY

'I don't want to be involved' you said,
As two cars crashed at the corner of the street.
One bleeding driver dazed, climbed out,
Then slumped forward in a heap.
The other dead, with his head
Where the windscreen had been.
Eyes staring. He didn't look as though he was asleep.
'I don't want to be involved,' you said.

You walk along. A man falls from a ladder.
With a crunch he lands at your feet.
With aid he could have lived.
'I don't want to be involved,' you said.

Jesus Christ lay there.
A spike from the railing through His side.
Matted blood on His beard, arms outstretched.
'I don't want to be involved,' you said
        And walked away . . .

*Maurice Colclough*

LOVELY NICOLA MANETH
HAD ONE BURNING AMBITION—
TO BECOME A
**PRIMA BALLERINA ASSOLUTA.**
SHE WOULD ALLOW NOTHING
TO STAND IN HER WAY,
AND SHE WOULD USE ANY MAN
TO ACHIEVE HER GOAL, INCLUDING
EMPEROR FRANZ JOSEF HIMSELF!
DESPITE THE EMPEROR'S PATRONAGE,
NICOLA'S AMBITION CREATED
POWERFUL ENEMIES,
BOTH BACKSTAGE AND AMIDST THE
DAZZLING DECADENCE OF
THE IMPERIAL COURT.
ONLY ONE MAN COULD PROTECT HER
FROM THOSE WHO PLOTTED
HER DOWNFALL—
AND THE PASSION SHE FELT FOR HIM
THREATENED TO DESTROY
HER CAREER!

# DESIRE AND DESTINY

"Nicky." Tonio's voice was tortured as he spoke her name. Before Nicola could protest, his arms enclosed her. She was well aware of the passion she had stirred within him.

"No, Tonio. You promised. You promised. I don't love you."

"I know what I promised," her dance partner said, "but I hold you at each performance, our bodies touch, and I cannot control myself."

"Then it would be best if we did not dance together again," Nicola said stiffly. At that point she realized it was David's arms she wanted around her, caressing and fondling her. David's voice she wanted to hear, whispering endearments and speaking of his love. *David, David, David*. It would always be David. She realized suddenly she was whispering his name over and over. . .

# NICOLA

**Dorothy Daniels**

LEISURE BOOKS 🕮 NEW YORK CITY

A LEISURE BOOK

Published by

Nordon Publications, Inc.
Two Park Avenue
New York, N.Y. 10016

# One

"Two hours warm-up, four hours rehearsal, a dress rehearsal and then the evening performance," Magda grumbled. "Lapin will kill all of us before we ever become soloists—or much older."

Nicola Maneth, already in her wool cross-over bodice, pulled on the knitted leg warmers. She was eighteen, a product of nine years of ballet training in the world-renowned school in Vienna.

Nicola said, "What of it? We're performing in the Burgtheater, aren't we? The most famous of all theatres. That's certainly worth something and a good step forward."

"That's all you think of, Nicky—a step forward, then another step and another. Where are you headed? Don't tell me—you have a hundred times and more."

"I shall become a *prima ballerina assoluta*. Don't laugh. I know what I want and I shall have it."

Her bright blue eyes sparkled with enthusiasm for that day in the future when she would have finally become the most important ballet artist in Vienna.

She walked to the *barre* and began her morning leg exercises. With bending and stretching, she warmed up until muscles were loose and coordination good for early practice.

She changed into leotards, black with a red stripe down the side. Now she was ready for more intricate work. The leaps and turns, the art of balance after a leap and the *en pointe* dancing that carried her gracefully across the stage.

She was lovely, even in this sweaty routine. She had bound her hair tightly so her neck muscles were revealed. Lapin, the ballet master, insisted on that so he could catch the action of the head movements, as important as those of the hands and torso. Her hair was a golden color, her face an oval picture of exquisite beauty with large eyes and a delicate mouth and nose. She was, without question, the most beautiful and appealing member of the entire ballet company.

Two hours of this and she was beginning to feel the first pangs of hunger for the day. She tried to satisfy it with a glass of water. Until early afternoon she and Magda rested, spending their time on a small balcony at the rear of the theatre, high enough so they could see the city spread out before them, especially part of the Ringstrasse, that circle of fine houses of the very wealthy, which ended at the Danube.

"I shall live in one of those someday," Nicola said. "With a fine husband and a great deal of money. Of course that won't happen until I reach *prima ballerina assoluta*. I'm not interested in men until after that."

"What nonsense," Magda said. "Each night after the performance, I see you look with longing at the young officers who haunt the stage door. I even think you are jealous of Heinrich, who comes for me each evening. Sometimes when I wish he wouldn't, because I'd not mind being asked to supper by some of the other officers. Most are better looking than Heinrich and you can rely on it, they'd be more generous."

"I am not jealous," Nicola declared. "I'm not even interested. But I do wish I could get along with Lapin better. He keeps calling me a dolt, a knucklehead and

6

maintains I'm not a good dancer when I know I am. I wish they'd fire him, except he is one of the best teachers."

"If you cut his throat, he'd bleed ice water," Magda said. "His pleasure in life is insulting us. Nobody escapes. He hates everyone."

"I have to agree with that."

"Don't you have any other ambitions in life? I know your father is in the diplomatic corps. You could travel with him."

"My father is a courier for the State Department," Nicola said. "There is no great prestige to his rank. No —Mama, before she died, wished me to become a ballerina and Papa insists I carry out her wishes. Not that I mind, because the dance is all I live for."

"I can think of other things," Magda said mischievously. "Especially when I'm with Heinrich. He's not bad at lovemaking."

"Magda, how can you say such things?" Nicola demanded, but with a smile. "Maybe you can get him to take you to the Court Ball. That would be something."

"A fat chance of that. Well, unless we want to be bawled out by Lapin, we'd better get to the rehearsal stage. If you're one minute late, he acts as if it was an hour. I wonder how he does it, with all his romances. They say there's scarcely an actress he hasn't kept overnight in his studio."

"I know I don't trust him," Nicola said. "But I have to obey him because if he suspends me, or fires me, I think I'd die. No one else would have me if he publicly said I was a poor dancer."

"If he does that to me, I'll kill him," Magda said cheerfully. "Let's go."

Lapin was French, a slightly built man, wiry and strong, with an instinct to make life as unbearable for his dancers as possible. Partially bald, a smooth-skinned man of forty-odd years, he considered himself handsome even if his ears were too big and his eyes too small.

He was dressed in black silk trousers and a white, frilled shirt. He was seated on a high stool close to the piano where the musician was already banging out a waltz by Millöcker. There was no finesse to the music, but it was loud and easy to dance to. The subtle phrasings would come during the actual performance.

"You!" Lapin aimed a finger at Nicola. "Come over here!"

Nicola took a quick breath and walked lithely to stand before him.

"I'm giving you fair warning that unless you do better during the rehearsal, I shall remove you from the *corps de ballet,* I cannot have a clumsy one showing up her inability to dance before an audience."

"I am doing my best, *M'sieur,*" Nicola said diffidently.

"You are not! You dance slowly. Your heart is not in it. . . ."

"My heart is in it. So is my soul and all of me," she said angrily, taunted into expressing herself this way by his ruthlessness.

"So you say, but it does not show. Now I want to see some fine *en pointe* work from you. Now . . . at this moment. Show me!"

She had to accommodate herself to the music being played for the whole rehearsing corps, but she made it and she rose on her toes, danced, pirouetted and gave a small leap.

"You come down like a piece of lead," Lapin said. "But you are some better. Now get over there with the corps and let's begin this atrocious exercise by dancers I wouldn't hire for a florin."

He clapped his hands. The corps assembled, the piano began and the rehearsal was under way. It lasted for three hours, a tiring, painful experience under Lapin's lashing tongue.

It was now time to rest, but not eat. No morsel of food culd pass Nicola's lips until after the performance. She napped in the hot dressing room, dreaming her favorite dream of dancing as the *prima ballerina,* coming back again and again for bows. She also began thinking of where her father might be at this moment. The last she knew he was in some small Balkan country, delivering some kind of an ultimatum from Emperor Franz Josef in this everlasting series of small wars and conquests. Her father often insisted everything was on the verge of change and that Austria, as it was now, would never again attain this kind of glory.

A sudden hush in the large room announced the entry of Lapin. All the chatter ceased when he entered. Nicola's dreams came to an abrupt halt. Lapin was walking toward her with obvious intent.

His catlike eyes studied her for a moment. "I came to apologize," he said. "I have been very harsh with you, Nicky, but it has been for your own good. You have the ability to become a fine dancer, but you need more discipline."

"Thank you, *M'sieur,*" she said with all the humility Lapin demanded of his charges, including the use of the French language when possible.

"I have that much faith, I insist that you come to my studio tomorrow for special exercises. You are a bit rusty in your leaps and especially your *balletrie.* Your feet come together with the grace of an elephant, but we can remedy that. Tonight. . .and this applies to all of you," he raised his voice. "Tonight, in the audience, will be the Emperor and his Empress. She is an articulate critic of bad ballet and you had better be graceful if you don't want to be told to leave this troupe forever."

He walked with his usual briskness to the door, turned and looked back at Nicola. "Tomorrow afternoon at two. I will be expecting you."

He walked out, closing the door noisily behind him. The chattering began again, this time with a hostile air and a few choice remarks about Lapin's birthright.

"Why does that silly cluck wait until just before the performance to tell us the Emperor will be in the royal box?" Magda asked loudly. "He disgusts me, this prancing peacock of a man."

At the dinner hour Nicola managed to get away from Magda to leave the theatre and walk to the Burgtheater where she would perform in three or four more hours. The opulence of this structure was evident even on the outside, with the dome rising from the top, surrounded by those figurines placed around it. The building was fairly new and represented all the glory, the gilt, and the pomp of Vienna in 1885.

She walked slowly, conserving her strength, and when she came close to a pastry shop or coffee house she crossed the street. The delectable aromas from such places made her ravenous. Yet she wouldn't have dared eat even a small cup of ice cream.

Presently the first of the carriages began to arrive and she watched the women in jeweled gowns, tiaras, furs and diamonds, helped down from the *landaus*. Bright uniforms of the reserve officers began to appear. Nicola realized she would have to walk fast now to get back in time to make up and warm up.

At nine the curtain arose on the *corps de ballet* already on stage. The music of *Swan Lake* began and the corps began their dance, with their eyes on the royal box where Emperor Franz Josef of the Hapsburgs sat primly erect beside his beautiful and glamorous Empress Elisabeth.

Nicola never tried too hard for fear of revealing any stiffness in her dancing, but tonight she was relaxed and she danced well. They had placed her on the end of the line so that she did much of the dancing just below the royal box. When the white-gloved Emperor clapped enthusiastically, she hoped she deserved some of the applause.

In the wings, while the soloists were doing their part of the act, Magda came over to stand beside her. "Watch out for Lapin tomorrow. He may not want you so much to rehearse your *en pointes,* as to rehearse you in his bed. He is a well-known lecher and often he demands favors from some of the girls, especially those as attractive as you."

"I shall be on guard," Nicola assured her.

"What if he says you will sleep with him or leave the corps? What will you do then?"

"I don't know," Nicola admitted. "Right now I'm concentrating on pleasing the Emperor, not Lapin."

Their cue was coming up. The line formed, danced out onto the stage and for the rest of the performance, Nicola felt that she had done well, certainly as well as any of the others. The ballerina seemed to have noticed it, for as she passed Nicola she smiled and touched her cheek in a token of approval and affection.

Then came the curtain calls and there were several. The Emperor must have been pleased. He stood up to bow to the dancers and signify his enjoyment of their work.

Nicola felt very good about the performance. She believed that she was coming along and before her was a fine future. She removed her makeup, chattering as much as the others in the corps, mostly about the Empress. Nicola was always careful to dress well and tonight she wore a black satin dress offset only with a single red rose embroidered at the hip. The triple rows of ruching at the hem were edged with red embroidery, as were the off-the-shoulder sleeves. The decolletage was low, partially exposing her young, firm breasts. The simple gown complimented her fair skin and blonde beauty. Also, it was effective and eye-catching—and expensive. Her father, who rarely objected to expenses, had grumbled at the bill this one brought.

Of course it meant little, or nothing. She would walk out the stage door, observe all the gaudily uniformed young officers and the wealthy young men in evening dress, but none would bow to her. They were all after the soloists or the ballerina. A few steadies sought out members of the corps, as Magda's young officer, who gravely saluted Nicola before he took Magda's arm. But on his face was a look of desire for Nicola, which he repressed when Magda roughly jerked his arm. Nicola sighed, drew on her gloves and began walking through the small crowd.

Suddenly a young, very handsome officer saluted, then bowed before her. "*Fräulein,* I am Lieutenant Loecher. May I have the honor of your company at supper?"

Nicola was stunned at this approach, but not for long. It had been hours since she'd eaten and her empty stomach reminded her of that fact. She was at last being asked to supper, just like the soloists and the ballerinas.

"Why. . .yes," she said. "It should be most pleasant."

He presented his arm and he escorted her quite majestically to a waiting carriage. A fine one, far better than she'd have expected of a mere lieutenant, even a handsome one.

"I saw your performance tonight," he said as the carriage pulled away. "You were the very best in the *corps de ballet.* Outstanding!"

"Thank you," she said graciously. "I'm very pleased to hear that. Are you from Vienna?"

"Of course. I am in His Majesty's army, on reserve duty at present. Would the Blue Castle meet with your approval?"

"As it is one of the best restaurants in the city," she said, smiling warmly, "I approve heartily."

"Fine. It's a favorite of mine too. Do you live in Vienna?"

"Oh, yes. With my father. He is in government service."

"It shall be my pleasure to see you home then," he said.

It was somewhat strange, she thought, that he was not betraying any ardor, even passion. Almost all the young officers did within moments of getting a girl in a carriage with the promise of a pleasant evening at a fine restaurant. This lieutenant seemed almost detached from the present and was making conversation more out of politeness than interest.

In the ornate and crowded restaurant, she saw two or three of her fellow dancers. Her escort bowed when she greeted them, their escorts bounded to their feet. Protocol was in full swing in Vienna.

"The menu is yours," he told her after they were seated. "Whatever you wish."

"You are very kind, *Herr Leutnant*, but we ballet dancers are required by our profession to eat very little. I shall have a small steak and large salad. No wine, thank you, but do not deprive yourself."

He gave the order and when it came, he began to talk again. In the same perfunctory way, he told her about himself. He came from a well-known family, it seemed. He had been destined for the military since he was a small boy. He'd gone through military college with honors, and he was presently attached to the brigade assigned to guard the palace.

"It must be an interesting life," she said. He should have been holding her hand by now and indulging in the usual sweet talk, his eyes warm with desire, but he was as formal and official as during the ride in the carriage.

"In a way, yes," he said. And then, as if on second thought, he added, "Would you care to see the palace? From inside, I mean."

"You can get me into the palace?" she asked in disbelief. "Without causing trouble for yourself?"

"I assure you, I shall be in no trouble, and it would be

13

a great pleasure to let you see how our Emperor lives."

"Why. . .why, yes, I'd like that. Who wouldn't? But it seems beyond belief, *Herr Leutnant*. Are you certain you are allowed to do this? Especially at this time of night."

"I assure you, it is within my province to let you see the palace. Almost all of it. You will find it a most interesting place. A museum, if you ask me, but a very exclusive one. We can go as soon as we have our coffee."

"You've made me very happy," Nicola said. "I'm quite pleased with our evening."

"It's not over yet," he said enigmatically. Nor did his eyes try to engage hers.

"To celebrate this privilege," she said, "I shall have a chocolate mousse, if you please. I shall eat only half, but I have been aching for a mousse many, many days. I do not have to dance tomorrow and I shall be sure not to indulge myself again."

He ordered the dessert with a tolerant smile, but she had the impression that he was in somewhat of a hurry to leave. She did regard his manner and this incredible offer as being very unusual and she wondered if there were some kind of a string attached to it. But the lieutenant seemed very sincere, although not interested in her as a girl who might arouse him. He acted, she thought, as if he were almost afraid to show any affection or indulge in the slightest attempt at lovemaking. His manner was almost overly formal.

He was, nonetheless, a gentleman and he was an officer, so his word must be good, though she could not understand how in the world he could take her for a tour of the palace at midnight. It seemed both foolish and impossible.

Yet he escorted her to the same carriage, indicating it was not one he had rented for the evening. The uniformed coachman drove them through the nearly deserted streets and on to the Hofburg, one of the royal palaces, this one in Vienna proper. It was a lovely, somewhat austere, but beautifully landscaped building. In the moonlight it looked unreal, lovely enough to take Nicola's breath away.

She hadn't heard him give the coachman any order, but he drove directly to the palace, rolled on up a curved drive, beside a great pool and fountain filling the night silence with the soft splashing of the water.

It was a magnificent building, two stories high and spread over a great area of land. She would have guessed it had at least fifty rooms.

The carriage went on by the main entrance to another at the north end of the building. Here two doormen came forward to help her and the lieutenant down, again an unheard-of service at this time of night. She began to realize this was no ordinary visit.

"I'm frightened," she said. "If you are taking me inside without permission. . . ."

"There will be no trouble, *Fräulein*," he insisted, then added, softly and mysteriously, "unless you make it and my advice is not to. Come along now and stop being as fearful as a silly spinster."

She entered a reception hall that looked as if it extended half the length of the palace. She walked on soft carpeting between rows of high-backed, stately chairs covered in brilliant red velvet. She glimpsed paintings on the walls, and a series of great chandeliers that would have brightly lighted her way if they were lit. The whole palace seemed to be asleep.

For a guide, the lieutenant was singularly silent, not bothering to describe anything or call her attention to some special *objet d'art*. When she dawdled, he seized her hand and urged her along. They began to mount a wide, curved staircase with what seemed to be gold balustrades. At the top, she found herself in another

15

long corridor, softly illuminated by candlelight as the first floor had been.

She began to tremble. There was something wrong. This was not a guided tour of the palace. There was something more behind it, but she couldn't fathom the reason for her being here. When the lieutenant opened a door along the corridor and stood aside for her to enter, she guessed that this was where he would show himself for what he was and what he was after. She hesitated and he seized her arm and piloted her into the room, indicating a very large chair.

"Sit there," he said, "and wait."

She sat down slowly, almost fearfully. The lieutenant backed away, saluted her, wheeled in military fashion, marched out and closed the door. She was alone in this massive room. She arose to look about. There were two candles burning, but casting only a faint glow. Yet she could see the splendor of this room. The walls seemed to be lined with gold leaf and the ceiling was one vast mural of a bucolic scene. Thick rugs were underfoot and near the windows was a bed, quite the biggest one she'd ever seen. Four people could sleep in it in comfort.

She heard the click of a door latch and she whirled about in fresh fear. Someone was walking slowly toward her. She was unable to identify the person, but she could tell it was a man. As he drew closer she saw that he wore an ornate, red and blue dressing gown. He had muttonchop whiskers and mustachios, and he seemed familiar. Then she cried out in astonishment and she curtsied deeply as the Emperor extended his hand to take hers.

"Rise, my child," he said. He didn't let go of her hand. "Are you surprised to see me?"

"Your Majesty, I don't know what to say. . . ."

"Do you know why you are here, my dear?"

"I. . .I was told I might see the palace. . . ."

16

"Oh, yes, and you will. But not by night. By day, whenever you choose. You need only to let me know. I will arrange it."

"I'm overwhelmed, Your Majesty."

"Do you know why you are here? I asked that before, but your answer was unsatisfactory."

"No, Your Highness," she said hesitantly.

"I watched you in the theatre tonight and you aroused me as no girl has done in many years. I sent for you because. . .I want you to spend a little time with me."

Nicola was too stunned to say anything and she was torn between a desire to push this fifty-year-old man to one side and flee from the room and the palace. But she was intelligent enough to know that would be unwise.

"Are you shocked?" His voice was pleasant and held no note of command.

"Perhaps, Your Highness. Yes. . .yes, of course I am shocked. This has never happened to me before."

He chuckled softly. "How enchanting you look when things aren't what you expect them to be."

"I'm revolted, Your Majesty," she said coldly.

"By me?" he asked, still amused by her behavior.

"Perhaps not by you personally. I wonder what I did tonight that made you believe I was the type of girl who submitted to men. Strange men."

"Since I'm your Emperor you cannot say I'm a stranger," he replied.

"I don't exactly mean that."

"What do you mean?"

She pressed her fingertips to her temples. "I'm disturbed by the thought you believe I could cheapen myself in such a fashion."

"My dear child, I think no such thing."

Up until now, she had avoided looking at him once

17

she realized why she had been brought here. However, his tone was so gentle that she turned, despite herself, to regard him. He made no move to approach her and his eyes fully revealed his admiration of her youth and comeliness.

"Then what do you think, Your Highness?" she asked indignantly. "To bring me here, point to your bed and say you wish me to spend a little time with you. Even though you've not laid a hand on me, I feel despoiled."

The Emperor's hands raised, then dropped to his sides. "I would never want to be the cause of you feeling that way. I know I am old enough to be your father. I also know I respect and admire your youth, your beauty and your modesty. All desirable in a young lady."

Nicola's features revealed her perplexity. "Then why would you select me from a room full of women, many of whom are far more exquisitely gowned?"

"No more so than you." He chuckled under those whiskers.

"Who have more poise."

"I doubt that," he said, regarding her with an amused smile.

Nicola sought desperately for some other reason he should desire the companionship of a woman other than she. "Are far more worldly and would know how to please you, make you laugh. . . ."

"It's no use, my dear. It is you I covet. That's the proper word in this instance and I use it without hesitation."

"I have not been made love to before, nor have I made love to a man. I've not even had a schoolgirl courtship."

"Good. I sensed you were a virgin. I will teach you."

"Please, Your Excellency. . . ."

He stepped back, giving her a clear path to the door through which she had entered, though he made no

18

gesture dismissing her.

"I am told you like the ballet."

"I love it, Your Highness. It's my life. I live it every moment of my waking hours."

He nodded. "I admire talent and ambition. Yes. I remember another dancer who paid me a visit—many years ago. She became the *prima ballerina assoluta*. With talent and ambition such as yours, certainly you should have no problem attaining that goal. Even *prima ballerina* is quite an honor. A command performance alone could do it."

Nicola could scarcely believe her ears. She held her breath as his words took on new meaning. He was telling her that what she yearned for was within her reach under a certain condition. She needed only to please him. Yet she wanted to get it on talent. She thought back to the number of girls who were brilliant —some even more so than she—who had struggled to attain the peak she sought to no avail.

Franz Josef read her mind and moved casually to close the distance between them. His hands stroked her upper arms where her gloves didn't reach. His thumbs moved lightly against her soft flesh.

"Please don't," she said, turning her face away from him.

"Do you find me so repelling?" His tone was lightly seductive.

She turned back. "I told you before, Your Highness, I do not. But I've never done anything like this. I feel that you've cheapened me."

"How wrong you are, my dear. You may not realize it, but many women in that room would have felt honored to have been singled out by me for such a purpose. I chose *you*."

She wanted to run from the room, yet she also thought of the advancement in her profession he had

19

hinted about. His hands were moving gently along the bare portion of her upper arm, even caressing her underarm. She felt a slight quickening of her heartbeat and resented the fact that he could arouse in her a sensation that was strange yet exciting.

"Look at me, my dear."

Nicola slowly turned her head. His eyes regarded her with affection.

"I want you to put your arms around my neck. If you are repelled, you may go. The same lieutenant is waiting to escort you."

"I don't think I could, Sir," she said, but there was a tremulousness in her voice that revealed he had aroused her, despite her reluctance to be a part of an assignation.

"I ask you, please try." There was no note of command in his voice.

She stood motionless for a few moments, then slowly raised her arms, placing her hands on his shoulders.

"Put your arms around my neck," he urged softly. "Then look into my eyes."

She did so.

"Now smile, my dear."

Once again, she obeyed. He placed his arm about her waist. "Is that so frightening?"

"No."

"I am going to kiss you—gently."

Nicola stiffened when he said that, but she didn't turn her head away as she had before. She didn't know whether she had fallen under his spell, if she were curious to learn what it meant to be made love to, or if it was because she had a burning ambition to reach the top of her profession. And he might help her.

His kiss was gentle, though lingering, and his lips moved lightly against hers. It was enough to awaken the fires of passion within her. He drew her to him and moved closer to her. A little cry escaped her, but one of desire, not fear.

He released her and stepped back. "Will you stay?"

"Yes," she whispered, now submissive.

"Why?"

"I want to," she exclaimed. "I understand now that you have honored me with this invitation."

"Have I aroused you?"

"Yes," she confessed. "It is an alien feeling but a beautiful one. I had no idea."

"You still haven't, my beauty. But I will teach you. And it will be a joy to do so. Please remove your gloves. Or no—let me."

He eased them off very slowly, letting his fingertips caress her skin until her gloves slipped free of her hands. He raised them and kissed her palms. He lowered the shoulders of her gown and fumbled for the hooks and buttons. Nicola smiled and helped him, even though her face flushed. The dress dropped to the floor and she was in her undergarments. Once again, shyness overcame her and once again he came to her assistance, pulling the ends of the ribbon bow on her corset cover, loosening it and undoing the buttons. He slipped her arms out of it and dropped it to the floor. Her full breasts were now exposed.

"Don't be embarrassed, my dear. They are not the first I've feasted my eyes on, but they are the most beautiful."

He cupped them in his hands, bent and kissed them. Nicola's breathing was faster and so was her heartbeat. He straightened, motioned to her corset and gave a brief nod of his head. Except for stockings and slippers, she was naked.

"Loosen the belt of my robe and slip it off me, the way I removed your corset cover."

Nicola's movements were shy, but she let her hands

21

slip inside the robe, move up beyond his chest and into the sleeves, slipping the robe off his shoulders. It was silk and slid to the floor. He was as naked as she.

His hands moved down to her buttocks, pressing her to him. Their moans mingled. His lips sought hers and imprisoned them. As he used his hands and his body to further arouse her, she relaxed and found she was as eager as he.

"Now, my precious, will you bed with me?"

"Yes, Your Highness."

"Come."

They headed for the bed. He removed her slippers, garters and stockings while she sat on the side of the bed.

"Lie down, my dear. Let me admire your lovely body."

She did so, submitting willingly to his fondling and caresses. He eased himself on the bed to lie beside her. She looked down at his manhood and felt her breath quicken. A smile of appreciation touched his lips as her arms lifted and went around his neck.

His mouth covered hers and moved in a way to arouse her further. She found herself responding, not only with her mouth, but with her hands, which were now caressing and exploring his body. Her heart was pounding as her passion quickened, for he was awakening bliss she'd never even dreamed of. His hands were experienced and as her ardor flamed, she moaned softly, first with desire and then with eagerness and an impatience to complete the act.

He eased her on her back and covered her with his body. Their passion was equal now and she arched her body to receive him. There was a brief moment of sharp pain which was over quickly, to be followed by an ecstasy that rose to a pitch she never believed possible. Their moans and cries mingled and their bodies and hands continued their movements even after their passion was spent. Finally, he murmured an endearment and complimented her on being such a desirable girl who had, in moments, become a passionate woman. He kissed her gently, then lay on his back. She rested her head on his chest and sighed in contentment, reveling in the fact that she now knew the joy and fulfillment of being a complete woman.

"You are a beautiful girl," he said. "And a most responsive one. It has been long since I have been this gratified. Tell me something about yourself while we rest."

"There is little to tell, Your Highness. I have always wanted to be a ballet dancer. I hope one day—and I shall get there—to become a *prima ballerina assoluta*. The very best in the world if I can accomplish that."

"I believe you can," he said. "You have a certain spark, my dear. It shows when you smile and when you dance and. . .when you make love."

"I'm glad that you are pleased, Sir."

"What of your parents?"

"Mama is dead. Papa is in the diplomatic service of Your Majesty."

"Oh? Have I heard of him?"

"It is not likely, Sir. He is a courier and at this time he is in Budapest on some errand."

"I have not asked your name. Usually I do not, but in your case it would please me if I knew who you were."

"I am Nicola Maneth, Your Majesty."

"*Nicola*. A beautiful name. Of course you understand that what went on here tonight is a strict secret. A state secret."

"Of course, Your Majesty."

"Nicola, I believe you will be famous one day, and soon I believe your papa will fare well."

"I am grateful, Your Highness."

He turned on his side and reached for her. "One thing more, my dear, dear child. So long as I live, you will have my ear. Remember that—you have the Emperor's ear into which you may whisper whatever request you

23

wish or any desire to remedy whatever trouble you may find along the way. And now, enough talk. We have more important—and wonderful—things to do together."

Nicola thanked him by kissing the tip of his ear.

# Two

There was a letter in the mailbox when Nicola arrived at the apartment she shared with her father. The message was brief, only telling her he would arrive at the Vienna railroad station in the early afternoon.

That meant trouble with Lapin, because he could very well extend that practice session until evening, out of spite if nothing else. She didn't take time to think about it until morning when she awoke late, with an enormous appetite which she satisfied with cereal and fruit. She was still hungry afterward, but if she reported to Lapin with a full stomach, he'd know it, as he did everything else.

She wondered how she would handle the situation with him. It was true that he was accustomed to providing private lessons for pupils of promise and then enticing them into bed. She was not inclined to surrender to such a man, but she did wonder what she'd do if there were an ultimatum in which her career were at stake.

She read her father's letter again, recalling somewhat dimly that when she first had read it a solution to this problem had flashed into her mind, to be forgotten because of her need for sleep. It was there—the way out. Lapin might be very angry, but there'd be little he could do. At least she hoped so.

Her father had added a postscript that Anna Croft would likely meet him at the station as well. To Nicola, Anna Croft was a dear friend of her father, perhaps even an intimate one because Anna complained frequently about the fact that she would marry her father in a moment, but he refused to ask her after his experience with Nicola's mother.

His duties required him to be away so often and for such long periods of time that there really had been no marriage. Or so it had seemed. He didn't wish to inflict this upon Anna.

It would not be difficult for Nicola to accept Anna as a stepmother. Anna was a tall, well-built woman, not beautiful, but voluptuous. She made no attempt in her apparel to entice a man. She didn't need to. Her deep brown eyes and full, beautifully shaped lips were sensual, but her dress was severe, almost mannish. Nicola believed she dressed that way deliberately to discourage lecherous males. Her work in the special section of the Department of State didn't serve to soften her serious image which, Nicola sensed, also pleased Anna.

Nicola had seen Anna with her father many times and had observed the smoldering passion in the woman's eyes when she regarded the man she loved. Nicola had surprised them twice in moments of intimacy. Once, when Anna's bodice was open, revealing her luscious breasts which Nicola's father was fondling. The second time was when she came home from school unexpectedly and found both Anna and her father on a couch in the parlor, their clothing in disarray. Nothing was ever made of it, but the incidents had sparked Nicola's curiosity about love.

However, of one thing she was certain. Anna's love was two-fold—for her job and for Nicola's father. And always she was kind to Nicola, which was how she knew that Anna had a sense of humor and enjoyed laughter and fun—but only with those she allowed to become a

26

part of her life.

There was time to arrange things, so Nicola hurried to finish breakfast, tidy the apartment in anticipation of her father's return, dress and be on her way to the government building where Anna worked. She sent word to Anna and she came out to the waiting room directly, looking somewhat worried.

"Has your father changed his mind?" she asked. "Have you heard from him?"

"He will be on the train as his letter to you specified," Nicola said. "I have come to ask a favor of you—if you can get off early."

"I can always do that," Anna replied. "I'm more or less my own boss. What do you have in mind?"

"M'sieur Lapin, our ballet master, insists I report to his private studio this afternoon for special lessons. He claims I am failing."

"I saw you dance last night and if you are failing, there were certainly no indications of it so far as I could see. Is he that much of a perfectionist?"

"Yes, indeed he is. But something more as well. I have been told that the girls who go to his private studio for instructions are very often forced to submit to him and I am not about to do that."

"I should think not." Anna's tone held a hint of anger. "You want me to accompany you, is that it?"

"I would be very grateful, Anna. We can go from the studio to the railroad station. If you are not with me, he'll never let me off to meet Papa. So there are two reasons why I wish you would come with me."

"Wait here. I'll be about fifteen minutes. We'll make a day of it. I'm going to be so happy to see your papa again." She touched Nicola's cheek in a gesture of affection. "It is always good to see his little girl whom he adores—and of whom I am also fond."

"Papa will be pleased to see you." Nicola hoped her face didn't flame as the memory of the previous night

27

came to mind. She no longer felt like a little girl.

"You do not mind sharing your papa with me?" Anna asked, her eyes studying Nicola's face intently.

"I am pleased you give Papa his company—and your time. And your love," Nicola added daringly. Somehow, after last night, she felt she could speak a little more boldly.

Anna smiled, revealing beautiful, even teeth. "You understand then."

"Perfectly. And I am grateful."

"You are a dear child. It makes my heart warm that you came to me now. It proves you do not resent me."

"I never did, Anna," Nicola protested.

"You are so beautiful, my dear," Anna said poignantly. "Forgive me if I envy you that and your youth."

"You are brilliant and if I may be so bold, I have seen lust in men's eyes when they look at you."

Anna shrugged. "My body. That is all they want. What I give to a man I give only to your papa. I hope he is true to me. But he is away so much. . ."

"Don't look so sad, Anna. I am sure Papa is faithful to you. Even if he were inclined to be otherwise, he is kept so busy. . ."

Nicola didn't finish the sentence, but she and Anna exchanged glances and laughed in the manner of two women who understood one another and understood life. It was apparent they felt a closer rapport with each other in this moment than they ever had.

When Anna joined Nicola again, they walked the half mile to Lapin's studio. It was located in a rather drab building just off the Ringstrasse. They went up a flight of narrow stairs, and walked down a dark and dismal corridor to the door on which Lapin's name was inscribed. Nicola knocked and the door opened at once.

Lapin was scowling. "You're late. I am not accustomed to wait for my pupils. I. . ." he saw Anna.

"Who is that? I don't want silly people cluttering up the lessons I give."

"This is Miss Anna Croft," Nicola said. "She works for the Department of State and she is my best friend."

The fact that Anna seemed to have an important job with the government softened Lapin's objections, though he still scowled and was inclined to be very curt in his instructions and especially in his criticism.

He confirmed, just once, what it would have been like if she'd come alone. He did it subtly, but there was no question of what he was after. He held her at the waist while she did a series of turns *en pointe,* and when she faltered just the slightest, his hands moved quickly to engage her breasts.

She stopped instantly and flushed with anger. He stepped back. "You are too clumsy," he said, realizing what he'd hope for wasn't going to develop now or at any other time. "I cannot teach a cow to dance like a feather. You have little coordination and you are always off balance."

Anna Croft walked toward them. "*M'sieur,*" she said in a stern and uncompromising voice, "if you call my friend a cow, you have no right to try to teach her, nor to supervise any kind of ballet, let alone the Royal Ballet. She danced well last evening. I was there and I know. I heard comments about her skills from people I never saw before. What do you want of her, *M'sieur*? A dancer or a courtesan? I saw what you did a moment ago. I know your reputation, and I strongly advise that you behave yourself and stop this criticism of Nicola's dancing. She is as good as anyone in the *corps de ballet*, and you very well know that."

Lapin made an elaborate, sardonic bow. "I am grateful for your comments, *Madame.* However, in what you said there is but one word of truth. You said I am the ballet master of the Royal Ballet and that is a fact. That title gives me the privilege of picking my dancers as

29

I see fit. Nicola, you are fired. Pick up your practice clothing at once, but take none of your costumes. Good day, ladies."

Nicola was angry and at the same time on the verge of tears. Anna was beside herself with rage.

"I should not have talked to him that way, but he made me so angry. I saw him fondle you and I know how right you were in not going there alone. That man is impossible. He may be a great ballet master, but he is not a man fit to be in the company of respectable women. Still, I can't forgive myself."

"It wasn't your fault, Anna. If you had not been with me, I would have been forced to scream for help, or fight him, and either way it would have brought on the same thing. I would have been fired. But there are other ballet troupes. Perhaps even better ones."

"Do not try to fool yourself, Nicola. The Royal Ballet is the only one worth its salt. Perhaps that impossible man will cool off and realize he made a mistake. I would not give up hope yet."

"How can he change his mind? You heard what he said. Anna, please don't tell Papa about this. Not right away. It would spoil his homecoming."

"It would—yes, no question of it. I'll be silent."

"Could we have the carriage stop at the theatre so I can gather up my practice clothes? I'm afraid if I don't he may throw them away. He's like that. I'm well rid of the man, even if I do have to start all over again."

"There may be something we can do about it. Of course we'll stop by the theatre."

They hired a carriage from a line of them outside a hotel. Anna remained in the carriage while Nicola hurried into the theatre by the stage door. Magda was in the dressing room, eating a breakfast biscuit which she hastily thrust under a pile of towels on her dressing table.

"Oh, it's you," she said and resumed eating the biscuit. "What happened? You look like you've been crying or are ready to."

"I've been discharged," Nicola said. "Lapin told me I danced like a cow. He was angry because I brought Anna Croft to the studio and he never had a chance to make me do what he wanted, though he did let me know what he was after."

Magda scowled. "He's done that once too often. We're going to have to take some drastic action."

"What can we do? He's the ballet master. His word is law."

"It may be law, but it can be changed if he's ordered to change it. I'm meeting Heinrich in a few moments and I'm going to ask him if he knows of anything we can do."

"Please, Magda, don't get yourself into trouble because of me. I appreciate what you wish to do, but remember that Lapin is a most vindictive man."

"If he fires me, I'll gouge his eyes out. That prissy little skunk. I tell you, he is not the Emperor, though he often seems to think he is."

The Emperor! Nicola drew a sharp breath. What was it he had said only last night? She had his ear. He would listen to what she said and act upon it. She could go to him. But how impossible that was. She'd need an excuse to ask for an audience and if there developed the slightest hint of any closeness between her and Franz Josef, the Empress would be angry. Nicola decided she couldn't take a chance on that.

"You have any ideas?" Magda asked. "You seem to be thinking hard enough."

"No, I have no idea how to make him change his mind. And right now I can't do anything about it anyway. Anna is outside. We're meeting Papa in—" she consulted the watch attached to her chatelaine—"about twenty minutes. I've got to run."

"Come by when you can," Magda said. "I'm still

going to tell Heinrich.''

Nicola rolled up her practice clothes and hesitated a moment. "Magda, I don't want Papa to know I've been discharged. If he sees my practice clothes, he'll guess. May I leave them with you?"

"Of course," Magda said. "I'll take care of them."

Nicola returned to the carriage and urged the driver to go as fast as possible. She didn't want to keep her father waiting.

"You didn't bring your clothes," Anna observed.

"Magda is taking care of them. We can tell Papa about it tomorrow, but not tonight. I didn't want him to see the clothes."

"A good idea. Nicky, if your papa is ever promoted and given work that keeps him in Vienna, would you object if he and I were married?"

Nicola quickly embraced Anna. "I'd be delighted. Papa needs you. Everyone needs love. I'd welcome you as my new mother. I will pray Papa gets that promotion, but I wouldn't count on it."

"I'm not," Anna sighed. "I know enough about the way he is regarded to realize he is the most trusted courier we have. In these troublesome days, that is a rare commodity. They'll never change his position."

"Sometimes I wish he wasn't quite so conscientious," Nicola said. "But that's the way he is."

Otto Maneth, in a long, dark coat and a black slouch hat, was the first off the railroad car. A slim, assured man blessed with classic good looks, he saw them instantly and broke into a trot in his eagerness to greet them. He embraced and kissed Anna first with an ardor that betrayed his affection for this unusual woman. He then turned to Nicola, kissed her and held her at arm's length.

"It seems to me that you grow skinnier each time I come home. Are you sure this dancing isn't affecting your health, my dear child?"

"Of course not, Papa. Stop fussing. Oh, I am glad to see you again, to have you home once more."

"I'm glad to be here and that's an understatement," he said. "Both of you have been well?"

"Very well," Anna said. "I've been looking out for Nicola. She comes to me and we have good talks. Sometimes about you."

"They must be dull."

"No more than you, Papa," Nicola said jokingly, giving him an adoring glance.

"Will you be with us long?" Anna asked, her tone hopeful.

"I'm afraid not. There are certain matters which came up, that I happened upon. They could be most dangerous. I will have to explain them to my superiors and I know they'll send me right back to Budapest to verify what I shall report."

Anna linked her arm under his. "No more talk of business or diplomacy. I insist that we stop at your favorite restaurant for supper. Please don't refuse your daughter and me, dear Otto."

He nodded cheerfully, but Nicola realized that something of great importance bothered him. He was too quiet, even during the fine supper that Anna selected from the menu.

Nicola indulged herself with the unspoken excuse that she had been fired from the ballet anyway, though she did restrain herself when it came to the rich, whipped cream dessert.

They had their Viennese coffee strong—with a mound of whipped cream. In Vienna, everything seemed to be covered with whipped cream.

"My dearest," Anna said, "you may as well be dining alone. Something is troubling you."

"I have to tell you," Otto said. "Since the Turks were defeated and Macedonia was taken from them, there has been trouble over who gets the land. Bulgaria,

33

Serbia and Greece are fighting over it already. Franz Josef insists on mediating the problem and he favors giving most of it to Greece. At least, that is the talk in diplomatic circles. So, either Serbia or Bulgaria—I haven't been able to find out which—have plans to assassinate Franz Josef on the assumption that upon his death Franz Ferdinand may become emperor and will be easier to handle."

Anna shook her head. "They are mad, these people who fight over the spoils of war. I would suggest it is Serbia that is to blame."

"I am inclined to agree," Otto said.

"What are you going to do about it?" Nicola asked.

"One thing. The Emperor must be told so he can take measures to protect himself."

"It would be wise to let him know at once," Anna suggested.

"I intend to make my report first thing in the morning."

"Papa, how did you discover this?" Nicola asked.

"By chance. Just plain luck. One of the conspirators hinted about my being paid a large sum if I would cooperate in a project he had in mind. I led him on sufficiently to guess it was a plot to assassinate someone. I pretended to go along with it, and I then heard enough to know whom they were going to kill."

"But isn't it dangerous if they guess you are going to tell the Emperor?" Anna asked.

"Perhaps. But I doubt they have the slightest suspicion that I will stop their plans or that I know enough about them."

"Do you know these schemers by name?" Anna asked. "They should be apprehended and punished before they hatch another assassination plot."

"I know who they are," Otto said. "They go by false names, but they can't change their faces. I can identify them and I will. No doubt they'll send me back and take precautions so that when I point out these men they will be promptly arrested. The Serbs won't have any idea why I am back."

"It was the Serbs then?" Anna asked.

"Well, yes. They are the main plotters. I can assure you their plans won't work. But now let's go home, Nicola. I'm tired and I have an important day tomorrow when I report."

When they reached Anna's apartment, Otto accompanied her to the door and they stepped inside. He was gone only minutes, but when he returned Nicola noticed his quick breathing. She felt guilty being with them. Had there just been the two of them, she felt certain he would have spent some time with Anna. They would have made love and she would have helped him forget the frightening plot he had uncovered. Also, the tension he must be so filled with was still with him. She made no attempt to talk with him as they continued on to their apartment.

Once inside, Otto shed his hat, coat and tie, removed his shoes and Nicola quickly supplied a footrest for him.

He smiled his gratitude, though it was weary. "I'm tired, daughter, but I don't wish to go to bed yet."

"Would you like to talk?" Nicola asked, seating herself on the floor in front of him.

He nodded. "About Anna. Would you resent my marrying her? I have enough love for both of you."

"How wonderful that you have given the matter thought. Anna and I discussed that very subject today. She too, feared I might object to sharing you. Do you think me so selfish, Papa?"

"No, my child."

"What made you change your mind? I'm referring to all the traveling you do and how you feel it interferes with marriage."

"It does, but I cannot go on alone. I need a woman's arms about me. A wife to fulfill my needs. Anna has

35

been a faithful companion. I believe you understand what I mean.''

"Papa, you are a man and Anna is a woman. You are both human, blessed with good health and a capacity for love. It is natural. Living alone is not. You need each other.''

"Then you are in favor of a marriage between us.''

"With all my heart. I will rest easier knowing she will be with you.''

"Oh no,'' Otto objected quickly. "Her work is much too important for her to give up. She is brilliant. And I think it would be a mistake for her to do nothing but travel with me. She would become bored. I just want someone to come home to. And I want it to be Anna.''

"Anna wants it as much as you,'' Nicola assured him. "As for her work, I have no idea what she does, though I sense it is important, just as I sense she is extremely competent. She has never discussed it with me, but I believe she still thinks of me as a child.''

"So do I.'' Otto leaned forward and pinched Nicola's cheek lightly.

"I'm a woman, Papa,'' Nicola said seriously.

"Of course,'' Otto mocked. "A woman with a secret lover. Come, my child, you will be a woman soon enough.''

"Papa,'' Nicola wished to get the subject away from herself, "just what does Anna do? Or can't you tell me?''

"Of course I can. She is attached to the cipher division. It is secret and important work. That is why I wouldn't want her to give it up. She would be lonely and unhappy—like your mama who spent her time just waiting for me to return and cried her heart out every time I was sent off again.''

"When will you propose to Anna?''

"Before I leave.''

"Will you marry before you go away?''

36

"That will be up to Anna."

"When will you be going back? Have you any idea?"

"Soon, I suppose, but there is no great need for haste. It takes a long time to put one of these assassination plots into motion. The schemers have no idea I know as much as I do. When I go back, we'll surprise them."

"You're sure there is no danger to yourself, Papa?"

"I doubt it. As I said, they are not aware of how much I know."

"But don't they have spies everywhere? I've heard there are so many spies all around us, they almost rival the army in numbers."

"True enough, but the majority are not dangerous. I don't worry about them anyway. Tomorrow I'll make my report and discharge my duties, until they see fit to send me back. Maybe it will be for the last time. I deserve a promotion for this because it is a matter of the greatest importance. Saving the life of the Emperor should be rewarded in some fine way. Now I'm going to bed. Wake me early, Nicky."

Nicola slept badly that night, even though there was great comfort in having her father home. She was worried about him. He had a tendency to accept things with an amazing nonchalance. She had rarely known him to worry or fret over any situation. Perhaps there was no danger if the assassins didn't know he was going to reveal their plot.

Her thoughts switched to the disaster with Lapin. She was no longer a member of the Royal Ballet. Finding another troupe would be so difficult that she surmised she would have to leave the country in search of one. Lapin wielded a great deal of influence in his field. If he said she danced like a cow, she was doomed.

Every plan, every dream she ever had, was now gone,

vanished in the angry words of a disappointed man who gave praise only as a reward for the sexual favors he demanded. Nicola hated him with an ardor as great as her sense of loss.

There was no use crying about it. When her father left to visit his superiors, she planned to go to the theatre and retrieve her clothes. By evening she felt she could tell her father the truth about her dismissal. He would feel badly about it, but she depended upon his asking Anna to marry him to soften his disappointment over her failure. She was pleased he would ask Anna's hand in marriage.

At least Nicola knew Lapin had made an unfair decision. She was a good dancer. She'd trained the better part of her life and she could have danced as a soloist and done a fine job of it. But it was gone now. Not because she wasn't skilled enough, but because she was not about to let Lapin have his lecherous ways with her.

She saw her father off late in the morning and after his departure, she cleaned the apartment. She realized that when her father and Anna married, they would have to look for a larger place. Apartments were scarce, but anyone with the diplomatic corps could wield a great deal of influence. When both man and wife were employed there, it was unlikely they would be denied what they wished in the way of living space.

Nicola walked to the theatre, a rather long distance, but she needed time to think and to accept this dismissal. Nevertheless, it was agonizing to hear the music of *Giselle* as she entered the theatre. It was one of her favorite ballets and it made her cry. Her whole life seemed to have stopped in its tracks.

The corps was hard at work warming up. A few of the girls were testing steps to the piano music. Lapin, in tight pants and lace shirt, was angrily telling one girl how badly she danced. He looked up and saw Nicola.

"So you finally decided to show up!" he said. "Do you think you are a prima ballerina who can come and go as you please? Get into your warm-up clothes and go to work. What nonsense to behave this way. Report back here and be quick about it."

"But, sir," Nicola said in amazement, "yesterday you told me. . ."

"Yesterday, yesterday! What about yesterday? It's done with. This is today. You will know it too before the day is over. You will be learning the second solo for the next performance, and if you stub your toe I'll have your head. Go—get busy. This is ballet, not musical comedy."

She was still dazed, but she obeyed him. Magda managed to leave the *barre* where she'd been warming up and accompanied Nicola to the dressing room.

"What in the world happened?" Nicola asked. "To have him change his mind like that! And I'm to be second soloist. It's unbelievable."

"Someone," Magda guessed, "put a flea in the ear of someone else. I told Heinrich and he said he would do what he could, but that poor clunk of a man does little except talk. Yet this time he seems to have accomplished something."

"Whatever made Lapin change his mind," Nicola said, "I am most grateful. I thought I was surely finished."

"So did I. He could see to it you never danced again, that stinker. I wonder if he has something in mind. You know what I mean. A grateful girl would be more apt not to resist. . ."

"He knows better. After yesterday he certainly realizes there is no chance." Nicola frowned slightly.

"There was something else that caused him to relent. I'll find out some day. I'll know whom to thank."

She reported to the floor, warmed up for two hours and then took Lapin's instructions for her solo part, which was not too difficult a task, but a decided advance in her career. She danced very well, even though the part was somewhat strange to her. Lapin had the grace to compliment her.

"You are fulfilling my earnest hope that you will be a success and soon a prima ballerina, Nicky. I am proud of you."

She could only smile and nod. She was speechless. Magda was not. In her practical manner, she issued a warning.

"You were lucky," she said. "But take care. This isn't going to make you well liked by the others. They are going to say that you got this featured spot and all this praise because you went to his private studio yesterday. . .and you know what they'll believe that means."

"Anna Croft was with me every moment," Nicola said. "So I can put a quick stop to such gossip. Still, there has to be some reason. . ." She stopped talking abruptly. Something Magda had said before rang a bell. What was it? Something about someone putting a flea in Lapin's ear. That was it! The Emperor had said she had his ear for anything she desired. He had learned of Lapin's dastardly behavior, informed him of his anger and instructed him to take her back. That had to be it! Nicola smiled and felt a glow of warmth. It was a pleasing sensation. The Emperor's statement had not been made only in the warmth of passion. He had meant every word.

"Now what are you thinking about?" Magda asked. "Such a beautiful smile. I stand here like a dummy while your thoughts go sailing off into space. Besides, we'd better get back to rehearsal before Lapin changes his mind again."

Long after the others had gone, Nicola prevailed upon Tonio, the second male soloist, with whom she would dance, to remain and practice the more sensational part of their *pas de deux*. Nicola, *en pointe,* was required to take fast steps, throw herself up to be airborne and safely land in Tonio's arms without breaking her neck. They were clumsy at first, not having worked together before, but after a dozen tries they developed a grace that both knew would stand well with any audience. Nicola's solo part also went well and she could improve it by practicing alone.

"We are going to be great," Tonio proclaimed. "We will show up the prima ballerina and that partner of hers, that Loren, who thinks he is a virtuoso."

The performance was not for four days, on a Saturday night, when the elite would be sure to attend. Nicola knew her chances of achieving stardom would not be far off if she succeeded in dazzling the audience that night.

Her hopes, so miserably dashed a few hours ago, now soared higher than ever. The Emperor had remembered. It never entered her mind that he would. But that was their secret and she would show him how well she could keep it.

At home she found an exultant Otto and Anna. Something else had happened. Otto explained it before Nicola could tell them her good news.

"I have made my report and action will be taken when I return to Budapest, this time with enough men to make the proper arrests. The Serbian government will be warned not to interfere with us. And after that, my dear Nicky, I am to be given a desk in the State Department. An important one. The Emperor himself ordered it after I reported personally to him. It was wonderful news."

"It's even more wonderful that your father and I are going to be married as soon as he returns from this last mission abroad," Anna said happily. "You may congratulate us, my dear soon-to-be daughter. Oh, Nicky. We shall be such good friends."

"I'm sure of it," Nicola said happily. "And I've got good news too."

"He relented," Anna said promptly. "Lapin took you back."

"Indeed he did."

"What's all this?" Otto's attention switched to Nicola. "Took you back from where?"

"Oh, it's of no consequence," Nicola began, already sorry she had intruded in their gaiety.

But Anna would not be denied. Her arm went around Nicola's shoulder as she addressed Otto. "Yesterday that miserable excuse for a man—that Lapin monster—ordered Nicky to report to his private studio for instructions. She knew what those instructions would entail, so she asked me to go along. My presence angered Lapin, but while I was there, he tried to arouse Nicky, placing his hands on her breasts during the dance. There was no excuse for his behavior. When she gave him no response save a plain rejection of what he wanted, he fired her and said she danced like a cow."

Otto's voice was that of an angry man. "If ever the opportunity comes across my desk to punish this man, I'll make him sweat. But Nicky, I'm proud of you."

"There is more to the story." Nicola's smile was reassuring. "He not only took me back, he acted as if he had never fired me and. . .I'm to be second soloist at the next performance!"

"Whatever made him change his mind?" Anna asked. "He was so insulting when he fired you."

"I don't know," Nicola said. "I wish I did, because someone must have reached him and been quite persuasive in making him back down. I'm gratified that it turned out this way. I've already practiced with Tonio, and he is as ambitious as I. I have confidence we will perform well together."

"I hope I don't have to miss that performance," Otto said, adding firmly, "I won't miss it. If they try to send me back, I'll protest. A father has a right to see his daughter become a ballerina. A prima ballerina."

"Oh, Papa, not yet," Nicola said. "Give me a little more time."

He smiled mischievously. "Perhaps a week or so? I'm pleased and very proud. I suggest we open a bottle of champagne. Two bottles. We have two wonderful things to celebrate."

# Three

There were days of rehearsals, productive ones, for her solo part was now perfect and her role with Tonio in the *pas de deux* was without a flaw. She had learned how to project herself. Leaping into his arms became routine and she no longer feared it.

Her father, meanwhile, had been assigned to an important desk in the diplomatic service with chances that one day he might be granted an ambassadorship. He was yet to return to Budapest to identify the spies, but his superiors thought it best to let them prepare their plans before striking. In that way they might be able to capture not only those her father could identify, but perhaps even more important ones.

Nicola was beside herself with joy. In the next twenty-four hours three very important incidents in her life were to unfold. First, she was to perform this night. It had been arranged that her father be allowed to remain and witness her performance. The next morning her father and Anna were to be married and that very day they would go to Budapest, apparently on their honeymoon. As a new bridegroom, Otto would surely not be suspected of having plans against those who plotted the death of Franz Josef.

They were in a gay mood late in the afternoon. Anna had purchased an evening dress for the occasion and brought it to their flat where she would dress. Nicola persuaded her to model it. When Anna emerged from Nicola's bedroom, both she and Otto were speechless, for Anna looked magnificent, like a goddess. The dress was of ottoman and silk. The bodice and train were burgundy and the skirt a hunter's green. The brief sleeves touched her shoulders and the bodice revealed that Anna, despite her large frame, had a small waistline. Her full breasts were shown to advantage in the low decolletage, and Nicola noticed her father give what he thought was a private nod of approval to Anna as he eyed them. Nicola didn't blame him. Anna was sensuous from the top of her head, crowned with auburn hair, to the tips of her toes. Her curves, though generous, couldn't help but arouse any male who viewed them. Nicola felt her father was a lucky man. But then, so was Anna, for Otto was a commanding figure, with piercing blue eyes, prominent cheekbones and a face that revealed intelligence. But his was a serious nature, as was Anna's, and they saved their fun and lovemaking only for each other.

Tonight they were to dine at one of the best restaurants after dropping Nicola at the theatre. A carriage would call for them at five-thirty. That would give her plenty of time for a little more rehearsal and to make up her face and dress.

"Would it," Otto asked his daughter, "make you too lonely if Anna and I went off to Paris for a week or two after we finish our work in Budapest?"

"Of course not, Papa." Nicola embraced him as further assurance. "What kind of a honeymoon is searching for assassins? Go to Paris and enjoy yourselves. Please don't worry about me. I'll be busy every moment and will need plenty of rest in between. Don't forget, I am to solo in seven more performances and then I'll likely be given a part in another ballet. I'm hoping for *Sleeping Beauty*. There is a very important second solo there and I already know most of it.''

"Well, in that case," Anna said, "Otto and I will stay for a month if I can persuade him. He has that much time coming to him and so have I. But if you are to perform at any time during those weeks, let us know and we'll come back. I wouldn't miss it for anything, not even a honeymoon.''

"Nor I," Otto added.

In pure joy, Nicola kissed her and embraced her father. Everything was perfect, even the finding of a larger apartment right on the most important section of the Ring.

When the time came to leave, Anna was helped on with her cloak by Otto. Nicola put on her plain brown lightweight coat. She removed the theatre tickets from her purse and placed them on the table.

"Don't forget them," she told her father. "The performance is a sellout and you'd have difficulty getting in without them."

He went into the bedroom to survey himself in the full-length mirror while Anna adjusted the flower at her waist. Nicola went to fetch her gloves.

They walked downstairs, singing, laughing and without a care. The carriage waited outside. Suddenly Anna grasped Otto's elbow.

"The tickets! You didn't pick them up."

"Damn," Otto exploded, in pretended annoyance. "You two women make me forget everything. But that's a small sacrifice for what pleasure you give me. I'll fetch them."

"No," Nicola said. "I will."

"Let me," Anna said. "We can't let Nicky expend herself on such an errand up so many steps. She needs

46

all her vitality for tonight. Besides, I forgot to slip my sachet into my bosom.''

"We'll be in the carriage," Otto said. "Come along, Nicky. We'll relax in the carriage until Anna joins us.''

Nicola and her father stepped out of the apartment-house foyer to stand at the top of the four brick steps. Otto called to the carriage driver that they would be with him in a few moments.

A young man came by, glanced up, tipped his hat and bowed slightly.

"That is Leopold Kramer, a lawyer with whom I have had a little business some time back," Otto raised his hat. "Nice fellow."

The departing Leopold Kramer almost collided with a man who was hunched over, walked with a shuffle, wore a hat with a rather large brim, and kept his head down until he was opposite the entrance to the apart-ment house. He came to a stop, straightened up and at the same time leveled a revolver at Otto. He pulled the trigger twice, and Otto flew back against the apartment house door to sag slowly to the brick steps in a rapidly growing pool of blood.

Nicola, too stunned to move, saw the lawyer whirl about at the sound of the shots. He yelled something at the assassin who immediately began to run. It was then that Nicola found her voice and she screamed.

There were people on the street and some of them made half-hearted attempts to stop the murderer, but he was able to elude them. The assassin was almost at a corner around which he might disappear and never be found, but at that moment two young officers con-fronted him. They knew nothing of what was going on, but the assassin, at the sight of the uniforms, thought they had come in answer to Nicola's screams. He started to turn and run back. One of the young officers responded with remarkable speed. He jammed a fist into the face of the murderer and the other wrestled the assassin to the sidewalk. It was all done in the space of five or ten seconds. The assassin scrambled to his feet and made another attempt to get away, but in his haste, he forgot there was a curb where the sidewalk ended. He tripped and fell heavily, emitting a cry of pain. By then police had arrived, the street was beginning to fill with the curious, and vehicles had come to a stop.

At the entrance to the apartment house, Nicola knelt and tried to raise her father's head. His eyes had rolled back so only the white showed and he was unconscious and limp. But she thought he still breathed. The lawyer was at her side, feeling for a pulse.

"I'll get him to the hospital," he said. "You stay here and wait. I'll come back."

He picked up her father in his arms and yelled to the coachman to get back in the carriage. He placed Otto on the back seat, got in beside him and the coachman used his whip as the carriage went off in a burst of speed.

Anna came out the door and looked about in amazement. She saw Nicola still kneeling, saw the blood, and her face went pale. She cried out in anguish.

"Nicky. . .Nicky. . .was it Otto?. . ." She helped Nicky to her feet.

Nicola, still dazed, nodded in assent. Then she pressed her face against Anna's breast and wept. "They've killed him, Anna. They've killed him. That man fired twice. I'm sure Papa is dead."

"Don't lose courage, my dear," Anna said, her concern now for Nicola. "You don't know that he is dead. But do you know who shot him?"

"He has been taken," Nicky said, her voice breaking. "Something happened and he fell and I think the police came. There were uniforms. . ."

"We can at least be glad of that. Did your father speak?"

"Not a word. What am I to do, Anna?"

Anna's arms enclosed her. "Now you listen to me, Nicky. Your father lived to see you become a great ballet dancer. You may not know it, but his ambitions were not the equal of those he had for you. No matter what has happened, he would wish you. . .even order you. . .to go on with the dance. You must! Your whole future could rest on it. Do it for him. He was a dedicated man and a brave one. Now you must prove part of him lives in you."

"What are you asking, Anna? Could you?. . ."

"Yes, I could. Don't forget—tomorrow was to be my day of days. Your papa and I were to be married. Perhaps we will be. You don't know how badly he was hurt. Now listen to me. You must stop trembling. Please, Nicola. Will you listen and try to be calm?"

"Yes. . .yes, I'll try."

"I can see the police are here in force and soon they'll come to question you. The fact that you have to dance tonight means nothing to them. They'll never let you get away just to perform at the ballet. There is a rear door to this apartment building. Come with me!"

She pushed Nicola inside, closed the door and led her to the rear of the foyer, into a corridor that extended to the back of the structure. There they descended a few steps and opened another door to emerge into an alley. There was no one about. Anna wasted no words. She accompanied Nicola to a quiet street, down along it until they saw a carriage. Anna hailed it.

"Dance, Nicola," she said. "Dance for your father. He will live and he will be very proud of you. He is not dead. We would have heard by now if he was."

Nicola didn't understand how that could be possible. Her father must have either reached the hospital or not even arrived there yet. But she knew Anna was right. Her father would have wanted her to go on, to act as if nothing was wrong. Give a fine performance and weep afterward. She knew Anna was doing her best to bolster her courage.

"I'll do my best," Nicola said. "Anna, will you go to the hospital and see him? Right now?"

"As soon as I find another carriage. I'll tell him how brave you are. He'll like that. Now, in with you."

Anna gave the driver the name of the theatre and told him to drive fast. Just before the carriage began to move, she checked it and spoke to Nicola.

"You'll be driving through the crowds that have gathered. Don't let the police see you. You must not be stopped, or your performance will never take place."

She opened her purse and handed the coachman a bill. "Take this and get to the theatre as quickly as you can. Don't stop for anyone."

The carriage pulled away and Nicola dried her tears and kept her head down as they rolled along the boulevard in the direction of the theatre. A large crowd had already gathered on the street, everyone seemed to be asking questions. The police were everywhere, but there was no attempt made to stop Nicola's carriage.

She reached the theatre, but by then she had barely composed herself. She hurried inside. As a solo dancer she had a dressing room to herself and her costumes were all laid out. She was glad she didn't have to talk to anyone except the maid who would assist in dressing her. Nicola applied her makeup and was gratified that it hid the redness of her eyelids and eliminated all traces of the tears that had coursed down her cheeks. She kept telling herself silently that her father was not dead. The range from which the assassin had fired was not close. Perhaps some of the force of the bullets had been lessened. Perhaps one of the bullets hadn't hit him. Her father was a man with a great zest for life. He'd fight death and he'd defeat it. She told herself this again and again. It was the only way she could conquer the fear and agony that threatened to overcome her.

The music had already filled the theatre. Nicola, in a pink tutu and a flower crown on her head, emerged from the dressing room to run into the excitement of the performance already going on.

Tonio joined her. "I was getting worried," he said. "You didn't arrive too early, you know."

"I'm sorry. But I'm ready. We shall do well, Tonio. We must!"

"Don't worry your pretty head about it, Nicky. We have the routine down so we could do it with our eyes closed. But I don't think you should close them just before the leap. You might wind up in the orchestra pit."

Magda danced off stage with the *corps de ballet* while the principal dancer was still in the midst of a solo. Magda rushed to Nicola's side and embraced her.

"Be good, darling. Be the best dancer in the business. Show that insolent pup of a Frenchman you didn't need his help. And here he comes. Kick him once for me."

She passed Lapin with an expression of contempt which, fortunately for her, he did not see. He grasped Nicola and turned her about to face him.

"Why the devil did you have to be late tonight? This one night and you're not here to rehearse. That's what every ballet dancer needs. Rehearse and rehearse, right up to the moment they go on stage. If this happens again, I swear it will be the last time I'll give you a chance like this. And perform badly just once, and you're out of the ballet for the rest of your life. Do you understand?"

"Oh, come now," Tonio said. "You know very well we are very good."

"You keep out of it," he snapped back at Tonio. "What happens to you isn't worth a fig to me. But

51

Nicky is. She can dance and she can go far. Are you ready, Nicky? This is but one step. However, no other step will ever be as important."

She recalled that her father had once said that. She nodded slowly and reached for Tonio's hand. The music cue was to come in a few seconds. She was in another world now. One where there was nothing but music and dancing. She could think of nothing else, only how to make every step and move graceful and beautiful.

"Now!" Tonio said, and they emerged onto the stage. It was not a long sequence but a lovely one. The music was lilting and happy. Nicola danced. She was air- borne and she fell into Tonio's arms with all the grace she'd practiced to attain. Then she was alone and now she went into her solo, every move perfect. Even before she finished, the audience began applauding.

She made her exit and fell into Tonio's arms. He held her, and looked down at her. "What's the matter, Nicky? There is something wrong. I could sense it."

"Did anyone else, do you think?" she asked.

"You were perfect. No one ever danced that sequence better than you. I'm proud of you, proud to work with you because you make me look better than I am."

Lapin was there at her side. "You did well," he said. "Better than I hoped for. There are a few little. . ."

"Damn it," Tonio said tightly. "She never made a mistake. Don't destroy her confidence. We've another sequence to do. Why don't you just go away from us, Lapin? Give us a chance and keep your everlasting criticisms to yourself."

He glowered at Tonio, but he turned away, muttering to himself.

"Thank you, Tonio," she said. "I needed your help."

"What is wrong?" he insisted.

"My father. . .an assassin. . .just before I came to

52

the theatre. . ."

"Oh, my God!" Tonio said. "Nicky, I'm sorry. How bad is it?"

"I don't know. There's no way I can find out. I've prayed every moment while I danced that he is alive, but I don't know."

"I'll say one thing, he would have been the proudest father in Vienna if he had seen you dance. Now, even though it's painful, try to put it out of your mind. We'll go on in about twenty minutes. Stay with me. Don't be alone. I'll talk myself hoarse to keep you from thinking. . . ."

She reached up and kissed his cheek. "Thank you, my good and kind friend. I'll be as good as I can. As you said, assassins fail most of the time. But I do wish Papa could have been here."

"There'll be other times." He led her away from the crowded wings. "Many, many other times, because you have the spark to become a famous dancer. A prima ballerina."

She tried to smile. "You left out one word, Tonio."

He frowned. "Now what could I have left out?"

"*Assoluta*! That's where I'm bound, Tonio, and I hope you are with me as *primo danseur*."

He embraced her and held that embrace while she grew silent and rested her head just below his shoulder and wept, but only a little. Their next *pas de deux* came up and they danced onto the stage to perform with a skill equal to, if not better than, their first appearance. This time the applause was sustained and they took three bows before the show went on.

Then it was over and all this make-believe dissolved as Nicola found herself back in a more sordid world where violence had struck. She hurried to her dressing room to find Anna there alone. Nicola needed only to look at Anna's somber expression to know what she was about to say. But Anna didn't put it into words. She only shook her head slowly in a gesture of defeat and hopelessness.

Nicola wept.

"He never recovered consciousness," Anna said. "I was at his side. He died a martyr, Nicky. A martyr to the cause that has saved our Emperor from death and the nation from perhaps another vicious war. The assassin is in police custody and Franz Josef has given orders that he is to be tried as quickly as possible. They'll shoot him, likely. He deserves worse than that, but at least he did not escape. I arrived in time to see part of your last dance. Oh, Nicky, he'd have been so proud. You were wonderful. You should hear the comments that went on while you were on stage. There's not a soul in this troupe who doesn't know you are bound for great things. If that becomes the truth, then you will have honored your father's memory far more than I could have done."

Nicola wiped the tears from her eyes. "You know, Anna, I had a feeling he was in danger. I think he knew it, but he wouldn't admit it. Perhaps not even to himself. I'm sorry. . .for you, Anna. You would have been my stepmother and that would have made me so happy."

"I can still pretend I am. We are not going to let this break us up, Nicky. He wanted us together and that's how it will be. Just as if he were alive."

"Yes, Anna. Dear Anna. If I can, I'll make up for what he meant to you. I'm all right now. I won't break down again. I know the truth and I don't have to wonder any more. We must not be overwhelmed. There is too much to be done."

"I've already heard there is to be a state funeral. The Emperor will march and every dignitary will be there. If you're ready, we can leave now."

Nicola was dressed. She pinned on her hat and they left the dressing room to walk between the many admirers who had managed to get backstage. No one spoke to Nicola was grateful. If they did, she might have broken down again.

Only Lapin moved toward them. Anna scowled at him. "Get out of our way," she commanded.

He stepped aside hastily, and seemed perplexed by such treatment.

The police were at the apartment lobby waiting for her. A high-ranking officer accompanied them to the apartment. Anna excused herself and accompanied Nicola into a bedroom.

"If you don't feel up to this," she said, "I'll try to handle it."

"No, Anna. I appreciate this, but I have to face this now. I think tonight I grew up very suddenly. Papa told me once that tonight would be a turning point in my life because he believed I would dance so well. But he had no idea how sharp a turning point it became. I have to stand up to it. He would have, and I can do no less."

The police official asked countless questions, but always came back to the important one. "If you saw this assassin again, would you be able to recognize him, *Fräulein*?"

"Yes," she said. "I'll never forget what he looks like."

"He is, and quite a surprise it is too, a very important man in politics. A respected man whose story, that it was another who shot your father, will perhaps be honored by some. And he has a brother and a father who are even more important. They are going to call you a liar, *Fräulein*."

"I saw him. I will know him again in a crowd of a thousand. That's all I have to say."

"Do you recall the man who was there when it

happened? The one who took your father to the hospital?"

"Oh, yes. He was very kind and most helpful."

"He is a lawyer named Leopold Kramer."

"My father knew him. Just before it happened he mentioned his name."

"Good. He was positive at first as to the identity of the assassin, but now he isn't quite as sure. He will testify that he saw the murderer, but a good lawyer may be able to weaken his testimony. That's where your evidence comes in. It will be the most important of all."

"I will testify," she said. "I know what I saw and no one can make me testify to anything different."

"Fräulein Croft has stated she was not at your side."

"No, sir. I had taken the tickets for the ballet from my purse and placed them on that small marble-topped table. I warned Papa not to forget them, but he was forgetful at times and this time. . .well, he didn't take them. Anna went upstairs to get them and it happened while she was gone."

"I saw nothing, unfortunately," Anna said.

"Well, I think we have a good case. That will be all for now. I ask that you hold yourself in readiness to testify. The funeral will be tomorrow and the next day this murderer will be tried. The Emperor has commanded that there be no delay."

Fortunately for Nicola, everything did move so quickly she had no time to be alone or to think too deeply. The Emperor had caused the murder to receive maximum publicity by making a statement honoring Otto Maneth as a hero worthy of the elaborate funeral the following day. The procession stretched for a mile and the uniforms reserved for ceremonial occasions predominated. Nicola rode in a carriage with Empress Elisabeth and found her both sympathetic and charming. There were a few moments when Nicola actually felt ashamed of herself for what happened between her and the Emperor, but common sense told her it was not of her doing, nor had it been willed by her. Likely it had happened many other times with other girls. The Emperor had a reputation for not being true to his Empress.

The ceremony was long, and speeches extolling the bravery and virtues of her father would have made him blush if he could have heard it all. Then there was the firing of the guns, the bugle call, and it was over. Nicola curtsied before the Empress and she was embraced by her.

"I will not forget that your father gave his life so that my husband's might be saved. Be proud of him the rest of your life, my child. As I will be."

Anna rode with her in the carriage that took them home. As they entered the apartment, Nicola came to a stop and looked about.

"Until right now I never noticed how lonely it is, and will be. Will you live with me, Anna?"

"I have thought about that, but I doubt it would be beneficial to either of us. Please don't think that I dislike the idea, but I'm thinking of you. There is so much in life waiting for you, Nicky. I would only be in the way. You are an independent person, you will weather the loneliness better than I. However, I shall never be far away. You may reach me at any time and whatever I can do, I shall. I'll stay with you for a few days, of course."

"Thank you," Nicola said. "I do believe you are right. I'm going to continue to devote myself to the ballet. I'm more determined than ever to reach the absolute top if I can."

"You will, Nicky. I have no doubts, nor has anyone else. You were superb that night, despite the grief that must have weighted you down."

"I succeeded mainly because I knew that was what Papa would have wanted. And now I go on from there."

"With a small interlude. A disagreeable one. Tomorrow you have to be in court."

"I know. I don't dread it. I can face anything now."

"Perhaps you should drop the whole thing. It will be a horrible ordeal."

"No, Anna. I want that man punished for what he did. It was to keep Papa from identifying those who planned to assassinate the Emperor."

# Four

Nicola and Anna took their assigned seats in the front row of the courtroom. Both wore black. "They're bringing the assassin in now," Anna said.

Resolutely, Nicola trained her eyes on the man she recognized. He was about twenty-five or six, a really handsome man with a great shock of curly light brown hair and a pleasant-looking face. He was well dressed now, not wearing that sleazy coat and the sloppy hat. He looked coolly at Nicola and she quickly averted her eyes.

"The nerve of him," Anna said. "I've found out a few things about this man. It surprises me, just as he does now by looking like anything but some stupid assassin. He comes of a fine Serbian family and his relatives are important people in Serbia. Some even here in Austria. He is well educated, a very ambitious young man. He has never been in trouble before, he isn't known to be any kind of revolutionary and he doesn't look the part. It may be that he'll be found not guilty, no matter how positively you identify him.. I know he has good lawyers."

"He is guilty. I don't pretend to say I wish his life to be taken, but I do believe he should never again be allowed to be a free man, nor permitted to ever forget what he did."

"They forget," Anna said with a shake of her head. "That's the easiest thing to do. Your father was dangerous to the cause this man represents. Killing your father was a necessary thing to them."

When the trial began, a dozen witnesses testified to seeing the prisoner run away. No one had ever seen him before, nor heard his name—Michael Sander—ever spoken. The two officers who had intercepted him had not seen the murder and had not seen a gun in the hand of the accused, though they found one in the gutter. They knew only that they realized there'd been a crime committed and they believed this prisoner to be guilty.

The trial went into its third day. Fortunately there was some time during the day when Nicola could report to the theatre and dance, but there were no performances. Each day she sat in court and listened to the testimony of people who wanted to help, but just didn't know enough to convict Sander.

Leopold Kramer, the young lawyer who had been almost beside the assassin, gave very direct and damaging testimony, but the lawyers for the accused man were able to weaken it, though not disprove it. Kramer was not intimidated by the questions.

He described the man who had passed him by, a man he looked at casually. He'd seen him as a person, probably poor, badly dressed, humble enough to keep his head down. He admitted the garments the assassin had worn certainly were nothing the almost dapper accused would wear. But he insisted he had seen enough of his face to recognize him now. Still, he had not seen the shots fired. He had not seen a gun. He saw the man running away and had to admit there were a great many other people on the street.

Anna said, "It's going to depend on you, Nicky."

"I will testify to what I know. No more, no less."

When she took the stand, her story was brief,

straightforward. She could not be induced to change a word of it or her identification of Michael Sander as the man who had suddenly straightened from a slouching walk, raised his head as he raised his gun, and fired two shots. Again and again she swore that the murderer was now seated in the defendant's box. She was calm and confident, and showed no trace of fear.

Sander's self-assurance was beginning to crumble as she answered the countless, repetitive questions in a quiet voice.

The trial day ended when she was dismissed from the stand. She went directly home, but as she left the courtroom she saw a man on an end seat who had attended every session of the court. She'd noticed him because he seemed somehow familiar. Like someone she had seen, or who had been pointed out to her. She had no idea of what his name was; she knew she'd never met him.

He was a sturdy-looking man of no more than twenty-seven or eight. A man with a ruggedly handsome, compelling face and confident manner. He would be afraid of nothing, she thought. He was expensively dressed too, but again with a difference she couldn't lay a finger on. Expensive clothes, but not quite like those worn by Viennese gentlemen.

On the last day, when Sander was to testify, this man found it possible, perhaps by arrangement, to occupy the seat next to her. The judges were not yet on the bench.

The man at her side spoke softly, though the tone was deep and masculine. "*Fräulein*, you are as brave and intelligent a lady as you are a dancer *par excellence*. I saw your performance."

Anna leaned over. "Is he bothering you, Nicky?"

She shook her head. "He has just complimented me, Anna. I don't think he means any harm."

"Thank you," the man said. "I really don't, but I do intend to make an offer which I hope you will not

61

refuse."

"An offer?" she asked. "Whatever do you mean, sir?"

"This isn't the place for it."

"I don't mind, and you have made me very curious. Besides that, I have a feeling I've seen you before somewhere. . . ."

"My name," he said, "is David Jackson. I'm an American."

"The actor!" she exclaimed and all but forgot she was in a courtroom. "Of course. How stupid of me. I've seen your picture dozens of times and I've heard of your accomplishments on the American and British stage. I'm very happy to know you, even under these conditions." She indicated the crowded courtroom with a brief gesture of her hand.

"The rest can wait. I would be honored to take you to supper when this is all over. You. . .and your companion. It will be a business proposition I have to offer."

"You may call upon me whenever you like, Mr. Jackson."

"Thank you. I've been all over Europe searching for someone. When I saw you dance, I knew you were the one."

Sander was on the stand. He made an impassioned denial of shooting Otto Maneth. "I was there, close by," he admitted. "The man who did the shooting was an uncouth sort of person. I do not claim that Fräulein Maneth is trying to have me executed just out of some imagined recognition of me as the man who murdered her father. I believe, in her opinion, she has given honest testimony, but she is mistaken. No one else identified me positively. Not even Herr Kramer. He too was honest and fair. I ask that Fräulein Maneth be once again questioned as to the authenticity of her former testimony. I am an innocent man and all I ask is justice.

I have indicated often enough that I admit my clothing was shabby too, but I like to dress that way occasionally."

"He's lying," David Jackson said. "He's very convincing, but he lies. I'm an actor and I know how it's done. He's not a bad actor himself, but he's guilty. There's a little shifting of the eyes, a slight tremor of the voice when he says something dishonest. You are not making a mistake, Fräulein Maneth."

Nicola took the stand again and for two hours she fought off all the insinuations that she was using Sander as a scapegoat to satisfy her own ego that she was not mistaken in identifying him the first time. Her testimony was just as calm and assured as before. When she was dismissed, she returned to her seat while the justices on the bench conferred with one another.

Without leaving the bench, they found Michael Sander guilty and they sentenced him to be shot within the next two days. He was led away with his head high and a gleam of hatred in his eyes as he looked back at Nicola.

Anna held her arm as they left the courtroom. David Jackson made no attempt to accompany them, respecting the agony Nicola had gone through these past few days.

"Well," Anna said, as they were being driven home, "he got what he justly deserved. If he'd been found not guilty, it would have been a great travesty of justice. You did very well in giving your testimony."

"You were afraid for me, weren't you?" Nicola asked. "You said so a few times, even if you were perhaps not aware of it."

"Of course I was afraid for you. That man killed your father and he has many friends and allies, none of whom would be averse to killing you if it would keep you from testifying."

"I thought, more than once, that they might try."

"If they'd killed you, that would have been a complete admission of guilt on the part of Sander. They couldn't stop you from giving your testimony. Everything is over now. I'm not sorry, but there's just one thing. I wish that you would not fall into conversation with any handsome man who comes along."

Nicola laughed for the first time in days. "Why, Anna, he and I are of the theatre. He is one of the most illustrious young actors in the world. He means nothing, except that we share a love for the theatre. It's possible I shall not see him again."

"Nonsense. He said he would call. And I know he will. There was a look in his eyes. I recognized it. He's an admirer of yours. Don't get involved."

"I shall only listen to what he calls 'an offer'. I am not saying I will consider it for a moment. I'm quite satisfied with what I am doing now."

"Most handsome men are philanderers," Anna reminded her. "Take Sander, who will be shot the day after tomorrow. He's a handsome dog who killed your father without any compunction."

David Jackson called on Nicola the following afternoon. Anna was not there, being busy at her government desk. Nicola admitted him happily, because with Anna away, the apartment seemed lonely and there were too many memories to dwell upon.

"A most attractive apartment," he said as he sat down. "Homelike, which is something I miss, since I live mostly in hotels."

"Papa used to say that too. He was always glad to come home. Will you be in Vienna long?"

"That depends a great deal on you, Miss Maneth."

"Really? What is it all about?"

"We are going to do a musical show in New York. Likely it will travel around the world if it's successful. A completely new kind of show. You might call it a light opera. I know you have these here. In fact, Vienna is noted for its operettas, but this one will have a book. . . a story—and the music will be a part of it. Then, to make it completely different, the book demands a solo dance by someone who can do ballet. Someone who is young but highly skilled.''

"You interest me," Nicola admitted.

"The idea breaks away from tradition and that's what is going to put it over," he said enthusiastically. "I searched the United States for a girl to fill this part, but I guess we're rather provincial there. More so than Europe. Ballet has not reached the popularity it enjoys here. Perhaps something like this will change all that. At any rate, if you are interested, I'll bring a script and the music the next time I call."

"I trust I won't be required to leave Vienna overnight. I have my father's estate to settle and then there is this disagreeable business about his assassination."

"You will have no less than six months, but once you make up your mind, there will be a contract. I can tell you now that the terms will be generous and I'm certain you will earn a great deal of fame from this. We believe the show will last about two years."

"Naturally I will have to think about it and see the script and music, but I admit I am intrigued, Mr. Jackson."

"Good. I hoped you would be. It's a radical step, I know, but as I said, it may be highly profitable careerwise."

"Thank you for giving me the opportunity," Nicola said. She didn't want him to go. Not only because he relieved the loneliness, but he was interesting to talk to.

"May I serve you tea? Or coffee?" she asked.

"I'd be delighted. In fact, it's a perfect excuse for not leaving."

She hurried into the kitchen and discovered that he had followed her to watch her prepare a pot of coffee and set out some of Vienna's pastries.

They sat at a small table in the parlor, beside the window overlooking the Ring and all the movement on the streets. He told her about himself, how he had come from a family of actors and been initiated into the theatre when he was seven. His father and mother were now dead. They'd been quite famous in their day, doing musical comedies mostly.

He had gone to the legitimate stage as soon as he was old enough to handle the more difficult roles and had been lucky enough to have opened in a show that ran for months and was highly acclaimed, with most of the praise for the actors.

"I'm devoted to music," he explained. "I like singing and dancing. I'm better at the first than the second, but I get by. It would be my pleasure to show you New York, and perhaps, a number of other cities if the show is a success."

"It would be wonderful," she admitted. "I have no contract here. Not yet."

"Please give me a chance before you sign anything," he begged. "I really want to work with you."

"I'm sure it would be my pleasure as well," she said. If he'd had a contract with him and offered it, she had a wild thought that she would have signed it.

"Perhaps," he asked hopefully, "supper tonight? If you are performing, a late supper? We could talk more about this show and what it could mean to you."

"I'd be very pleased," she said without the slightest hesitation. "I am not performing, so we can make it an early supper. It is up to you."

His face was alight with pleasure. "I've traveled far to find someone like you, Miss Maneth, and it was worth every mile. I'm going to be very persistent, I warn you."

"We shall see," she said. "I do have to rehearse this afternoon, however, but you may call for me here at, say, eight?"

66

"Fine. And thank you for considering my proposition and for agreeing to have supper with me."

He held her hand for a long time and looked directly into her eyes. He wasn't trying to mask his feelings and she knew they were genuine. For the first time in her life she had met a man she knew she might fall in love with, if she had not done so already. And she hadn't missed the admiration and warmth in his eyes. Before the evening was over, she felt that she'd know for sure, but she cautioned herself to be wary and not encourage him. There was her career.

After David left, she hurried to the window to look down at the street for another glimpse of him. She was old enough to know better, but she did wish to see him, even from such a distance. He, in turn, stopped across the street and looked up, scanning the building to fathom which of the windows were hers.

Anna had said she'd be late, so Nicola dressed quickly and went straight to the theatre. She put on her warm-up clothes and joined the half dozen dancers already at work on the *barre*. Lapin had not yet put in an appearance. Tonio wouldn't be here, so Nicola practiced a few steps of her solo and thought of nothing else except her engagement for supper with David Jackson. It annoyed her, in a pleasant sort of way, to be distracted from her dancing.

It was after five when she decided she had to leave and return home in time to devote some extra care to her appearance. Before she could get out of her warm-up clothes, a middle-aged, bespectacled man approached and gave her his card.

"I represent Michael Sander," he said. "The man sentenced to death."

"What do you want with me?" She glanced at the card. "Herr Hahn?"

"My client asks that you come to see him. I'm a

67

lawyer.''

"To see him? Impossible," Nicola said. "I want nothing more to do with him."

"He insists it is of vital importance, to you and to him. He also says if you do not come, he will tell everyone that you were afraid to face him because you know you were mistaken and are sending an innocent man to his death."

"No," she said. "Absolutely not! I fulfilled whatever duty was required of me in court. I have no wish to carry this any further."

"Then," he said, "I am required to hand you this note."

She accepted the folded bit of paper and glanced at it.

"You will see," Hahn went on, "that it is from Anna Croft. I interviewed her prior to coming here to see you because I wished to find out what your reaction would likely be. You can read for yourself that she thinks it wise to talk to the man. It can do no harm. Certainly not seeing him might be far more harmful."

Nicola tore the note into shreds. She was accustomed to following Anna's advice and there seemed to be no reason why she should refuse this time. It was true that Sander might possibly make trouble for her somehow, perhaps even with David Jackson.

"Very well," she said. "I will go directly to the prison, but it must not be a long interview. I am very busy this evening and I have little time."

Hahn bowed slightly. "May I remind you that he has even less time."

He left and she finished removing her warm-up clothes and quickly dressed for the street. She wished to get this unpleasantness over with.

During the carriage ride to the prison, she fell to wondering what he could possibly want of her. He was doomed. Nothing could save him. The trial had been fair, the judges so impressed with his guilt they'd not even left the bench before finding him guilty. Possibly he would ask her to change her testimony, but this she would never do. It was her duty to tell the truth. Whatever the result, it was up to the court to pass judgement, not her.

The gray-walled prison was an austere, forbidding place, close by the outskirts. A rather lonely place she thought, for the few streets were deserted. She applied at the gate for permission to enter. It was granted so promptly after she identified herself that she thought she must have been expected.

A deputy warden met her outside his office. He was tall, angular man with a fringe of gray hair around an otherwise friarlike bald head.

"Fräulein Maneth, I have seen you dance and you are wonderful," he said. "My wife has commented on this too. Also I think you did a brave thing testifying against this assassin who will die tomorrow."

"What can he want with me?" she asked, after she thanked the man for his generous comments on her dancing.

"Only one thing. A condemned man's last request. He knows he is going to die and he is concerned with trying everything he can think of to save his neck. If he becomes too insistent, just call out and a guard will escort you out. Also, I may add, that there is no law compelling you to answer his request for an interview. You can turn around and leave this minute if you so choose."

"No, I'll see him."

"Then come with me."

Behind bars, Sander seemed remarkably cool for a man about to die. He wore prison clothes that detracted considerably from his once suave appearance.

"Thank you for coming to see me," he said brusquely. "I'm sure you know why I asked you to come. I beg of you to go before the court and tell the judge now that you have thought it over, but you are no longer certain I am the man who killed your father.''

"May I ask why I should do that?'' she asked calmly, though her heart was pounding.

"A token of pity, an expression of mercy. I am not much older than you. I have a wonderful life ahead of me if I am set free. There is much in this world for me to do, and I swear it will be beneficial. You are cutting off my life in its prime. I will not kneel before you to beg. I ask this of you in an unemotional manner because I speak the truth. I did not shoot your father. You are mistaken. This I swear. I do not accuse you of being dishonest, or of seeking revenge for the death of your father. I say only that you are mistaken. If you let my life become forfeit, you will have to live with your guilt for the remainder of your days.''

Nicola sat on the edge of the hard chair, her spine as rigid as her determination not to be swayed by this man. Though he said he would not beg, his eyes appealed to her for mercy.

"You were not more than ten feet away,'' she said. "You looked at me directly as you fired. You were waiting to kill my father. You are a member of a violent group against Franz Josef. You shot my father. I saw you do it and I will not change my testimony.''

"Not even if I predict dire consequences for you if you do not?'' he asked in a voice gone cold.

Nicola spoke with quiet determination. "I suppose you are inferring I will be murdered as my father was. I will not be intimidated by your threats. If you have nothing further to say, Herr Sander, I will leave.''

She began to rise. "You can give a dead man a few more seconds,'' he said. "I have to warn you, *Fräulein*, that you have made a hasty decision you may regret.''

"Good day,'' she said.

"I am not an ordinary man, *Fräulein*.'' He arose as she did. "I am an important man, with much to do with my life. If you choose to cut it off, that act will haunt you to your dying day."

"Herr Sander," she said in a flat, unemotional voice, "your death will not haunt me in the slightest. My father's death will, and you were responsible for that."

"I don't mean 'haunt' you in any ordinary way. I am not referring to ghosts, or to your guilty conscience. I refer to something physical. I mean that you will be in danger so long as you live. You will be stalked as an animal would be by a hunter, eager for the kill."

She walked briskly to the door without looking back.

The deputy was waiting outside. He walked with her to the prison office.

"Was I correct?" he asked. "Didn't he ask you to change your testimony?"

"He not only asked me to, but threatened me if I did not."

"Threatened you? He's in no position to carry out any threats, *Fräulein*. The man is probably terrified. He anticipates the death that will come to him tomorrow."

"I agree," Nicola said. "However, he knows his threat did not dissuade me. I told him I was not afraid. You may be assured I will do nothing to aid this murderer."

She walked out of the prison, reached the sidewalk and saw a closed coach at the curb with a driver on the box, looking at her expectantly.

She gave the driver her address and opened the door of the coach. Before she could climb in, a hand reached out, seized her wrist and she was roughly pulled into the coach. Before she could scream, a large hand clamped down on her mouth. She was dragged onto the seat.

The coach door was still open and she was able to observe a man emerge from the shadows of the prison wall, move to the edge of the sidewalk and look up at the barred windows, as if by prearrangement, to look for some kind of signal. It was apparent he must have seen something, because he turned abruptly, entered the coach and sat down beside Nicola so that now she was squeezed between the two men.

The newcomer produced a bottle and a bit of cloth from his coat pocket and held them before her eyes. "This is chloroform," he told her. He removed the cork and thrust the bottle under her nose. "I do not wish to use this, but I will if you make the slightest sound or try to struggle. If you behave yourself, you will not be hurt. Do you understand?"

She nodded as best she could with the hand pressed tightly across her mouth.

"That's better," the man at her side said, slowly releasing his hand from her mouth. "We are taking you to see someone who may change your mind about asking for Sander's freedom. It will be a reasonable request. We have no desire to harm you. Only to explain matters as we see them."

She nodded again, but she placed no faith in what he said, and she was right. Suddenly a heavy sack was brought down over her head so that she could scarcely breathe, let alone see.

The coach was in motion. It wasn't going to be possible to see where she was being taken. She could rely only on the promise that she would not be harmed and she placed no credence in it. Sander had said that she would be haunted by physical reminders of her refusal to help him. This was likely a part of that threat carried out after Sander had managed to give some sort of signal from the window of his cell.

The two men on either side of her never uttered another word. She tried to estimate the time involved in getting to wherever they were taking her. When the coach slowed, made a turn and came to an abrupt stop, she thought it had been a ride of about fifteen minutes. Then she heard the sound of an iron gate being opened. The hinges must have been very rusty on one side, because the gate squealed loudly. But the second gate swung open almost soundlessly. So one gate was in need of oil, the other was in better condition. She stored that bit of information away.

She was determined to remain as cool as possible, to learn all she could and to defy them under any conditions. This was a last ditch effort to free the man, silly as she believed the attempt to be. It would gain them nothing.

The man on her right spoke. "I am getting out of the coach. I will help you down. Do not try to remove the hood over your head. I shall be compelled to take very drastic action if you do. As I said, behave yourself and you will not be harmed."

"Whatever it is you want of me," she said in a voice muffled by the hood, "get it over with."

Suddenly she remembered that David Jackson would be calling on her in an hour, perhaps even less. But there was nothing she could do. It was still daylight, she knew, and she must have been brought to some place so private that it didn't matter if she were led across an open space and up a dozen stairs while her head was encased in a hood. She would have attracted all sorts of attention if this was a public street. Apparently her abductors felt perfectly safe here.

She heard a door open, she was guided into some sort of building and she heard the door close. The man grasped her elbow and brought her to a stop.

"We are going to climb some steps," he said. "I'll make certain you don't fall."

She counted the steps. There were twenty-one, so this must be a structure with a high-ceilinged first floor. She was unable to distinguish any smells; the hood prevented that. At the top of the stairs, she was turned to her left and then down what must have been a corridor. She heard a door open and whispered voices held some sort of consultation.

She knew she was then led into a room of some size, because when those present began to talk, their voices sometimes came from a moderate distance.

"You may sit down," her captor said. She felt a chair pushed against her legs. She lowered herself cautiously and waited. Nothing was said; there were no movements. She surmised this was a form of intimidation to allow her time to develop a healthy fear so that she would be more willing to bow to their demands.

A man's voice said, "We know you refused to spare Michael Sander's life. That was a mistake. You will pay for it if you still refuse. There is time to change your mind. To save his life, which is in your power to do. I'm sure you understand what I am saying."

"I understand," Nicola said. "Sander also threatened me, and my answer to you is the same as I gave him. I will not change my testimony. I told the truth."

"So you say. Remove the hood."

It was yanked off her head, but the difference in her ability to see was not improved. She was able to distinguish some shadowy forms across this long room. There was someone seated in what must have been a high-backed chair, because the figure was not in profile even though the room was faintly illuminated with a shaded candle situated somewhere behind her. All she could see were shadows. There was no way of identifying anyone.

"It will do you no good to threaten or to harm me," she said. "You seem to forget that it was my father who was killed."

"Let me speak." A man's voice came from the darkness. It seemed to originate from the direction of that tall chair, but Nicola wasn't sure. It could have come from someone behind the chair, or beside it. No matter, it was clearly meant that she was to believe the occupant of the chair was speaking as the leader of this group.

She thought there were three, possibly four people in the room. She was sure one of her captors, the one who had been inside the coach, had not come upstairs. So if there were four men here, three of them she had never seen. The fourth one she had. She'd managed the barest glimpse of the second man in the coach. Neither had looked in the least familiar.

"Fräulein Maneth," the voice said, "this man, whose life dribbles away while you refuse to help him, is a figure of some importance. In due time, if he lives, he could be one of the most important personages in the world. He is young, he is clever and intelligent. He is in line to take command of forces that will accomplish much. Even change history. If you allow him to die, you will deprive the world of a great man."

"I will deprive the world of nothing more than a cold-blooded murderer who gives his victim no chance. The great man you refer to is a rank coward at heart."

"Too bad. A pity to be as young and pretty as you and so obstinate."

"I am only doing what I must, and that is to keep telling the truth. Sander killed my father. That's all I have to know. What he would become in the future is of no consequence to me. I refuse to believe he has a future beyond tomorrow. Now you may inflict whatever pain you wish upon me, but I will not change my testimony and there is no use in asking me to do it again, nor to threaten me further."

"We do not threaten you with pain. We can do better than that. We threaten your future. Michael Sander was on the threshold of something he had striven for all his life. There was a pinnacle which he sought to attain and he was on the verge of it. Now he is going to die. While you will live. You, a dancer with a bright future ahead in the ballet. Oh yes, we know all about you, Fräulein Maneth, from the day you were born to the moment when you agreed to meet an American actor. So one day

75

you will come to the same pinnacle as Sander. You will have reached your goal, what you fought for all your life. You will stretch out your hand to grasp it. Fame, fortune, adulation—and you will die. Just as Sander will die at the threshold of his moment of achievement. Do you understand me, Fräulein Maneth?"

She tensed, poised herself for a quick leap from the chair. She could move faster than they could stop her. What she intended to do was reach whoever sat in that big chair and seemed to be in command.

"Answer me!" the voice commanded harshly.

She leaped to her feet and dashed in the direction of the chair. But someone she had not seen in the dark stepped before her, and she collided with a man who held her tightly in his arms.

"This one needs to be taught a lesson," the man who held her said. "Do I have that permission? It will be my great pleasure."

Nicola was closer to the figure in the tall chair, but she could see nothing more than a deep shadow. Only the dim outline was visible. She saw whoever it was nod slowly. The man who held her shouted in glee and took her into his arms.

"Open the side door," he called out.

Someone moved to obey. She was carried through a door, her legs striking the side of it. There were half a dozen more steps and she was violently thrown upon a bed. She tried to wriggle off it, to escape somehow, but the man was atop her now. His hands tore at her shirt-waist, ripping off some of the buttons. He opened her corset, pulled it from beneath her and cast it aside. He squeezed and manipulated her breasts until she cried out in pain. She turned her head aside when he tried to press his mouth against hers. The gesture either angered him or filled him with sadistic glee. His head moved down to her breast and his teeth pierced her flesh, forcing a moan from her.

His hands tore at her skirt, pushed it down and kicked it free of her ankles with his feet. Her efforts to fend him off seemed only to increase his carnal desire. He kicked her legs farther apart and entered her with such brutality she screamed. He slapped her across the face so hard she grew dizzy and faint. She went limp and made no further move. It would serve only to further his brutal appetite.

When it was over, the man slid off her, but sat on the side of the bed, his hands still moving over her flesh. Her legs were spread wantonly, but when she tried to bring them together, he forced them apart roughly. His hands squeezed her thighs, forcing a moan from her which served to further excite him. Her eyes were closed, but she could hear his breathing deepen as his lust arose. His body covered her again and his hands slid under her buttocks, raising her into position to receive him. She wondered how she could endure more of this horror.

The same voice came from the dark. "That will do—for now."

Reluctantly, the rapist moved his hands, letting her drop to the bed.

The voice spoke again. "Fräulein Maneth, will you think once again about the incident concerning your father? Think about the wisdom of going to the authorities and telling them you were kidnapped. Being such an honest person, you would naturally also tell them you were raped. Think of how that will enhance your reputation as a lovely young ballet dancer. It will get your name and picture in every newspaper. Whatever chance you had to improve your standing as an actress will be driven into the muck of sensationalism that newspapers dote upon."

She said nothing, nor did she move. Her body was seething with pain from the ordeal. She wondered if she would ever be able to forget the horror and humiliation of what she had been forced to endure. She heard the sound of movement. Then a voice—that of the man who had taken her prisoner.

"Get up and dress. Your clothes were not completely destroyed. You will be placed under the same hood and you will be released in a short time. You will then go home and you will say nothing of this to anyone."

"And you will remember," the leader of the group said, "you will remember that when you reach the apex of success, whenever it may turn out to be, you will die as Sander will die. Your only chance is to recant. To go to the authorities and tell them you were mistaken. If that happens, nothing more will happen to you. Otherwise, you will see success in your grasp and then you will be no more. What you have suffered tonight was but a mild lesson. What will happen to you next will be much worse. Think about it. There is still time. Precious little, but enough."

# Five

With the hood still in place, she was thrown out of a carriage onto an open, grassy spot in one of Vienna's parks. By the time she managed to recover her wits and remove her hood, there was no sign of the carriage, or whoever had accompanied her from the mysterious place where she'd been taken and where she'd suffered the worst indignities.

Her shirtwaist was torn but still wearable, and though her skirt had some buttons missing, those remaining were adequate. There was no sign of her handbag, though. She searched for it, but her efforts were futile in the darkness. She couldn't recall having it when they hustled her out of the house.

With a sense of relief she realized they'd dropped her off not very far from her apartment, which was no more than a ten-minute walk along quiet side streets. Despite all she'd been through, she had not forgotten her appointment with David Jackson, though she realized the chances were remote of his having waited all this time for her.

She was fortunate that few were about, with her torn clothing and her hair missing most of its pins. However, the lobby was empty and she reached her floor without being seen. At the door she recalled the loss of her handbag, which meant she had no key. In a desperate gesture, she tried the door, and to her surprise, it was unlocked. She entered the parlor to find a startled David Jackson seated in a chair near the window with Anna sitting opposite him. Both stood up immediately. Nicola's badly mussed hair and a slight swelling on her left cheek was grim evidence that something was wrong. Anna and David went to Nicola's side.

"What happened? Where have you been?" Anna asked. "Nobody knew when you left the rehearsal. Your clothes are torn. . .you look awful."

David placed a comforting arm around her shoulders and spoke with quiet concern. "What happened, Nicola? Were you in an accident—"

"No."

"What then?" Anna asked.

"I was kidnapped, then taken somewhere. My captors urged me to recant my testimony, which I would not do. I was threatened and then. . .raped."

Anna held her. "Let's remove your torn garments," she said.

While David waited in the parlor, she bathed carefully and slowly, for her body was still outraged at the indignity. She chose a simple blue dress, then put up her hair, no easy chore, for her arms had been tightly squeezed, not only when she'd been kidnapped, but by the rapist. Fortunately the bruise on her cheek was superficial and would heal in a day or two. She was fortunate that her face bore no other marks, though her body would be black and blue by morning, if not sooner. She looked in the mirror, then closed her eyes and took a few slow, deep breaths in an effort to steady her nerves.

Her thoughts shifted to David. She was grateful for his understanding and sympathy, though the thought of having to talk about what happened wasn't easy. She turned and went back to the parlor. Anna had resumed her seat, but David was still standing. When she entered the room, he went to her, guided her to the settee and eased her down beside him. Anna got up and took a seat in a chair facing them.

David said, "You're trembling, Nicola. Don't talk until you're ready."

"I want to talk about it," Nicola said quietly. "It was horrible. I will understand if you don't wish to see me again."

"I not only want to see you," he said, "I want to help."

Anna said, "I would like to kill the man who did this. How can you be so calm?"

"Because I must be," Nicola said. "During the afternoon rehearsal period, I was approached by Sander's lawyer who begged me to go to the prison to talk to Sander. I refused, but he was persistent, saying if I did not go, the word would get around that I was afraid to talk to him because I knew he was innocent. I had made up my mind not to oblige him, but then he handed me your note, Anna."

"My note? What note?" Anna asked.

"I can see now that you didn't write it, but the handwriting did resemble yours, though I admit I didn't study it very carefully. It was stupid of me, but I was excited. I took it for granted you had written that you advised me to go to see the man. I saw him, against my better judgment. Sander was cold, austere, but he didn't seem to be afraid, I'll say that much for him. He asked me to go before the court and say that, after thinking it over, I wasn't positive in my identification of him. That's all it would take to have his sentence changed. But I refused. When I left the prison, I was seized and

81

thrown into a coach with two men. They drew a hood over my head. When the hood was removed, I found myself in a partially darkened room. I never did know exactly how many people were there, but one man, seated in a high-backed chair so there would be no profile of him to recognize, took charge."

"Nicola," Anna said, "if it pains you too much to tell. . ."

"I was asked to save Sander, and again I refused. I tried to get away from them, but in the gloomy light I didn't see a man standing close by. He seized me and he asked permission of someone. . .a leader I'm sure. . .if he could teach me a lesson. Or something to that effect. He was granted permission and. . .he raped me. I suppose you might say I was lucky they didn't kill me."

"Nicola," David said, "you are very courageous."

"I'm not sure what I am."

Anna's features revealed her anxiety. "Nicky, aren't you going to the police?"

"I haven't made up my mind yet, Anna. There is so little I can tell them."

"But you could ensure that that beast goes to the wall."

"I'm sure he is going anyway."

"I wouldn't be too confident of that," Anna said.

"What do you mean?" Nicola cried out apprehensively.

"We heard the news a little while ago," David explained. "From a man in the lobby. I was waiting there for you when Miss Croft and another gentleman entered. Anyway, this man told us he just heard that Sander's lawyer has succeeded in getting the court to listen to a plea for mercy."

"Now," Nicola said, "I understand all this."

"I don't," Anna said.

"I think I do," David said. "They are banking on the fact that you will not appear in court to testify again because of what happened to you."

"Why else would they have done such a thing?" Nicola asked. "They must have known I'd never change my testimony. In fact, I couldn't if I wanted to, but now, with this new plea and me too ashamed and terrified to go into court. . .don't you see, Anna? If I appear, they will force me to tell that I was raped."

Anna clapped her hands to the sides of her head and rocked back and forth in fresh agony. "My God! What kind of people are they? I never thought of that. Nicky, everyone will know. How can you ever go on a stage again and dance? You will be ridiculed, called names."

"Anna, my dear one, I shall go on stage. I shall dance and tomorrow I shall go before the court and beg them not to spare this monster. If I am ostracized later, that is how it must be."

"I'd not worry too deeply about it," David said.

"Perhaps you wouldn't," Anna said angrily. "It's Nicky who is in this terrible trouble, not you, Mr. Jackson."

Nicola stood up. "I shall change again, Mr. Jackson. It may be a somewhat late supper, but I still intend to enjoy it. I hope I don't sound too bold."

"You sound delightful," he said, smiling.

Anna accompanied Nicola to the bedroom. She gasped in horror when Nicola undressed, revealing the rapidly darkening bruises on her thighs and breasts.

"Please, Nicky," she implored, "see a doctor immediately. You are badly hurt."

"Not physically so much," Nicola said quietly. "The bruises will go away. The rest of it, I'm not so sure. But I'm going to try and make it go away, Anna. Believe me, I'm going to try. Tonight I am going out with David. I am going to appear in court tomorrow and, whatever the consequences may be, I shall face up to them. Please help me with my hair. I want to look nice tonight. Luckily the bruise on my face is scarcely noticeable, and with this high-necked gown those on my body will not be visible."

"Lovely," David said when she returned to the parlor. "You're going to make me very proud this evening. You'll catch every eye."

"Thank you," Nicola said, fighting to throw off the memory of what had happened earlier.

Anna said, "I'm staying right here until you come back. Take special care of her, Mr. Jackson. I'll worry every moment."

"Then I shall not be required to do so," Nicola said lightly. She wondered if there would come a moment she'd break down and submit to the awful memory that she had so far crushed. David reassured Anna and they left.

He had made reservations in the finest restaurant in Vienna. David had apparently ordered in advance. A bottle of champagne was already cooling and the waiters needed no instructions. David raised his glass.

"Let me say this now. What happened to you this afternoon has no bearing on my plea that you join my show. The offer remains, with no change. I mean it now more than ever."

"Thank you, David," she said, using his given name for the first time. She sipped her champagne.

"Tomorrow in court will be difficult for you," he said somewhat gloomily. "I believe that's the reason they did this. To humiliate you to a point where you'd say the devil with the whole thing. I can see how wrong they were. Now, before the food is brought, do you want to talk about what happened? Will telling the story make you feel better? Maybe I can help."

"There's little to tell. I was about to enter a carriage

waiting in front of the prison gate. I suppose I should have suspected it was waiting for me, but of course I didn't. I was pushed inside. Two men accompanied me. They threatened to use chloroform if I made any trouble so I took care not to. A hood was placed over my head. The carriage drove for, I would say, about ten or fifteen minutes.''

"What else?'' he asked.

"We turned onto a side street. I believe that's what it was. The smooth ride changed to a rough one because I'm sure the pavement was uneven brick.''

"Some of the side streets are, though that won't help too much. Go on.''

"A gate was opened after the carriage came to a stop. I recall there were two gates, two doors. One of them squealed as if it needed oil, and other was silent.''

"Interesting,'' David commented.

"I was led up four steps—outside steps—and into some kind of building. . .I'm sure it was a house. Then up twenty-one stairs to a second floor and into a very long room. Like a ballroom. Yes, that's what it reminded me of, now that I think of it. And in Vienna, an upstairs ballroom is not unusual.''

"Could there have been another reason for you believing it was a ballroom?'' David asked.

Nicola thought a moment, then smiled. "I don't suppose I thought of it, but now that you mention it—yes.''

"Tell me.''

"The floor was as smooth as glass. Strange that it didn't occur to me before, but it makes me more certain I am correct in naming the kind of room I was brought to.''

"Then what happened?''

"The hood was removed from my head. I tried very hard to see those present, but the only light came from a dim candle—at least that's what I assumed it was—far behind me. I believe there were three or four men in the room. The leader sat in a high-backed chair. Now and then I seemed to view a dim shadow. I never heard his voice, but there was a blur to one side of the chair and I believe it was one of the men. He is the one who spoke after being told what to say."

"What makes you so certain of that?"

"Because there was a pause after I spoke, a silence long enough for the leader to tell the man at his side what to say."

David looked thoughtful. "Apparently this leader—as you refer to him, did not speak because he feared you might recognize his voice."

"That has to be the reason," Nicola exclaimed.

The first course of seafood was placed before them. Nicola ate with enjoyment, though she ate only a ballerina's portion. David attacked his food as if he were famished, which he probably was. He looked up and saw her looking at him, and their eyes met. He reached across the table, caught her hand in his and squeezed it gently. Then, to her surprise, he bent forward and kissed the back of it.

"You're very beautiful, you know," he said. "It's difficult to look at you and still keep my mind on what I feel I have to know."

"What do you have to know?" She spoke as he released her hand.

"Where you were taken. I believe it's possible to find it."

"I would rather you didn't."

"Why not?"

"They're dangerous men. They'll stop at nothing."

"But we've got to find the people who did that horrible thing to you."

"Will nothing I say stop you?"

"Nothing," he replied. "You're as brave as they were cowardly. Yes, they're dangerous, but they know they didn't frighten you. I fear you're still in danger. Anna does also. I'd rather you stayed out of it."

"I couldn't. My father was murdered. I'll never forget that. I believe if they doubted before, they won't now."

"You've been through a lot," David said.

"I'm very touched by your concern, David, truly I am," Nicola replied.

"Concern is only a part of love, Nicola." He touched her hand.

"David. . ."

"I'm sure it's been said millions of times before, perhaps in those exact words. Just give me some hope, Nicola. I rehearsed what I would say in my hotel tonight, but you know, I can't remember a word of it. I'm sure though it isn't what I just said."

Nicola could scarcely believe her ears. She was sitting here, having this wonderful man tell of his love while she still bore the bruises of a rape. It seemed utterly incongruous, and yet it did not when she really thought about it. David loved her and she knew she was falling in love with him. The black memory of the afternoon and early evening was rapidly fading. No one could have prescribed better therapy than this supper with David. Still, she was worried about tomorrow.

"You mentioned about warning me," she said. "I know you were only using the word lightly, but it reminded me of something else that happened and I'm afraid this does scare me."

"Tell me," he urged.

"I was told that Sander is a very ambitious man. He was on the verge of attaining his goal when he was arrested. I don't know what it was, but I gather it was important and influential. Something he dreamed about since his youth."

"If he was about to attain something that important to him, I doubt he'd have taken the part of an assassin and performed his murder in broad daylight in front of witnesses."

"Perhaps. I believe that Papa knew a great deal more than he told me, and some of what he had discovered may have been dangerous for anyone to know. Perhaps what he could have done against those rebels, or whatever they are, might have destroyed the lot of them. I believe they felt he had to be assassinated—and quickly. And Sander was there and he must have known Papa was coming out of the apartment-house door. The opportunity presented itself and he fired."

"I agree it was possible. There is something else, isn't there?"

"No. If I seemed concerned, it is because I was told that as Sander would die at the very peak of his hopes and dreams and success, so I too would die when I reached that same pinnacle."

David's face grew somber; his eyes were cold. "After working your way up to the highest point in the field of ballet, they'd kill you?"

"Yes."

"It sounds like nonsense to me, but the kind of nonsense that sometimes makes real sense and must not be underestimated. Someone must hate you very much, or love Sander very much, to take it upon himself to prophesy such a thing. I don't blame you for being afraid."

"I must confess that I am, David."

"Why not come back with me? It'll be harder for them to follow you to the United States. In fact, we could keep our address and our moves as secret as possible, though we will be on stage in a successful play."

"It's tempting, but I want to wait and see what happens tomorrow. The day after that I'm to dance another solo part. That will be the test of it. Either I'll be degraded and shunned, or people won't pay any attention to what happened."

"I've an idea it will be neither. I think they'll applaud you."

"Oh no, it won't be that way. There are too many straight laces around Vienna. They may come to see me perform, but it will be a sort of cannibalistic curiosity. After it's over, they'll devour me as they shower me with scandal."

"We shall see. I'll be in the audience, of course."

"That will delight me more than anything else. Now let's talk about the dancing in this new show of yours. I'm very intrigued."

They talked into the late evening. The owners almost closed the restaurant, but David saw to it that the impatient waiters were well taken care of. Then Nicola and David rode back to her apartment.

David escorted her to her door. Nicola kissed him briefly on the lips, resisting the impulse to let him take her in his arms. She couldn't quite come up to that. Not yet. The memory of her ordeal had evaporated to some extent due to the perfection of the evening, but not quite. Not until the door closed did she hear David's retreating footsteps.

Anna sat by the open window, fanning herself, for it was a warm night. She shook her head as Nicola entered.

"I don't know how you managed to do that, Nicky. I'd have been in bed for a week at least."

"I had fun. Weeping would have made me miserable, and could not have changed what happened."

"No doubt. He's a very nice young man. Is it serious yet? Oh, listen to me! Talking like that after what was done to you."

"I'm trying not to dwell on it." Nicola draped her folded evening coat over the back of a chair. "I'm going into court in the morning. I'll not be intimidated. If those judges show the slightest tendency toward mercy, I'm going to ask to be heard and I'll tell them the whole story."

"Up to a point, of course," Anna said.

"Up to the finish of the whole ugly incident. I will not allow myself to be shamed because of something that was forced on me. I don't care what others think. If those people believe they have frightened me into silence, they are making a bad mistake."

"It could wreck your career," Anna warned.

"So long as Sander doesn't get away with it, I'll not weep over that either. He was sentenced to be shot and he will be shot. If that makes me sound cruel or hard-hearted, so be it. For me it can end no other way."

"Your ambitions were so high and you were moving toward them so fast. . . ." Anna said worriedly. "And now this."

"Papa is dead. He loved you as he loved me. Would you allow these people to frighten or intimidate you so that you'd recant your testimony and let Sander get off? I don't think you would, Anna. I believe you're too worried about me to think of what your feelings toward this monster can be. I hate him. Sander and all those who do his bidding."

"Vienna isn't the most moral city in the world," Anna said. "But we do pride ourselves on not going too fast, in most instances. They will understand that what happened was not your fault, but they will blame you anyway—in their hearts. You are young, attractive, a talented new ballet dancer. Those things also act against you. I've run across jealousy before."

"We shall see. Anna, do you know what it was that

Papa discovered? The secrets that made his death so important to others?''

"He never told me. He talked very rarely about his work. I think he was sworn to secrecy and if he was, neither you nor I could drag anything out of him. It was a funeral for heroes, Nicky. He was a hero."

"Perhaps," Nicola said thoughtfully. "But until this happened, a very minor one. Death made him the hero, Anna. That's what makes me bitter about Sander trying to get out of this. I swear he will not."

# Six

Sander, in chains, was brought into the courtroom as Nicola and Anna took their seats. Nicola looked around and saw David at the back of the room.

Attorney Hahn, Sander's lawyer, who didn't look impressive, stood up to face the same court and make an impassioned plea, proving that he was not only a skilled lawyer but a clever one as well.

"On behalf of my client, I wish to thank this court for reopening this case, if only to hear my plea. I base my contention that my client is innocent. He was convicted on the evidence of Fräulein Nicola Maneth alone. I have stated before that I do not accuse or suspect her of lying. Only of being honestly mistaken. She was, rightfully so, very upset at what happened. Shocked, and quite likely unable to have recognized anyone at the moment of the assassination. She saw my client immediately afterward. Yes, he was there. It has never been indicated that he was not. But while he may have then looked like a down-at-the-heels person, you can readily see that he is not. He was wearing shabby clothes because he liked to go to the poorer sections and listen to what the people there had to say. If he went well dressed, they'd have said nothing. He ran away because he foolishly didn't want to become involved."

"Get to the point," one of the judges said. "If you have fresh evidence, say so."

"Your Honor, there is no further evidence. But this girl wants someone punished for the murder of her father. She thinks my client was the assassin and will never consider anything else. The shot may have come from across the street. . . ."

"She and Attorney Kramer swore that the man in the shabby clothes fired the shots," one judge reminded the attorney.

"He was just as excited. . ."

"Herr Hahn, get on with it," the chief justice ordered. "You promised that you had something fresh to offer. Where is it?"

"It may lie in the further testimony of Fräulein Maneth. I ask permission to cross-examine her again. She may shed new light on the identity of the assassin. My client deserves that chance."

Nicola grasped Anna's hand strongly as she began to arise. "Wish me luck, Anna."

"Don't do it," Anna begged. "Nicky, don't do it."

"I must," she said, and then she moved out into the aisle to face the court. "It is my wish to testify once again, Your Honor, not to be questioned by Herr Hahn."

"I don't quite understand you, *Fräulein*," the chief justice said. "But if you wish to change your testimony. . ."

"No, Your Honor. Only to explain why this lawyer and Herr Sander think I might change it."

"I'm still confused, but take the stand, *Fräulein*. You do not wish to testify, but to make a statement, is that it?"

"I wish to be sworn and to make a statement, Your

Honor. The testimony I gave before will never change. I contend this is only a last-ditch effort on the part of the accused to delay his execution, or to have his sentence reduced.''

"You may be sworn," the chief justice agreed.

"Yesterday," Nicola said, after she was sworn, "Herr Hahn came to the theatre where I was rehearsing and asked me to see Herr Sander. At first I refused, but he showed me a letter written by Fräulein Anna Croft, my very close friend and advisor, that I should see the man. Fräulein Croft has since pronounced the note a forgery, for she has stated she never wrote such a message."

"She is here to testify to that?" One Justice peered down from the long bench.

Anna Croft stood up. "I am Anna Croft, Your Honor, and I did not write any such note. I will testify to that under oath, if you wish."

"We will see. Let Fräulein Maneth continue."

"Herr Sander asked me to change my story and I refused. He then threatened me with. . .some sort of revenge. I didn't understand him. I refused again. When I left the prison, I was kidnapped by two men. . . ."

There was a series of gasps from the courtroom audience, and the judges on the bench assumed stern expressions as they listened.

"I was taken somewhere in a carriage. I don't know the location because my vision was cut off by a hood drawn down over my eyes. I was led into a building and to what I believe was a large room. The hood was then removed. I sensed the presence of several people who were careful not to let me see their faces. The room was in darkness, except for what was probably a small candle which was apparently placed in a far corner so no faces were visible. I was asked to recant my testimony by someone who I assume was the leader of these people. I refused again. They warned me of dire circumstances if I continued to refuse. Nonetheless, I repeated my refusal."

Sander's lawyer jumped to his feet. "I wish to examine the witness," he said. "It is only fitting. . ."

Nicola said, "Herr Hahn wishes to ask me what happened after that because he believes I will be most reluctant to tell, and therefore he will try to declare all I have said as worthless. What happened afterward, and what Herr Hahn and Herr Sander feel sure I would be too ashamed to tell, is the fact that because of my refusal to obey these people in the darkened room, I was turned over to one of them who raped me."

One could feel the growing tension in the courtroom. All eyes were on Nicola.

"Please, *Fräulein*, give us more details about the kidnapping. Tell us exactly what was said," the chief justice ordered.

"I can tell very little. . . ."

"A likely story," Hahn called out, on his feet once again. "It is all nonsense. I had no intention of asking anything about her being degraded by rape. The whole thing is a fabrication."

"Sit down," the chief justice ordered sharply. "*Fräulein,* have you any proof of this?"

"None, Your Honor, except that when I returned to my apartment, Fräulein Croft noted my condition and a friend, Mr. Jackson, also noted how distraught I was and that my clothing was torn. If it is necessary for me to exhibit my body, which is severely bruised by the man who raped me, I shall do so to a physician."

David strode to the bench. "I am David Jackson," he said. "I ask that Fräulein Maneth give a more detailed account of her kidnapping. Let her relate the few details she absorbed once she was taken from the carriage. I have a reason for making the request."

The chief justice nodded. "*Fräulein. . . .*"

"The carriage in which I was taken required about fifteen minutes to reach our destination. It turned off onto a street I believe to have been laid with rough brick. The vehicle stopped and a gate was opened. One side of the gate had hinges that squealed as if in need of oil. The other half of the gate moved without sound. I was taken into a building. I ascended twenty-one steps and I was then led into the room I already described. That is all I can tell."

"Mr. Jackson," the chief justice leaned over the bench slightly, "what is your purpose in this?"

"I will tell the court that I searched for this place last evening. I searched along all manner of rough, brick-laid streets. I found a gate where one section squealed and the other did not. I found a house where it was necessary to climb twenty-one steps to reach the second floor. I found a long room, something like a ballroom. Just off it a bedroom, a bed with rumpled bedclothing . . .and something else."

He held up Nicola's handbag which he'd been concealing behind his back. "Fräulein Maneth, do you recognize this?"

"It's my handbag," Nicola said excitedly. "I didn't have it after I was taken from that house and released."

"Inside it is enough evidence to prove it is her property," David said.

"Now hold on!" Hahn came to his feet again. "Where is your proof? All of this could be so easily prepared. Where is the proof?"

Nicola wondered too. It wasn't like David to make up this story and the fact that he produced the missing handbag was proof to her that he was not lying. But the judges still had to be convinced.

David said, "Will the court please question Josef Strauss? He is an inspector of police. I prevailed upon him to help me find the house."

The bulky police officer gave terse testimony. It was he who had really found the handbag and there was no longer any need to furnish more proof. The chief justice conferred with his colleagues and then looked directly at Sander.

"This court approves the sentence passed upon this defendant and orders that it be carried out immediately. As for you, Herr Hahn, we shall take up your part in this business later. The court is adjourned."

"Now you've done it," Anna whispered dismally as Nicola sat down beside her. "You didn't have to be so frank. . . ."

"It is done as I wished it to be done," Nicola said. She stood up and those in the courtroom began to clap their hands. It was like a triumphant moment after a solo on stage. They pressed around her to express their praise for her bravery. She had difficulty reaching David, who stood by so that he would not intrude on a moment that was Nicola's alone.

"What did I tell you?" he said when she was at his side. His eyes revealed his pride in her.

"Thank you, David. It was you who turned the case in my favor." A smile touched Nicola's mouth as she spoke, but her eyes held a worried look.

"What is wrong?" he asked.

"I'm wondering if it will be the same way on stage as it was here."

"Of course it will. Here you were judged by your honesty. On stage, you will be judged by your talent. You have nothing to fear, my darling."

"I'm not so certain."

"You should be." Anna had reached their side and overheard Nicola's statement. "I was wrong. You captured the sympathy of everyone in the courtroom. I'm proud of you, Nicky."

She embraced Nicola and beamed as she held the girl at arm's length. "I'm proud of you."

"Thank you, Anna. You had me thinking I'd done the wrong thing."

"I was mistaken. You have nothing further to worry about. I must go now. Neither of you will miss me. You must both have plenty to talk about."

David bent and kissed her cheek lightly. "Thanks, Anna, for coming here and doing your part."

"I was going to thank you, David, but we each know why we did it. God bless you both." She turned and strode briskly from the courtroom.

Several times on their way out of the court building, Nicola was obliged to stop and acknowledge, with thanks, the comments from several groups of people who had witnessed her conduct on the stand. Finally, David guided her skillfully to a side door. Once in the open, she breathed a sigh of relief.

"Were you frightened?" David asked.

"Mostly of the crowds," she said. "I wasn't afraid on the witness stand. The judges were very understanding, don't you think?"

"Yes. Well, that's the end of Sander and the whole ugly business."

"Unless what those men told me comes to pass. I'll worry about that, David. They meant me to worry and I'm afraid I'm not going to disappoint them."

"I'm going to be with you from now on," he said. "You understand that, don't you?"

"I'll rely on you. You and Anna. It will help greatly to have you both at my side. David, I'm so grateful you found that house."

"It belonged to Sander. We never thought of that. At least I didn't, but when we got to the place, or close to it, the inspector did. He was very cooperative and I learned a great deal from him. The plot to assassinate Franz Josef was real enough. The plotters in Budapest were arrested and the whole scheme was broken up."

"Thank heaven for that. What a strange man—this Sander. Fine looking, very intelligent. I wonder what his bright future was."

"It depends on what you call bright, and from what angle you look at it. The police inspector knew the details. Sander had been under suspicion for some time. What he sought to attain was the leadership, perhaps even as king or emperor, of one of the Balkan states involved in the war with Turkey. Most of the states are fighting over the spoils of that war now. Sander hoped to consolidate some of the leaders and take over. But to do that, Franz Josef had to be eliminated and that was where the assassination plot came in. Your father stumbled on it and wisely revealed it all to the Emperor."

She linked her hand under his arm as they walked slowly along the street not far from the Burgtheater.

"Sander was indeed ambitious," Nicola commented. "I suppose, in time, he would have become a very important man."

"A dangerous man, I'd say. How about the coffee shop just ahead?"

"Please," Nicola begged earnestly, "cross the street with me. I'm starved and all those beautiful, fancy things are *verboten*. The penalty for being in the ballet."

"Tomorrow night you are second soloist again. Lapin should have made you first soloist. Are you looking forward to it?"

They reached the opposite sidewalk. "No," Nicola said. "I'm frightened."

"Of the audience? You saw what happened in the courtroom. You were regarded as a heroine."

"I don't feel like one, sending a man to his death, even if it was deserved. But remember, at this moment the story is going all through Vienna. That story is going to be changed in the telling after the first hundred times. I'm either going to be looked upon as a poor, half-demented girl suffering from the shock of the raping, or they'll say it couldn't have happened if I hadn't wanted it to. Gossip is one of Vienna's most favored pastimes and the stories they tell. . ."

She shook her head in dismay while David looked for a place to eat. They found a small coffee shop which didn't tempt Nicola so much. They lingered over coffee for two hours, getting better acquainted as they answered each other's questions, discovering similar things they liked to do, poets whose works moved them greatly and pausing from time to time to look into each other's eyes which glowed warmly with their newfound happiness.

Nicola knew it was more than that, though she didn't let herself dwell on it. Too much had happened recently —all of it bad. All of it except meeting David. His compassion and understanding had helped ease the ache and humiliation of what she had been forced to endure.

The waiter came to their table, placed the check on it and remained standing there. Even then, they had no awareness of his presence until he coughed politely. When he had David's attention, he made a gesture with his hand toward the check.

Outside again, they ambled along with the late after-noon crowds to Nicola's apartment house. They paused, each reluctant to have the magic of the hour end.

"I'll not see you tomorrow until after the per-formance," she said. "I neglected my rehearsal today and I'll pay for it in the morning. Until tomorrow, David." She stood on tiptoe and kissed him. "David, my love."

He held her, but briefly. He knew she was tired and the next day would be exhausting. As before, he saw her safely up the stairs.

Anna was waiting for her. Tea and some special cookies, made with as little butter as possible, were on the table.

"I saw you cross the street and got things ready," Anna said. "Why didn't David come in?"

"He understands I must devote my time to my dancing until after the show tomorrow night. Isn't it wonderful that he went to the trouble of finding Sander's home, and taking with him a police inspector who actually discovered my handbag? After that, nobody doubted my story."

"I don't think there were any doubts even before that. They. . .shot Sander about two hours ago."

"I can't bring myself to say 'rest his soul'. From what I hear, he would have been a very dangerous man if his plans had succeeded."

"I know little of politics. My services consist only of trying to cipher and decipher some of Franz Josef's crazy codes. Bad as he is, you should try to read one of Franz Ferdinand's. He tries to be clever and all he does is confuse us until we are ready to scream."

She had poured the tea and they nibbled cookies as they talked. Anna said, "You're a very brave girl, Nicky. I'm proud of you. But what about the performance tomorrow night? I. . .think you should know that I heard some gossip this afternoon."

"They're saying I invited being raped, I suppose."

"Not quite as openly as that, but they do agree that it's very rare a man can rape a woman and not have real cause—like an invitation."

"Let them think what they like. I know what happened, and gossip isn't going to influence me in any way."

"It's the performance tomorrow night that I dread," Anna said. "If enough of those malicious gossips are there, they might. . .well, not encourage you very much. I thought your triumph in the courtroom would end it."

"I must continue to believe it. I respect your opinion and I love you as dearly as if you were really my mother, but this time I hope you are wrong."

"So do I, but you'd best be prepared." Anna lifted a sofa cushion to remove a newspaper. She handed it silently to Nicola who looked at the front page and gasped in horror.

Someone had sketched a very good head-and-shoulders likeness of her. It was reproduced in the middle of the front page with a bold headline.

BALLERINA ADMITS TO RAPE IN THE SANDER TRIAL

The article revealed in great detail the episode of Sander's death before a firing squad. Then it went on to relate that Nicola was heroic in her testimony, but it insinuated that people of the theatre are not the most moral. There were more insinuations mixed with some faint praise for her, but it brought on a flood of tears. She wept on Anna's shoulder and murmured her fears as to what David would think when he read the paper.

"This is a scandal sheet," Anna comforted her. "It thrives on innuendoes and on the troubles of important people. They are very careful, so you cannot sue them, but they do their best to increase circulation at the expense of someone like you. I'd not worry about it. Everyone knows what this paper is. As for David, he worships you. It shows each time he looks at you."

"I don't know if I should risk going to the theatre tomorrow," Nicola said while she dried her tears. "I might even make trouble for the whole company."

"Your pipsqueak of a ballet master will surely make something of it. Don't pay any attention to the beast and. . .for heaven's sake, dance well. You have to go through with it. If you let what happened destroy your role in ballet, then Sander will have won the final victory. I say go, dance, and show them your real courage, along with your talent as a dancer."

Nicola nodded. "You're right, of course. Ruining me as a dancer is what those men are after. That will be their revenge. But I'll be damned if I'll let them destroy me this way. Wake me early. I need the practice."

"Not too early. You also need rest," Anna said. "But there will be plenty of time. I have to report for work in the morning too. Remember?"

"Of course," Nicola said. "Thank you for staying the night. For all the nights since Papa was killed."

"I was glad to do so, my dear Nicky. If you recall, I was to marry your papa the next day. I have memories too. Sad ones, and if I'd been alone, it would have been much worse. We needed one another, but beginning tomorrow I think I'd best go back to my own place. We have to learn to face loneliness. Not that we won't see one another often. Daily, I hope. But we must also have our own lives. You have David, thank God. As for me —I have memories of happy hours spent with your papa."

"Good night, Anna. I am very tired. So much so, I feel out of trim for my dancing. Thank you once again."

Nicola prepared for bed quickly, for she felt she was on the verge of exhaustion after this awful day. There'd been no physical tasks, but the anxiety of the courtroom and the crowds, and then the newspaper, made for stress dancers must avoid at all costs.

She sank gratefully back on her pillow, and became wide awake in seconds. She had turned the lamp down low and she tried once again to court sleep by blowing it out. Even the darkness didn't help. Her mind slipped back to the few seconds of time when she and her father

103

had stood outside the apartment house and Sander had suddenly appeared with leveled revolver. She saw again the blood on her father's white shirtfront, more on the stairs. She recalled dancing that same night, not two hours after her father was dead. It had been a question of forcing circumstances from her mind and concentrating solely on the dance. It had worked then, but it wasn't working now. No concentration on any subject removed the strain and the sorrow she felt. It was like being all alone in the world, with no one to turn to. David could have comforted her, but David was not there. She began to cry softly. She turned on her stomach and buried her face in the pillow to muffle her sobs.

She heard the bedroom door open. It was Anna. She struck a match, lit the lamp, then sat on the side of the bed. "Poor Nicky. Now it all comes back. This will be the worst of it. Go ahead and cry. Here, let me hold you. Just so you know you're not alone now. Cry for a kind and good man we both loved. And tomorrow you will dance. You will smile, and bow to the applause and take an encore, perhaps. The audience will love you for your brilliance and your beauty and skill. Because, you see, we have to go on with life. That's how it has always been. It will never change."

Nicola sat up, propping herself against the pillows. She opened the drawer in the night table and reached for a handerchief. She dried her tears and blew her nose. "It hit me all of a sudden, Anna."

"Of course it did. Until now you've not had time to properly remember. When you did, the tears came. Those tears you hadn't shed before because there wasn't time to think. You let David take your mind off the ugly episode. So much has happened to you."

"I don't think back on that, Anna. It happened and it's over. I hope the man who did it is found and

104

punished, but there is some satisfaction for me in that it didn't work. They hoped they would save Sander that way, but they did not. And you're right. We have to go on. At least, I know what I want."

"What do you want, Nicky? What is it that drives you? Is it success?"

Nicola managed a smile. "Ever since I first entered ballet school, there has been one single ambition in my life. Perhaps it will sound silly to you. I want to dance, as prima ballerina, at the Royal Theatre in the Schönbrunn Palace."

"That is a very large ambition," Anna admitted. "Yet I feel that you are going to make it. And soon."

"If I ever ventured to tell this to Lapin, he would laugh his head off. Knowing that makes it more important than ever."

"Then make it, Nicky. Don't relax, don't doubt. Concentrate only on that goal. Never let your determination waver—even for a second."

"Thank you for coming in. I had hoped you wouldn't hear me crying, but I guess what I really wanted was for you to come to me. I don't feel so alone now."

"You'll never be alone. What of David? Have you plans?"

"He is getting together a new kind of musical in which a ballet dancer is required. But that will happen in America. I'm not ready for that now. I haven't told him because I never thought about it enough to make up my mind. What I want is to become known here in Vienna first. To be prima ballerina on the Burgtheater stage. Then I will feel capable of taking on such an assignment."

"Will he wait? Will the show he has planned, wait?"

"I don't know. I wouldn't expect that. Oh, Anna, I love him. I've never been in love before, but I know now surely this is real and how beautiful true love is. But I love ballet too, my dancing, Vienna, the Burgtheater. I don't want to leave any of this. How can I tell him? I'm afraid if I go to America, we'll soon marry and then. . . perhaps my dancing days will end. I could not abide that. Not now."

"Things have a way of working out for each of us. When the time comes to make a decision, you'll know which one is best. Now I think you'd better get to sleep. As you said before, you need practice for tomorrow night's performance."

"Yes, Anna. Thank you again. I feel better. I will need your counsel. Good night, my friend. My dear, dear friend."

Anna stood up, smiled down at her and gave a re-assuring nod before she extinguished the lamp and moved softly from the room. Nicola was half asleep as the door latch clicked shut.

# Seven

Until Nicola began work at the *barre*, she had no idea of the amount of abuse which had been inflicted on her body as a result of the mauling by the rapist. Now it was painfully evident. The slightest movement of a muscle in even a minor position brought pain. She couldn't even soften the hurt by groaning, for since she'd arrived backstage, the girls of the corps pressed around her, asking details. Some were genuinely concerned and sympathetic; others were merely curious.

None of this bothered her. It was to be expected. It was human nature, she told herself, but the aching muscles were another thing. She had hoped Tonio might be there to help her limber up, but this was one morning when he failed to appear on time.

Their questions and comments were interrupted by the appearance of Lapin, though no one was aware of it. He clapped his hands for attention. When that didn't work, he shouted with the same result. He then strode to the piano and beat upon the keys, making a cacophony of sounds until all voices were silenced.

Nicola wiped her face and turned to look at him. She was astonished at the breathtaking beauty of the young, blond girl who stood by his side, still in street clothes.

Lapin returned Nicola's stare, his small eyes gleaming with ill-concealed revenge.

"You," he pointed to Nicola, "have no further need to rehearse or warm up. This," his arm went around the waist of the girl at his side, "is Fräulein Lorette from Berlin. She is one of the finest soloists in Europe and she will take your place, Nicola. You may return to the *corps de ballet* if you desire. If not, your services are no longer required."

Nicola managed to retain her dignity, perhaps because of what she'd been forced to endure these past few days. Certainly she had cause to burst into tears, but she kept her voice calm and looked directly at Lapin as she asked a question.

"Since I was notified that the second solo was mine, who ordered the change?"

"You dare to ask that? You have the gall to question me after besmirching your name with vulgar notoriety?"

"I did nothing, M'sieur Lapin. It was done to me."

"There's no need to talk about it. You will certainly be no asset for increasing our box office receipts. For instance, what a wonderful *Sleeping Beauty* you would make now. A ballerina who dances in that role must have an enchanting innocence."

"Are you as innocent, *M'sieur*? Are you so vain that you believe nobody talks after you get your 'Sleeping Beauties' to your studio? You are a fine one to speak of innocence."

"You are fired," he shouted. "I will not have you working in my ballet."

"This is the Royal Ballet," she reminded him. "It does not belong to you."

"The operation of it does. I am in charge. I have full say about what happens to this company and you are no longer any part of it.''

Nicola hadn't seen him, but Tonio had entered during this dialogue. He strode over to face Lapin. "I dance with Nicola, or I do not dance. How can you expect me to take this girl, no matter how good she is, and dance a *pas de deux* tonight? Impossible! Nicola is the girl I will dance with and no one else.''

"Then you are fired also," Lapin shouted. "I shall cut the second solo. No one will notice the difference. They don't come to see the ballet. They come to see themselves. Both of you, get out of this theatre. Now!''

"I think," Tonio said, "that before I go, I'll make you remember me, *M'sieur*. I have been thinking about it for a long time and just waiting for the right moment.''

"Toni, don't hit him." Nicola hurried over to his side. "He's not worth it. He'll see that you never dance again. It doesn't matter so much to me. I already have offers that this bully cannot interfere with, but you do not have that protection. We'll leave quietly and see what we can do elsewhere.''

Tonio's eyes softened as he regarded Nicola. "You're right. I'd be a fool. I'd hurt only myself. But at the moment I am so disgusted with him, I feel like purchasing a ticket for tonight's performance just to sit in the audience and hiss.''

"Toni, please," Nicola pleaded.

"Don't worry. To behave in such fashion would make me as big a bully as he. Besides, I respect the talent of every member of the corps. Also, they're my friends as they are yours.''

Nicola relaxed, even managing to flash a smile. "If we can't dance, we can at least go to one of the coffee shops and indulge. It's a victory—of sorts.''

"Of sorts," Tonio agreed, then shifted his gaze to Fräulein Lorette, now standing beside Lapin. "I do not mean to offend you, Fräulein Lorette. My harsh words were spoken only to Lapin. You may be the best dancer in the world. One thing I will say for Lapin—he knows talent. All kinds. Have you been with him since you came from Berlin?"

"Yes," she replied in a puzzled voice. "I have been with him. He is a good friend. . . ."

"Of course," Tonio said. Without a smile, he added, "You must be very tired, my dear. Imagine, all that time with Lapin. Yes, you must be absolutely exhausted."

He took Nicola's elbow and they left the stage to return to their dressing rooms. They veered from a straight course to go out onto an iron fire escape landing for air.

"Oh, Toni," Nicola said, "I've ruined your career as well as mine. I'm sick over it. There was no need for you to interfere. Lapin was after me, not you."

"It doesn't matter. I'd never be any good on a *pas de deux* with anybody but you. We have established beautiful coordination. There are other ballet companies. Paris, Rome. . ."

"Toni, I'm going back and ask him to reinstate you—in the corps, if nothing else. You're much too fine a dancer to throw away your career like this."

"That idiot won't listen. . . ."

"I'll promise not to make any trouble if he takes you back. If he refuses, I'll tell him I'll go to all extremes. . ." Her voice tapered off.

"What extremes?" Tonio asked. "Nicky. . .you're daydreaming."

She exclaimed aloud as a sudden thought jarred her memory.

Tonio eyed her with puzzlement. "What is it?"

She didn't even hear his question. Her mind had slipped back to that night she spent in the company of Emperor Franz Josef and what he had said to her. That she had his ear if she was ever in any trouble. Certainly she was now. Yet she hesitated to call on him for his help. She was sure he had interfered before when Lapin had made himself insufferable and that was payment enough. To ask a second time would be taking advantage and might even annoy His Majesty. Besides, she would never reach him in time to dance second solo tonight. It had been an entertaining thought, but a hopeless one.

Tonio placed a gentle hand on her shoulder. "What is it, Nicky? Something is going through your head. You did say you had some kind of connection Lapin could not interfere with."

Nicola got her wits together. "I have. With an American actor who is putting together a new kind of musical show in New York. It requires a ballet dancer and he picked me. So you see, it doesn't matter so much with me. But you. . .please let me see what I can do."

"Nicky, you know what will happen if you offer to let him give you special lessons in his studio."

"Is that what you think?" she asked testily. "Because of what happened to me, you believe I shall give myself to anyone just for his favors?"

"Oh my," Tonio groaned. "I didn't mean that at all. I wasn't thinking. I guess I'm too stupid to be good at anything. Forgive me, Nicky, I swear that never entered my mind."

"Of course it didn't." She relented quickly and kissed his cheek. "I'm sorry I made an issue of it. I'm going to talk to Lapin. There must be at least a spark of kindness in him, however well he conceals it."

As she turned away, she saw a large and ornate carriage pull up in the alley at the stage door. A man in uniform got out.

Nicola said, "Tonio, is it true that the Emperor's coach has gold spokes on the wheels?"

"Gilded, yes. It is a mark of royalty. Only he or his entourage can use such a coach."

"Don't despair," she said. "I think something is about to happen. Come along. We're going back."

They ran back at Nicola's insistence, because she wanted to be there when what she suspected would happen, did. It was already in progress when they joined the crowd of dancers around Lapin, the girl from Berlin, and an officer attached to the Emperor's royal guard. It was the same young officer who had brought Nicola to the palace that night.

He saluted, bowed and took her hand to kiss it in courtly fashion. "Fräulein Maneth, it is good to see you again."

"Thank you, *Herr Leutnant*," she replied. "I still have happy thoughts whenever I recall our last meeting."

"You are most gracious, *Fräulein*. Now, I understand there is some trouble. . . ."

"Yes. M'sieur Lapin thinks that because of what happened in court and the publicity that came from it, no one will wish to see me dance again."

"What nonsense!" He turned to Lapin. "Please explain yourself, *M'sieur*."

"There is nothing to explain," Lapin said. "I fired her and that's all there is to it."

"Most unfortunate." The lieutenant clucked his tongue. "Yes, indeed, most unfortunate. I'm afraid His Majesty is going to be disappointed."

"His Majesty?" Lapin asked in sudden awe.

"He and Empress Elisabeth decided to attend tonight's performance mainly to see Fräulein Maneth dance—a solo and *pas de deux*. They were to come for that express purpose."

112

"I am sorry," Lapin said, deciding to stick to his decision."

"We are all sorry. M'sieur Lapin, you are not Austrian, I know. Do you have a passport?"

"Of course. I have a French passport."

"Excellent. That will enable you not to delay."

"Delay. . .?"

"You will be on the morning train for Paris, *M'sieur*. A man who sees fit to displease the Emperor is no longer needed. Especially since he is a foreigner. Good day, *M'sieur*."

"Wait!" Lapin cried out. "Wait a moment, please. I have expressed my reason for letting Fräulein Maneth go, but I could be wrong. Of course I could be wrong. Any man can be wrong. I do not wish to offend the Emperor. To have him come to see Fräulein Maneth dance tonight. . .she must dance. Of course. I shall see to it that the entire company puts on the best performance they have ever given." He clapped his hands. "Come, children, we must rehearse and rehearse. . . ."

"One moment more," the lieutenant said. "You will be kind enough to understand that this is the Royal Ballet and it comes under the personal attention of the Emperor. You are merely here to coach and train the dancers. In effect, your services can be disposed of with no loss to the company. At any time."

"Of course, of course," Lapin said eagerly. "I can promise you, I will do nothing to displease Their Majesties."

The lieutenant took Nicola's hand again. "The Emperor and the Empress will come backstage this evening to greet you in person for the first time. I can say that they both admire your dancing to a great extent and they have predicted a bright future for you, Fräulein Maneth."

He saluted, walked out, and a momentary hush descended over the company. Heidi, the prima ballerina, ran lightly to embrace Nicola.

"Thank you, Nicky. The greatest honor we have is to dance when the royal box is occupied and tonight the Emperor and Empress will come backstage. How wonderful. And I know very well that His Majesty must be an excellent judge of the dance if he has singled you out. Next performance I am suggesting that you have the first solo."

"And *pas de deux* with Tonio," Nicola said. "I thank all of you for being kind to me. I also hope that Fräulein Lorette will be given my place in the corps. I am sure she is a fine dancer."

Nicola floated back to her dressing room where she closed and locked the door, heeded none of the knocking, and quietly wept, this time tears of joy and satisfaction. She had no idea how the Emperor had known of her difficulties and sent his emissary in the nick of time. Somehow he had been told. Unless. . .unless the lieutenant was telling the truth and his visit was only to inform the company that His Majesty would be in the royal box. It was possible it had been a coincidence, but she doubted that. She had the Emperor's ear. He had said so.

There was no more time for idle chatter. Everything was running late now, but Lapin took care not to scream his usual threats to those who did not begin their warmup at once. He remained singularly quiet for the rest of the day and stayed away from Nicola and Tonio.

They went into final rehearsal late in the afternoon and it came off without a hitch. Even Lapin had to compliment them. Nicola and Tonio's performance was smooth and fascinating to watch. They were well keyed and could anticipate every move the other would make. Their style was superb, their grace and subtle miming were a joy to watch.

As no one could leave the theatre to eat or relax, the

entire company spent the time there until the curtain being especially careful with makeup and costume. Magda shared Nicola's dressing room at Nicola's request. She applied fresh makeup and chattered as she usually did.

"Was Lapin told this time." Her brows raised meaningly. "And so smoothly. Did he have a passport and would he use it getting the train to Paris in the morning? Did you see Lapin's face? For the first time he was being told the facts of life and that he was not Emperor Franz Josef. It must have been difficult for him, especially in front of his slaves. Meaning us."

"We were lucky," Nicola said. "Tonio and I were almost ready to leave the theatre. The lieutenant arrived just in time."

"I agree. It was almost as if everything was pre-arranged for the confrontation with Lapin."

"It couldn't have been, Magda. There's no way the Emperor could have heard of our troubles with Lapin."

"I wonder if he did tell the lieutenant to inform us that he was coming to see you dance. Or if the lieutenant made it up to scare the wits out of Lapin."

"I don't know," Nicola said wonderingly. "Though I hope Their Majesties come. We will dance our hearts out for them."

"We dance our hearts out anyway—not only because Lapin would banish us with an imperious wave of the hand, but because we are proud to have achieved such esteem. Isn't that so, Nicky?"

"Yes. But to have the Emperor and Empress in the royal box. What an honor." She sighed with pleasure at the thought of it.

"If they come and appear backstage afterward, you will soon be the most important prima ballerina in Vienna, or anywhere else," Magda predicted. "Every-one is aware that His Majesty is a well-known fancier of the ballet."

"No more talk," Nicola cautioned. "I am about to paint my mouth."

Even before the curtain went up, Nicola and Tonio could hear the excitement in the audience as the Emperor and the royal party arrived in the royal box. The curtain went up, the *corps de ballet* danced out of the wings, and the show was on.

The first solo, by an accomplished ballerina, was beautifully done. At the end, she received a full measure of applause. Soon after, it was Nicola's turn. She and Tonio were greeted by a wave of applause which so astounded Nicola that she almost forgot to dance. She had entertained severe worries that she would not be accepted even if the Emperor were present, but it appeared that she was not only accepted before she danced, but was given full approval by this usually restrained audience.

"Let's show them some dancing," Tonio whispered as he shared in her bows before the dance began. The music resumed, after having been suspended for a few moments in deference to the applause. Nicola danced as she had never done before. And Tonio matched her performance. The entree was spectacular enough, though Tonio's male variation was superb and the skillful partnership of this pair was absolute perfection. Tonio presented his ballerina to her very best advantage and when it came time for Nicola's solo, the audience seemed entranced. She put a dignity and grace into her performance, with an added passion that gave the part its real quality.

The applause was sustained. They were called back for bows, the audience refusing to allow the performance to go on without it. In the royal box, both Franz Josef and Elisabeth arose to applaud, with white-gloved hands. Both smiled down at Nicola.

Her heartbeat was fluttering wildly as she and Tonio made their exit so the ballet could go on. The entire performance seemed to have a special glow, as if everyone wanted to do his or her best, and make this company outstanding.

There were more curtain calls at the end than had ever been witnessed at the Burgtheater. Then the moment came when Franz Josef, in his heavily bemedalled scarlet coat and black trousers with red stripe came backstage with Empress Elisabeth on his arm. She was a beautiful woman, but she was exquisite in Nicola's eyes.

Nicola curtsied deeply and as she arose, she thought she saw a twinkle in the Emperor's eyes. She wondered if he was thinking of those moments in the palace that night when Nicola had become a woman.

"It is a delight to watch you dance, *Fräulein*," Elisabeth said. "The entire company deserves great credit. The *premier danseur* and the *première danseuse* were, as usual, superb, but I think I should warn them that there are two in the company who will one day take their places."

"I agree, my dear," Franz Josef said. "All of you," he addressed the assembly, "were perfect. A delight to the eye and a standard not to be easily matched anywhere in the world. The entire audience was as enraptured as the Empress and I. We shall see that the Royal Ballet is given additional funds to enable you to do even better work."

He extended his hand to Nicola who placed hers in it. He bent and kissed it, then straightened. She curtsied before him, then before the Empress. As quickly as it began, it was over. The royal party was gone, the audience had filed out, the theatre was quiet. But the excitement backstage seemed equal to the noise the audience had made with their most vociferous applause. Everybody was talking at once. Lapin pranced about in high spirits, praising everyone. Magda embraced Nicola before Tonio led her to a quiet place in the wings. There he kissed her, not as before, but with meaning and passion, drawing her close.

"I love you, Nicola," he said. "I hadn't meant to tell you this, but I have always worshipped you—from afar. Don't look so frightened. I shall not mention it again until you give me encouragement. However, I do want to thank you for the chance you have given me."

"We helped each other, Tonio, though it is recognition from the Emperor and Empress that has turned the tide in our favor. It is my wish always to dance with you. And no one else. We are too well attuned to accept other partners. As for your feelings for me, I am honored. However, I think perhaps you were carried away because it is such a special evening. I am fond of you, Tonio. I will always be fond of you."

"It was not the evening," he replied firmly. "It is you. I told you I would not press you, but I will hope."

Before she could answer, she caught sight of Anna and David. Nicola ran to him. Their arms encircled each other as their lips met. She didn't see Tonio's features sober as he realized the significance of their embrace. He turned and walked slowly to his dressing room.

"What a performance," David exclaimed. "Now, more than ever, I know how much I want you for my show. We'll have to talk about that soon, darling."

"Nicky," Anna said, "how proud your father would have been tonight! You were superb. And the Emperor and Empress coming backstage. It's unheard of. You have reached the top. From now on, you will be the most famous ballet dancer in Austria."

"What did you hear out front?" she asked them both. "How was I received? I mean. . .about the newspaper publicity. . . ."

118

"On that stage you were a dancer," David said. "That's all they thought about."

"Or cared about," Anna added. "A few expressed only pity for what happened, but they were few. The rest had nothing but praise for your dancing."

"Then I'm very pleased—and relieved," she said. "I'll run and change. I'll be as quick as I can."

David kissed her again and released her. "Take your time. They couldn't drive us away. We're going to the best restaurant in Vienna and you will have dessert. You don't dance again for a week, so you will have time to work it off."

She kissed his cheek and ran to her dressing room. Magda had set out the gown Nicola planned to wear if everything went well. She had chosen the dinner gown to please David. It was of magnolia satin with rosy tints and embroidered with beads of many colors. The satin train was long and at the top was gathered twice, forming two bouffant puffs below the waist. The apron was richly embroidered with beads and silk. One shoulder of the gown was decorated with roses. She slipped matching roses in her coiffure. Her slippers matched the gown. Her only jewelry was a diamond necklace that had once been her mother's. She slipped on her gloves, picked up her fan, then bent and touched her cheek to Magda's for telling her she looked as regal as the Empress.

In the now almost-deserted backstage, Anna kept David company until Nicola returned. Anna looked quite elegant in evening dress and David told her so.

She smiled her thanks. "I prefer my tailored clothes, but I dressed tonight, more to build up Nicola's morale. I feared there might be some in the audience who would not accept her after what happened."

"With the Emperor and Empress, plus their party in the royal box, we had nothing to fear," David said.

"My concern was that the memory of the horror Nicola was subjected to might intrude on her concentration and affect her dancing. A needless worry."

"Yes," Anna said with a contented sigh. "You look quite handsome in evening clothes, David. Of course, being of the theatre, dress is all important."

"I hope I have sufficient talent to supplement it," he replied seriously. "Nickey is a superb dancer. I was completely enraptured by her performance."

"So was everyone in the theatre," Anna said. "I feel like a mother hen clucking over her chick. Foolish, but that's the way this evening has affected me. It's been a triumph from beginning to end. Nicola will go far now."

David sobered. "Yes. I feel I don't deserve such luck. I love her, you know."

Anna laughed her deep laugh. "That's apparent in regard to both of you. But remember, Nicola is dedicated to her career. She may be reluctant to leave the Royal Ballet."

"I'll discuss that with Nicky." The furrow which appeared on his brow gave evidence he'd not given thought to the idea before.

"I don't wish to be a killjoy," Anna said. "Not tonight of all nights. I am just cautioning you so you will be prepared when you have your little talk."

"I was planning on taking her to New York very soon," he said. "The producers of the show are ready to talk business now. The last letter I received informed me that the financial backing was almost complete."

Anna said, "I do not think she will go, David."

"Don't say that," he admonished her. "She has to go. I need her. Not only as a performer, but I want to marry her. We're in love."

"David," Anna said patiently, "Nicola has two loves. The ballet, I think, may predominate. From now on, her association with the Royal Ballet will increase its prestige, and very soon she will be offered the role of prima ballerina."

"Her work in New York will create a great deal of fame for her, Anna."

"No doubt, but not the same as here. American ballet is not one of the same quality or renown that this company has attained. You might be wise not to insist that she go with you and away from what is the best future for her."

"I can't do that," he said. "My work is important too, and hers will be."

"If you love her very much, don't insist, David. She will go with you, but it will surely break her heart. This is where she belongs, for another year or two at least. I know how well she loves you and she will sacrifice her career for you, but please don't make her do this."

"I never thought of it that way," David confessed.

"You are both young. The life of a prima ballerina is short. You won't have to wait long. Let her rise to the very top of her profession. Once she has achieved that, she will be content for the rest of her life."

David nodded slowly. "I sympathize with what you say, but I'm not sure I can do it. And then there is this terrible threat they made that when she reached the peak of her profession—that she will be killed. What do you think of that?"

"I don't believe it."

"She does."

"Yes, but I still say they told her that to keep her in such a state of endless fear that her dancing would suffer. You know as well as I do that in everyone's life, there are moments of crisis."

"Luckily Sander is dead, and the group with which he was associated in Budapest has been destroyed. There can't be many of that outfit left. I hope there are none."

"My dear David, you are an American with little knowledge of the intrigue, the murders, and the plotting that go on in a Balkan country. There are thousands involved. Assassinations are only a part of it. They scheme and plan and one of these days they will come out in force. Believe me, if this threat to Nicola were real, she'd be in great danger."

"Well then, isn't she?" he asked.

"I don't think so. Sander probably engineered her kidnapping, merely as revenge against Nicola's refusal to change her testimony."

"I did think it was a strange kind of threat," David reasoned. "If they wanted to punish her, why wait years to do it?"

"My thoughts exactly, but now I'll be on my way. This night is for you two, without me looking over your shoulder. Besides, I'm tired. Be good to her, David. She's a brave, talented girl, with a great future. Remember that. Tell her I will see her tomorrow."

"Thank you for exchanging your thoughts with mine," he said. "Nicola thinks the world of you. And so will I from now on."

Anna smiled and walked briskly to the stage door. A few moments later, David watched Nicola walk toward him with the poised grace of a dancer and the smile of a woman in love. He took both her hands, looked longingly into her eyes and spoke her name.

"You are the most beautiful woman I have ever beheld. And the most talented."

"Thank you, David."

"I almost hate to take you dining because I'll have to share you with so many people. But I bow to your fame, and I realize that I must not be so selfish. Your beauty should be displayed. I'm proud to be your escort."

"You've made me very happy, David." Nicola looked around. "Where is Anna?"

"She thought we'd enjoy it better if there were just the two of us. Besides, she said she was very tired. An exhausting day at the office I suppose."

"She's always kind and thoughtful. Shall we go? I'm famished. That is a ballet dancer's song after every performance."

David brought her to a restaurant that was the most favored after the ballet. It was large and well-filled. He had reserved a choice table which gave them a clear view of the room and would give the diners a view of Nicola. He wanted to share her with others. She deserved it. Her eyes glowed with happiness. He wanted her inner happiness always to be as evident as it was tonight.

They paused at the top of the gilded stairs leading down into the restaurant proper. As if on cue, it seemed that everyone at the tables on the floor below who noticed them looked up. The gentlemen in evening dress and the ladies in their elegant gowns greeted Nicola with a wave of applause. It continued as they descended the stairs and were led to their table. Nicola smiled and nodded her appreciation, her eyes glistening with tears of appreciation.

After they were seated by the *maître d'hôtel*, David said, "They already think of you as the *prima ballerina assoluta*."

"How kind of you to say that, David," she replied.

"It's the truth. I've already ordered champagne. I will toast your beauty and your talent. Nicola, I can't take my eyes off you."

"When I look at you, I think my heart will burst," she said. "I'm so happy it's frightening."

"No reason for it to be," he countered quickly. "Smile, darling. You look frightened all of a sudden."

"All of a sudden I remembered Sander's threat."

"It isn't worth a thought."

"I hope you're right. Also, I realize some of this

123

applause—perhaps a great deal of it—is the result of the Emperor and Empress honoring our corps by attending the performance tonight."

"Possibly a very minute part of the applause is because of that. It was your tremendous talent that held everyone spellbound. You and Tonio together were almost like one. But your solo—that was breathtaking!"

"Thank you. This has been such a beautiful evening. Everything wonderful has happened to me. Nothing more possibly could."

"Something," he said with a smile, "is going to."

"What are you talking about, David?"

"Wait—and see. It won't be long."

They had finished their supper when the Emperor's emissary came marching between the tables, as rigid and austere as ever. He only unbent when he handed Nicola a sealed envelope, after a proper salute.

"From the Emperor, *Fräulein*. He will not take a refusal under any circumstances."

The lieutenant bowed again, saluted as usual and marched out. Nicola held the envelope, with its royal embossed crown, and tapped it gently against her other hand.

"Now what have you been up to, David?"

"Not me. I had nothing to do with it. While I was waiting for you to get dressed, the lieutenant came looking for you and explained what he wanted. I asked him to show up here, as a surprise."

In the back of her mind was the memory of the first invitation to the Palace, not by letter, but by direct contact. She opened the envelope and removed the card. She looked up at David with a startled expression.

"It's an invitation to the Ball at Court. That is the most prestigious social event in Vienna. David, we're both invited. I never expected this."

"The lieutenant was very careful to explain to me, a foreigner, that there are two annual balls held at the palace. And there is a difference. The Court Ball is also important, but is confined to army officers, court and civil dignitaries and a few specially invited people. The Ball at Court is something else. This is for the diplomatic corps, visiting royalty if any, the archdukes and duchesses and young, handsome army officers on active duty."

"The army officers?" Nicola asked.

"Certainly. To dance with the archduchesses and give them a small thrill by complimenting them outrageously."

"Nevertheless," Nicola declared, "it is the most important ball of the year and they say the banquet is beyond description."

"It comes between your dancing appearances, so you may enjoy some of it. Well, you have three days in which to get ready."

"Three days!" She glanced at the invitation. "That's not enough. I have to purchase a gown. Oh, so many things to do to prepare myself!"

"Tonight," David said, "there is but one thing to do —enjoy yourself. May I have this dance? We'll make it brief so I may toast your success with champagne. Soon the world will be toasting you. Nothing can stop you now, darling."

Nicola let herself believe that, but she was too overwhelmed to speak.

David guided her to the dance floor, placed his arm around her waist and led her into a spirited Viennese waltz.

# Eight

"My dear," Anna said enthusiastically, "it is quite the loveliest gown I have ever seen, on a girl equally as lovely. Poor David is going to be smitten all over again, and he will have many rivals tonight. I expect even stodgy old Franz Josef may unbend enough to dance with you. Unless he is terribly nearsighted.

"Anna, his Empress is far more attractive than I."

"His Empress is a handsome woman. You are a beautiful girl. His Empress is getting on somewhat, and there's not a great deal of love between them. Elisabeth travels more than she stays home, and it's said this is her method of getting away from him."

"Regardless of anything in this world," Nicola said, "I am going to have the best time of my life tonight and you may expect me home very, very late."

Promptly at the appointed hour, the carriage arrived. David got out and went to Nicola's apartment.

Anna said, "If your father were here, we would surely be a foursome, Nicky. He'd have swelled with pride because of you."

"I'll be thinking of him," Nicola said. "Good night, Anna. As I said, we'll be late. Don't wait up."

"Who said anything about waiting up? I'm going to my own place. I have to be at work tomorrow. I'm not among the fortunate lie-abeds like actors and ballet dancers."

"She's quite a woman," David acknowledged as they went downstairs.

"I'd be lost without her. She has been such a comfort to me after Papa was killed. But tonight I'm going to think only of pleasure. Never in my life did I dream I'd be invited to the Emperor's ball."

"I'm still wondering how I came to be included in the invitation. I'm not even Austrian."

"I am," she told him with a merry laugh. "We Austrians find a high life hard to resist. I am told there are no more lavish ceremonial balls given in all Europe than this one we are about to attend."

The Hofburg was ablaze with light. Carriages were pulling up and diamonds glittered as the ladies were helped down. A line of servants stood on both sides of the stairs leading into the palace.

The ballroom was magnificent, and Nicola and David, arm in arm, looked about in speechless wonder. There were blazing chandeliers, a score of them, and gold sconces, also bright with light. There were murals on the arched ceiling of the massive room, and the walls were covered with paintings of great value, many of which were portraits of Franz Josef, Elisabeth, the Emperor's daughter who had died years before, and a black-framed portrait of his son Rudolph, who had killed himself. That was the only somber note in the entire room.

David recognized members of the diplomatic corps in formal dress. Young army officers looked splendid in their colorful uniforms. The ladies wore expensive gowns and bedecked their bodies with fortunes in gems. Even headdresses glittered with rubies, emeralds and diamonds. Some of the gowns were decorated lavishly with feathers and plumes from rare birds. Many of the small fans the ladies carried and employed industriously, especially when they sought attention, were of gold and rare feathers. The air was heavy with the scents of perfumes which the ladies had sprayed generously on themselves.

David and Nicola mingled with the guests, fascinated by such a display of wealth and extravagance. All were waiting for the announcement that the banquet was about to take place. It would be held in another room, so far closed off.

As the ballroom filled, the excitement grew. Nicola exchanged greetings with ladies and gentlemen who had seen her dance and took the time to compliment her. The young army officers were eyeing her with plans to get her in their arms, and the sooner the better. Three of the bolder ones approached and saluted as required. Protocol was rigidly practiced here. Franz Josef had even given orders that the royal guards were to present arms even when a child of an archduchess passed through the gates.

Nicola's dance card was being rapidly filled, but David gave in gracefully. There was a loud thump of a staff to indicate the royal couple were about to enter. The orchestra, so far hidden behind palms, changed from chamber music to the grand march.

Nicola stood transfixed as Franz Josef, dazzling in medals and the brilliance of his uniform of an army general, moved slowly down the center of the room with Elisabeth at his side. The jewels she wore dazzled the eye, but no more so than the gown which was of coral faille. The train, of ivory Sicilienne, was embroidered all around with shaded olive green poppy leaves. The narrow skirt had two gathered flounces at the foot and diagonal drapery in front on which were three diagonal garlands of foliage. The *princesse basque*, buttoned in front, had fan seams that made it fit as plainly as a corset. Chenille ornamentation of green foliage was caught on the waist and train by red poppies. The square neck had shoulder straps that formed the sleeves and was edged in white. Her diamond tiara seemed to engulf her in shafts of brilliant color as the jewels caught and reflected the light from the chandeliers.

Couples fell in step behind the royal pair and the doors to the banquet hall swung open. Inside were more bright chandeliers, so large they seemed ready to fall. The tables, four rows of them, were laid with the finest china, rare crystal and gold service. Flowers, brought from somewhere in France, decorated the tables. The walls of the room were paneled in a dark wood, the chairs upholstered in scarlet velvet. The waiters, in formal clothes and wearing white silk gloves, lined the walls. They stood motionless, resembling statues, staring straight ahead.

The Emperor was helped into his chair at exactly nine. He was a punctual man and demanded this of everyone. Now all were seated as the Empress took her chair.

Suddenly the room became a sea of motion as the waiters came to life, serving a twelve-course meal accompanied by the finest wines in the world served in crystal glasses. The dinnerware was hand painted with historic scenes, each different. The rolled napkins were held in solid gold rings. The first course, tiny squares of puff pastry covered with caviar, was placed before each guest. Nicola managed to eat part of hers before the plate was whisked away.

She looked about. In the space of four or five minutes, the first course had vanished from the table and the second course of soup was brought. In five minutes this was taken away. Nicola looked about with a puzzled expression. She'd sipped only three spoonfuls.

To her left, a dowager in diamonds, bent her head slightly and whispered, "The Emperor eats quickly and if we don't, it is our fault if we go hungry. He will not permit dining slowly, even though we have about us the greatest elegance in the world."

"Thank you," Nicola said. "I shall act accordingly."

The following courses were consumed just as rapidly. There was little conversation, because one couldn't talk and eat as quickly as Franz Josef did. In an incredibly short time, brandy and cigars appeared for the men, and for the ladies, dainty lace handkerchiefs and perfume accompanied small cups of strong coffee.

Franz Josef arose, walked to the foot of the table to assist Elisabeth and they led the way to the ballroom where music was now being played for dancing. Franz Josef danced a few steps with his wife, then escorted her to the thrones situated at the end of the room. The guests promptly began the dancing and Nicola danced with David to the first of the Strauss and Millöcher waltzes.

"I'm not allowed to eat much," Nicola said in David's ear, "but that was ridiculous. I'm still hungry and each guest must have been tempted with thousands of florins worth of food."

"I ate my beef with the previous fish course still in my mouth," David chuckled.

"I was told by the lady seated next to me that Franz Josef doesn't like to spend time at the table."

"For a ballet dancer, it would work out fine," David said. "But for a man who saved his appetite for a banquet such as this one, it was the most frustrating thing I ever endured. For delicious and elegantly prepared food to be wasted in such fashion is a crime."

"I agree, but I forgive him. I scarcely touched my champagne, but I feel as if I drank a magnum of it. It's a thrilling evening. Everything I look at delights me, even the murals on the ceiling. Did you notice them?"

"There's so much to see, I won't retain any of it," David said. "Just now I'm noticing those gorgeous chandeliers swaying as the dancing gets faster and more spirited. If one ever comes crashing down, it will be a catastrophe."

"Even that would be exciting so long as no one got hurt," Nicola replied with laughter.

David smiled indulgently. "You are the most exciting part of my evening, Nicky. You always will be. But fortunately the dance ended in time so the chandeliers didn't crash. Unfortunately, I must relinquish you to one of those handsome officers. One is approaching us now."

Nicola gave David an adoring glance, then turned to the officer whose arms were already extended for her.

For Nicola, the dancing seemed to never stop, for she moved from one partner to another, many of them the army officers, who were lavish with their praise for her dancing and the radiance of her beauty. Nicola's head wasn't turned by all the compliments, and she was aware of the reason. She knew the lives these officers lived. Every young woman was a challenge.

A diplomat who had known her father danced with her, a middle-aged man as slim as the officers.

"Otto," he said, "was a friend of mine and I regret his death as much as if he were my brother."

"Thank you," Nicola said.

"I am Paul von Freiwald," he told her. "I have suggested to His Majesty that your father should be rewarded the highest honor the Emperor can bestow, even though it will be a posthumous ceremony. I think he has agreed. Naturally he would, for your father was instrumental in eliminating a well-thought-out plot to kill the Emperor."

131

"It is a consoling thought, Herr von Freiwald, that he didn't die without good cause."

"The cause was also perhaps instrumental in avoiding the beginning of a great war. It's coming, I fear, but he managed to have it postponed for a few more years. Be proud of him, Fräulein Maneth."

"I am proud—and grateful to you for telling me this. Also, deeply touched by the honor to be bestowed on my father."

"I know of your court appearance and that was also a brave act. However, I feel it my duty to warn you that not all of that gang of assassins were caught. Some escaped, some were working undercover and are not yet known. But they were led by Sander and they regarded him as an exceptional man. They have not taken his execution lightly, and I'm afraid they may one day strike at you."

"I have been warned of that," she said. "I shall be watchful, *mein Herr*. But tonight I don't believe anything frightening can happen, so I have resolved to enjoy myself."

"And I have enjoyed this dance. You dance as lightly as a shadow, but then you are one of the foremost dancers in Austria."

Somewhat out of breath, she joined David on the sidelines. "I feel like Cinderella. Some of the most important people in the world are here and I am part of it. I just danced with a duke."

"And a dozen handsome young army officers," David chided her good-naturedly. "I saw them flirting with you."

"It was flattering," Nicola admitted. "But I know their scandalous reputations. Besides, when I am dancing with them and think of you, their faces become a blur."

"Darling," David said softly, "your words quicken

my heartbeat."

"That is why I spoke them," she replied quickly. "Just looking at you quickens mine."

"You've spoiled me for dancing with anyone else. I could scarcely feel you in my arms on the dance floor. However, I shall be dutiful and ask one of the dowagers to dance. It seems the more diamonds they wear, the harder they step on my feet."

Nicola laughed and consoled him with, "I shall cream and massage them for you when the evening is ended."

"I may have to do that for you," David said, looking over her shoulder, "judging from the gentleman who is approaching. He is heavy and sweating profusely."

Nicola turned. Though her face was wreathed in a smile of interest, her words revealed her dismay. "I see what you mean. I shall endeavor to maintain a distance."

"Considering his girth, that should not prove too great a problem. Good luck," David consoled.

The man bowed. "Fräulein Maneth, I believe this is my dance."

Nicola nodded and smiled graciously. He was extending his arm for her when an amply endowed woman stepped between them and spoke in a loud, harsh voice.

"You can do better than dance with this—woman. If you do not consider your own reputation, please consider mine."

Nicola was too stunned to comment. The woman led the man, obviously her husband, away. He managed to look back. His face was beet-red, his eyes apologetic.

"That was done deliberately," David spoke with quiet anger.

"It stopped some of the dancing," Nicola said. "They're staring at me. I know what they are thinking."

"They are thinking that woman is a boor," David

133

said crisply. "If you don't believe it, look at the men who are coming your way."

"David, they've turned back. They started to come to me and they stopped. They turned back. . . ."

"True. All but one. Look to your right."

She turned and saw Franz Josef approaching. He extended his arm, and the orchestra began a slow waltz as he danced her onto the floor.

"Your beauty and your dancing take my breath away," he said softly. "I regret what just happened. It was uncalled-for, and the lady who made that remark will soon be told her presence here is no longer desired. Nor shall she ever again be asked to any of my palaces."

"Your Majesty's kindness has eased my embarrassment. I am indebted to you."

"You owe me nothing, Fräulein Nicola. You are welcome to come any time you choose and I shall be sure to include you at next year's ball."

"Thank you, Your Highness," she said. She couldn't think of anything else to say. Certainly she could not remind him of that night when she'd met him for the first time, nor could she thank him for having saved her from humiliations, or worse, at the hands of Lapin.

When he danced her to the edge of the floor, a line of officers was waiting.

"Stay happy and well," the Emperor said as he released her.

She curtsied and again murmured her gratitude. Then she was swept into the arms of an officer and the dance tempo changed. By the end of the evening, she was rapidly becoming exhausted. David came to her with a glass of champagne and they retired to one of the quieter corners where there were chairs and some degree of privacy.

"When you were asked to dance by the Emperor," he said, "any talk of what happened to you in the past, was completely erased. No one will ever mention it again."

"Then, despite that woman's rudeness, I have spent an evening I shall never forget. The Emperor restored all my confidence and I shall be forever grateful to him."

"It was a fine gesture. An unusual one because the old boy rarely dances anything more than the grand march. Well, I see he and the Empress are leaving. That means the festivities are going to get louder and faster. Do you wish to dance again?"

"Only with you," she replied.

"Considering your popularity, I am the luckiest man here tonight."

Gradually the guests began to leave. The older men of the diplomatic corps were the first to escort their wives from the palace. The army officers were under orders and promptly at one in the morning they assembled, gravely saluted the remaining guests and were marched out by a colonel.

Nicola said, "For the first time since I have been in ballet, I must admit that if I had to dance tomorrow I could not do so. But it was worth it because you were with me. You know it, but I had to say it."

"Thank you, darling." He smiled. "If you were not a ballet dancer who has to restrict the amount of food you eat, I would ask you to a coffee shop if we could find one open."

"Ask the driver. He must know of one."

"No," David objected quickly. "We've been around people all night. Forgive my selfishness, but I want you to myself."

"That's what I want also."

There were a few carriages outside the palace and they sought the first one. "Would Your Honor like me to go through the park?" the driver asked.

"A wonderful idea," David said. "It's a pleasant night and we're in no hurry."

"It will even make this wonderful evening seem a bit longer," Nicola said. "I hate to have it end."

"So do I," David said.

"We'll do it again next year. I've been invited already, which means you have been also. By the Emperor himself."

"I hope we can be there. I'm not sure."

"You mean—you must go back to New York?"

"I can't stay here forever, darling Nicky. There is that show and I have found my ballet star."

She leaned her head against his shoulder and refused to comment on this, though she would tell him, she thought, that she didn't want to leave Vienna—not yet at least. She prayed he would understand.

The carriage turned into the park where the gas lights were already dimmed. David put his arm around her and turned her to him.

"Let me look at you," he whispered.

"You've been doing that all evening," Nicola teased. She rested her hands on his shoulders.

"I want to do it the rest of my life," he said.

He kissed her brow, then her cheeks and her chin. His mouth sought hers and as they held the kiss, their passion grew. He shifted his position so he faced her and drew her close. Her arms went around his neck and as her emotion rose, a soft high of happiness escaped her.

David was raining kisses on her neck, her shoulders, then her breasts. He moaned softly and pressed his face against their softness.

"Kiss me, darling," Nicola whispered. "Kiss me. I want your lips against mine."

He did, his hands pressing her close to him. Nicola returned the kiss with abandon. One of his hands moved to the narrow band forming the sleeve of her gown and slipped it off her shoulder. He did the same with the other sleeve, loosening the decolletage so that it slipped below her breasts.

Both were oblivious to anything but their rising passion, so they were unprepared for what happened in the next few moments. Four ruffians came out of the darkness. One stopped the carriage by leaping onto the seat beside the driver and taking over the reins; another pulled David from the carriage while still another took his place and held Nicola roughly.

She watched, helpless, while the man's hand covered her mouth so she couldn't even scream, and the other three concentrated on attacking David. He managed to shove one of them aside, turn on him and deliver a powerful blow that sent him falling to the ground. But before David could turn, the other two were upon him. He was seized in a strong, unbreakable grip, his arms pulled behind him, while the other thug began to pound punches to David's stomach until he cried out in pain.

The one he'd knocked down was then on his feet. He pushed aside the man who'd been doing the punching and took his place in this act of deliberate brutality. When they let go of David, he slumped to the ground.

The man who held her touched Nicola's still-exposed breasts. He breathed in her ear. "If only I didn't have orders. If only they'd let me have you. . ." Then he released her. He jumped from the carriage and all four vanished into the night. The terrified driver managed to get down and hurry to where David lay. Nicola rearranged her gown, got out of the carriage and knelt by him. He was beginning to move and to groan a bit. With the driver's help, she got him on his feet though he had to be supported. When they got him into the carriage, he seemed to pass out again, but now Nicola could hold him.

She gave the driver her address and told him to hurry. She thought about bringing David to a hospital, but there was none close by and she wanted to care for him, unless she discovered he was so badly hurt he must have real medical attention.

He solved her doubt by regaining consciousness sufficiently to ask that he not be taken to a hospital. The drive to her apartment house was a fair distance, and by the time they arrived, David was more himself and he was able to get out of the carriage with Nicola's assistance. After paying the driver she helped David up the stairs. He had to stop twice along the flights to her floor, but he made it. Inside her apartment, he felt a little better. She found a bottle of her father's brandy and poured David a glass of it.

"Will you be all right until I change?" she asked.

"I'm fine. Just aching like one big toothache, but I'll survive. Don't worry about me. I'm much better and the brandy will make me feel even better."

She got out of her gown as quickly as she could and didn't take time to put on a dress, wearing only a robe when she joined him. He looked better. She noticed that they hadn't hit him in the face.

"David, I've got to see how badly you're hurt. Please take off your coat and your shirt. Yes. . .yes, David, I see some blood on the shirt. . . ."

He groaned doing it, but he got the coat and shirt off. He lay back on the couch while she looked at the rapidly coloring bruises. There was one laceration, not deep or extensive, but she went for a basin of water and towels.

She gently washed the wound and discovered it didn't

even require a bandage. She was kneeling by the side of the sofa and she placed her head lightly against his bare chest and cried a little.

"They take their revenge against you because they know I love you, David. What have you let yourself in for? Being with a girl like me who has these enemies."

"I'm a lucky man," he said. "Nothing you can say will convince me otherwise."

"I want you to stay here all night," she said. "I'm worried you may be hurt more than you think."

"I doubt that, but I don't feel like going back to a hotel room in the shape I'm in. I'll accept your invitation, Nicky. Also, you shouldn't be alone here."

"I want you to go to bed. In Papa's room. If you rest tonight, you won't ache so much in the morning. Let me help you up."

She assisted him into her father's bedroom, turned down the bed and then went to the kitchen to prepare a glass of warm milk spiked with more brandy. When she returned, he was in bed, wearing one of her father's nightgowns. He was propped up against the pillows and he accepted the milk and brandy gratefully.

"I certainly know I've been hit," he said, "but surprisingly, I don't seem that badly hurt."

Nicola said, "What manner of people can they be to take out on you their hatred for me?"

"We're in love and they know it. Hurting me also hurts you. They don't want anything to happen to you until they're ready to take their full revenge."

Nicola nodded. "I tried to convince myself they were only going to try and frighten me. To upset me so much I couldn't concentrate on my dancing as I should. But after what they did to you, I know they're intent on vengeance."

"Yes. They're going to try and make life a living hell for you. Possibly so you will have a breakdown. Destroying your career would destroy you, Nicola, wouldn't it?" David eyed her carefully as he asked the question.

She gave him an apologetic glance as she answered. "Much as I love you, it is my life."

"I know," he said understandingly. "And you're going to reach that peak of *prima ballerina assoluta*. I intend to be at your side as often as possible from now on. What happened tonight is my fault. I should have known better than not to be on guard when we were outside."

"My passion was as great as yours," she said. "How could we have foreseen what was going to happen?"

"We couldn't," he admitted. "But from now on, I will be at your side as often as possible."

"What about the show in New York?"

"The devil with it," he said promptly, but she detected a note of uncertainty in his voice. She knew how much he wanted that show.

"We'll talk about it tomorrow," she said. "Go to sleep now. Your body needs rest to ease the pain."

He handed her the empty glass. "I'll try to sleep, but I'm not sure I can. There's an aura of danger all around you. After the drubbing I took tonight, I suppose around me also. I must try to think of a way to find out who they are and expose them. Certainly everyone connected with that plot against Franz Josef was not captured by the police. Also, because you are in the public eye, they'll have no trouble keeping track of you."

She turned the lamp down very low, opened a chest, got out a blanket for herself and settled down in a chair by the bed, tucking the covering around her. David closed his eyes after sliding down in the bed. She watched him drift into a light sleep and she huddled closer under the blanket, for the apartment was chilly at this time of night. She couldn't sleep and didn't even try to. She was grateful for this brief time in which she could think and make up her mind about one of the most important decisions of her life.

What concerned her most was this attack on David. It could happen again and again. Being with her, being in love with her, made him a target. As David had said, hurting him was their way of causing her pain. And constantly reminding her that they meant what they threatened.

She thought also of New York, of a new type of performance she was not familiar with. David's future likely rested on the success of this show and it would hurt her more than she could bear if he failed. He had to go back. But alone. For the more she considered going with him, the more certain she was that she wanted to stay here—to perform at the Burgtheater, to work endless hours, striving for perfection so she would reach the top. She could be first soloist now; but if what she suddenly and unexpectedly planned came to pass, she might be prima ballerina in a matter of a few weeks.

Heidi, now holding that position in the Royal Ballet Company, was an accomplished and experienced dancer. She was attractive as well. She'd always been kind to Nicola, helping her, giving her advice and standing up for her when Lapin became too critical and sarcastic. She could fill the part. David would be satisfied with her because he'd be getting one of the most famous ballerinas in Austria, and one well known on the continent as well. He would have to look no further for his ballet soloist.

All this would take David away from her, and she wondered if she could really bear it. Yet, keeping him here was not only destroying his career, but if there were another of these attacks, he might not survive it.

In the morning, she would have to tell him. If he felt well enough, that would be the time to let him know that she wanted to stay in Vienna. She closed her eyes and tried to blot out all thinking. It would be morning soon. She was fortunate that she wasn't to dance again for three more days. She felt herself relaxing, felt the first stages of sleep and then opened her eyes quickly. David had reached out and was touching her hand.

She partially arose to turn up the light, but he gently objected and she didn't make an issue of it.

"How do you feel," she asked. "You've not had an hour's sleep."

"I haven't had any sleep. I've been thinking of you."

His fingers tightened around her wrist and he drew her down to him. She made no resistance. He turned the bedcovers aside, sat up and put his other arm around her neck. She bent and kissed him. His was a kiss of passion and desire and once again she responded to him. He whispered endearments without taking his lips from hers. She eased her body against his. When their passion surged, she slipped free of his arms, opened the robe, shrugged it off and moved close to him again.

Now his lips became more demanding, and she responded, her hands caressing his shoulders gently, then moving down his torso. She realized he had removed the nightgown while she dozed. Their bodies, warm and eager, pressed close and their lovemaking became more ardent as their passion rose. Finally their bodies joined in the fulfillment of their love.

She relaxed then and so did he. Their arms remained around one another. They were still locked in an embrace when she awoke. Very gently she extricated herself from his arms, slipped out of bed, put on the robe and went to the bathroom to prepare for the day. Her mind was clear, her body for the time freed of the desire which had overwhelmed both of them. She felt there could never again be any question of their love for one another. It was going to break her heart to tell him he must return to New York City alone.

# Nine

His body was covered with bruises in the morning, reminding Nicola of her own black-and-blue body after the assault in Sander's house. But David ate eggs and hot bread with a fine appetite and finished the pot of coffee.

"It was," he said, his smile warm, "a lovely night. I didn't dream it, did I?"

"No, darling, it was no dream. I hope I pleased you."

"More than you know. I suggest we get married in New York. That will make you a citizen of the United States. We can be together forever, Nicky. Under no circumstances will I ever leave you. After last night we know we were meant for each other."

"I want you to listen to me, David, and try to understand. Please believe me, I don't want this to happen, but it must. The truth is, I don't wish to go to New York. I want to remain here in Vienna, at least until I have reached the top of my profession. If I go anywhere else, I'll have to start over again. I'm now the first soloist, I have Tonio to work with, and we seem to have blended our talents until we've become a fine team."

"But what of the show in New York?" he asked in dismay.

"I've thought about that too. You came here looking for a ballet dancer who was capable enough of filling the part you have in mind. I think I know who would do that part splendidly."

"Damn it," he exploded, "I don't want anyone else. If you can't go back, I won't either."

"David, you have your career just as I have mine. You are already quite famous in musical shows. Please don't wreck that reputation now. We can wait. We're young, and once we attain what we wish in our professions, we'll be that much happier when we do marry."

"I don't agree with you. I think you're trying to get me to go back alone because you're afraid those thugs will attack me again."

"I've thought of that, but my other reasons are even more important. I don't want you to end your career. Darling, you know how long a ballerina lasts. I have perhaps three or four years before I have to give way to a younger girl. From then on, it's downhill for a ballerina, and I don't want that to happen. Before it does, I'll be with you. Your work won't suffer with age as mine surely will. Then we can work together. Perhaps you can even find a part in one of your shows for an old, retired ballerina."

"I have to think about this," he said sternly. "I don't like it. What if those people corner you and harm you again? What if they rape you again?"

"I will do my best to see that they do not. David, my heart is breaking as I tell you this. After last night I don't know how I will endure the loneliness I know I'll have to bear when you are gone. And yet, I love you so completely that I will face it somehow. The pain won't last forever."

145

"I said I'd have to think about it. I want the woman I love with me."

"You agree that Heidi is a fine ballerina."

"Yes, I agree," he said impatiently. "She would do very well indeed. But it's *you* I want."

"I want to stay here and grow with the Vienna ballet. David, it won't be for long. With Heidi gone, I may step into her shoes. Who knows? Lapin may not like me, but after all, he is a ballet master and he has to pick and choose from those he knows can do the dancing. He knows I'm capable of it."

"I've planned this for so long and believed you were amenable. After last night I hadn't any doubt. Now you wreck all my plans and hopes. Give me time to think, Nicky."

"You have to go back soon. You told me they were growing impatient in New York. If my ballet life ends first, I'll come to you. If your show is not a success, I'll be here when you come back to me. It has to be that way. May I talk to Heidi about this?"

He arose, tightening the belt of her father's dressing gown that he was wearing. He went to the window overlooking the street and stood there peering down at the traffic.

"I suppose you're right." He spoke without turning around. "I know how devoted you are to your ballet and changing companies is not easy. I also realize I have an important show to do and the ballerina you suggested will be very good for the part we have in mind. I have to consent, Nicky. My ambitions and my pocketbook and reputation say I must, but my heart tells me that I cannot go away from you."

"Darling, it won't be for very long. Please don't regard our separation with anger. We have so much time."

"I'm not so sure, but I won't break through that wall

of stubbornness." He turned about quickly. "All right! If Heidi will take the part, I'll sail with her in three days' time. I'll cable New York that I've found the girl, and to get things ready at once."

She went to him and put her arms around his neck. "Dear David, it's the only way and I hate it as much as you do. But everything will work out for us. You'll see."

"Even though I know you're right, I'm disappointed. I shouldn't have asked you to go back with me. It's the first time in my life that I hope my show fails, even though I know it won't. It's bound to last for months —maybe a year. That's what makes this so hard."

"While you're gone," she said, "I'll polish my English until it's as good as your German is now. Eventually we'll work here half the year, and in New York the other half. There will be more shows in which I can dance, perhaps even with you."

"Ballet?" he scoffed. "If you ever started to run across the stage to launch yourself into my arms, I'd drop dead of fear that I'd miss you and you'd go flying off into space. It's bad enough watching you go through that routine."

"You feel better about it now, don't you?" she asked.

"Not one damn bit better, but I can at least face it, consider it and maybe even plan for it. But I'll never like it, and all I'll do is worry about you and wait for the day when I can come to you—or you will come back to me."

"David, my love."

"See about Heidi, will you? I'll begin preparations for going back. Frankly I should have done so days ago. Some of my recent cables from the producer haven't been exactly polite. Yes, I've a fine show to do and I want to do it. You have your ballet. My work is in New

York; yours is here in Vienna. We'll make the best of it, but next time nothing in this world is going to keep us apart.''

She kissed him and slipped her hands under his robe to draw him close once more. She cried a little on his shoulder. All she could think of was how dreary the days were going to be until he returned. Yet it was her choice.

David went off finally and Nicola dressed quickly. She walked to the Burgtheater and as she approached it, she regarded the building with a love for it and her profession, and the knowledge that what she had decided was proper and correct. She was grateful for his understanding. All her life had been spent in the anticipation of dancing at this theatre. In the space of a few days, actually, she'd progressed at a speed she'd never before thought possible. She was a soloist now; she was ready for the first solo part and suddenly she might be in line for prima ballerina. This rapid promotion was unheard of, and she was afraid that by asking Heidi to leave the troupe, she'd be accused of arranging matters so she would step into Heidi's ballet slippers. Yet there could be no deviation from her plans.

Armed with a copy of the script David had given her to study, she went directly to Heidi's dressing room. Heidi often care early in the belief that she needed more practice than any of the others. Luckily Lapin was nowhere about to interfere. Nicola tapped on Heidi's door and was quickly admitted.

"How nice to see you," Heidi exclaimed. "And how well you are doing. I've watched you progress from the first day you came here. You're going to take my place one of these days. And it won't be long. I'm getting a bit old. . . ."

"You're the best ballerina in Vienna, in all of Europe, for that matter. But I have a proposition that may hurry everything along. First of all, believe me when I say that I am not doing this because I want to succeed you. You know David, of course.''

"Of course. I wish I'd seen him first."

"David wants me to join the cast of a musical he is going to star in and help produce. It's a ballet-dancing part. In New York, of course."

"Well, congratulations, Nicky. I'm happy for you. I wish I had that chance."

"You have. That's what I came to talk to you about. I want to stay here. My whole life has been around this theatre. All of my dreams have been concerned with it, even though my chance with David could be of even more importance than leading this ballet company."

"Tell me about it," Heidi said with brisk curiosity. "I might be very interested."

"The part is a solo ballet dance during the performance. But the dance is an integral part of the show itself. This has never been done before. There will be some acting too, besides the dancing. It's a sensational part and an original idea. If it wasn't for. . .well. . . my chance here, I'd take it eagerly and gladly."

"Let me study the script," she said. "It's not a long one, I see. I'll have it read by the time you finish warming up. When would I have to leave?"

"In three days."

"As soon as that? Oh my! Theodor is going to be angry."

"Your partner? Are you that close?"

"We're not close at all. He's a good *premier danseur*, that's all. I enjoy dancing with him, but he's a jealous sort. He'll consider this a big advance in my career while he stands still. He won't be easy for you to dance with if Lapin actually unbends and uses his brains to give you my part."

"Heidi, I can stand anything if only you'll do this for

me. I want David to have the best possible dancer. You are the only one who can do it perfectly."

"Come back here in two hours," she said.

Nicola bent and kissed her cheek before she went to her own dressing room to change into leotards, leg warmers and her plain dancing slippers. She was at the *barre* when Lapin arrived. Since the Emperor and the Empress had come backstage to congratulate the company, it had gone to Lapin's head and he had become foppish in his street clothes. He wore a waist-hugging, black morning coat with a fur collar, a huge black cravat on a ruffled shirt, a black homburg tilted rakishly to one side, and to top it all off, a gold-headed cane.

"Good morning, girls," he called out.

There was a mumble of replies from sweaty, breathless girls. He beckoned to Nicola. She walked over to face him. He regarded her critically, but he had learned his lesson. He knew he could never again attempt to seek her favors.

"Do you think you can handle the first solo?" he asked.

"Yes, *M'sieur*. I know I can. I'll want Tonio, however. I'm used to him."

"Very well. You shall have him. The first soloist and her partner are going to head up a road company we are sending to many of the capitals of Europe. Something you may look forward to one day, if you are good enough."

"Thank you, *M'sieur*."

"The Emperor was well pleased with your dancing. I must say it has improved considerably. You have listened to my instructions and my advice. I trust you will continue to do so. You will dance first solo day after tomorrow."

"I'm grateful, *M'sieur*. I'll do my best."

"If you don't," he wagged a finger under her nose, "I'll have your head. You have somehow acquired quite a reputation as a dancer. See that you do not destroy it."

He pulled off his coat, hung it up with his hat, but he retained his cane, brandishing it about like a man who might enjoy using it. But Lapin was now a well-tamed man. He lived in fear of the Emperor's wrath as much, or more, than his dancers lived in fear of him.

Tonio heard the news from Lapin and hurried up to Nicola to embrace her. "It's wonderful. The solo. . . and you insisted I be in it for the *pas de deux*. Thank you, Nicky."

"I may be premature in telling you this," she said, "but it's possible you and I are going even higher, and much sooner than anyone suspected, including you and me. I'll know in a little while."

"Higher? You mean *premier danseur*? Theodor will kill me! What of Heidi?"

"I said I'll tell you soon."

"And this part in New York? What about that?"

"I'm not going. I've offered it to Heidi."

"But why? You're in love with this David, are you not?"

"Very much in love with him, Tonio."

"I know, but you can't blame a man for hoping. Why don't you and he have a fight?"

"Not in this world, Tonio. I always said I'd fall in love but once, and I fell. Now I'm going to see Heidi. If the monster wants to know where I am, tell him I'm resting. Get warmed up. We're to go into rehearsal as soon as I come back."

Heidi was on the last page of the script, beside herself with happiness. "It's meant for me, Nicky. I've never read such a play before. It's enchanting. And the music! What I can read of it seems wonderful. Imagine the

151

scene where I solo. A blue light, an evening backdrop—and Debussy? If you have changed your mind, I'll fight you for this chance."

"I'm as happy as you, Heidi. You're going to be famous before that show is over. Look out for David. For my sake?"

"I'll repress all my passion and desire," she promised with a smile and a hug. "I think I'll find me an American millionaire. Now I have the greatest of pleasure telling M'sieur Lapin that I'm leaving the company. I asked him for a contract a year ago and he told me, profoundly of course, that he dealt in dancers and not contracts and if I stubbed my toe he'd fire me. What a pleasure to quit. What a good thing for my career! Much as I love this theatre and the troupe."

"You'll dance one more time, of course? The night before you sail."

"I wouldn't miss it. I shall weep and take a hundred bows and tell everyone how sad it is to leave this theatre."

"Thank you again. I'll tell David this evening and arrange for you to talk to him as soon as possible."

"And in return I'll put a big flea in Lapin's ear about who should succeed me."

"I'll wait for the storm after you tell him. I'd better get back now before he sends me to the corps again."

She and Tonio began their rehearsals. As they danced, she told him what had happened. Out of sheer joy he lifted her high and set her down with a grace he possessed in full measure.

"You're not sure you'll get Heidi's part, Nicky?"

"No one is sure what Lapin will do."

"He'll give it to you. He has to. The Emperor singled you out. He can't deny that. The Emperor may come again to see you dance, he liked you that much. Lapin looks out for himself. If you can draw the Emperor and the people around him, Lapin can take the credit. Yes, you'll have a chance to dance as prima ballerina."

"And you as *premier danseur*," she said.

"He'll never let Theodor go. He thinks he's the best dancer in the world."

"He's not bad, but you're better and we dance well together. I'll insist you dance with me. Listen to us, Tonio, talking as if we were prima ballerina and *premier danseur* already. We both know things don't happen that way in ballet."

"Anything can happen in ballet," he countered. "Even that. And we're ready for it. We must work hard to make it happen."

Half an hour later, Nicola heard Lapin's shout of dismay and his anger expressed in French. He stalked from the stage and disappeared for almost an hour. Nicola was in her dressing room when Lapin knocked.

He came in and sat down, propped the cane between his legs, both hands resting on it, and glared at her. "I have heard of sneaky ways to get yourself promoted in this business, but none as clever as yours. Why didn't you tell me this friend of yours wanted a dancer for his American show? I could have provided him with half a dozen. Did you think if you got her away from the troupe, I would make you prima ballerina? You're not much more than a child. No one advances that fast. You may be a fine dancer, but the feature role. . .no. Never! Not for another three or four years."

"*M'sieur*, I look for nothing. I am first soloist and proud of it. I want no more than that for now."

"Perhaps after the next performance you won't be even first soloist. Or second, for that matter. A year or two more in the corps de ballet may do you a great deal of good and teach you respect and humility. This ambition of yours has become an obsession."

"I have ambition, yes. If you say I must go back to

the corps, who am I to argue with you regarding your judgement of my talent?"

He eyed her resentfully. "You know as well as I do, I can't send you back. If the Emperor heard of it—and you'd see to it he did—he'd have my head. You will dance first solo. With Tonio."

"Who," Nicola asked sweetly, "will take Heidi's place?"

"I don't know yet. There are plenty of dancers capable of it. I'll find one. It won't be you, that's all. And watch your pirouettes. You're beginning to turn like the hands of a run-down clock."

"I'll watch them, *M'sieur*. Thank you."

That night she met David at one of their favorite restaurants. Heidi was to join them later. She told David of Heidi's reaction and of her interview with Lapin.

"This happened so fast," David said, "that he can't get another ballerina in time. I'd be willing to bet you'll get it whether he wants you to have it or not. That man is selfish. He inflated like a balloon when the Emperor praised the performance. He hasn't forgotten that, but he won't let you think he can't get anyone else who would please Franz Josef as much as you do."

When Heidi came, she and David talked long about the show, the script, their plans for sailing. Nicola sat through it all, her features cheerful, her heart heavy. She wondered if she was selfish in wanting her career. She should go with David, she thought, and the devil with the Hofburg and Schönbrunn. But even now she knew she couldn't do it. Her lifelong dreams and plans for Schönbrunn were too firmly imbedded in her mind to disregard or delay.

She didn't enjoy the evening until they dropped Heidi off and continued on to her apartment.

David helped her remove her coat. He placed it on a

chair and turned to face her.

"Before we talk more about our future," she said, "I want to say that I would like you to spend the night with me."

He clasped her shoulders, bent and kissed her brow. "I was hoping you would let me. Having known the fulfillment of love with you isn't going to make my leaving any easier. I doubt if I were in a more staid profession such as medicine or the study of law, I would be so understanding. But as one of the theatre, I know the dreams and hopes we cherish and how hard we work to fulfill them."

"Do you think me selfish, darling?"

"No more so than I," he replied. "We're different. Also, more tolerant. Only one thing bothers me. You don't have the slightest fear I might be attracted to another woman. Not even of Heidi, who has a great deal of charm and knows how to use it. It's apparent she has spent much time cultivating it."

"You're wrong," Nicola said. "I have thought of losing you and of your being attracted to Heidi. Listening to both of you discuss the show and your plans for leaving depressed me. I wanted to tell you I would go with you. After last night when our love knew fulfillment, I wondered how I could bear the separation. I know there will never be anyone else for me."

"How do you suppose I will endure the separation?" he asked, his eyes rebuking her.

"It will be difficult," Nicola reasoned. "You will be subjected to the wiles of women who will fall in love with you just watching your performance. I'm sure they throw themselves at your feet already. Also, I noticed Heidi appraising you."

He chuckled. "Don't worry about Heidi. My interest in her is strictly professional. I'll keep busy and write you frequently. I wish I could write poetry so I could ex-

155

press my love in the proper manner. However, I do it best in person."

"Let me see how I do." Nicola moved close to him and raised her hands to cup his face, drawing it down to kiss him. He gathered her to him hungrily and held her close.

"How can I leave you?" he asked. "I'll go mad with desire."

"It is the same with me, darling." She bent back slightly and unbuttoned the bodice of her dress. She pulled at the ends of the pink-ribboned bow of her corset cover, loosening it and exposing her breasts. She put a hand behind his head and stood on tiptoe to kiss him. It fired their already rising passion. David's hands sought her exposed breasts and fondled them gently.

"I can't wait, darling." Nicola spoke between kisses.

"I don't want to," David replied huskily.

He swept her up in his arms and carried her into the bedroom, her lips still captured between his. He placed her on the bed, undressed her, then himself. She was as eager for fulfillment as he. Afterward, they lay side by side and spoke the language of lovers as they swore undying devotion. They spent the night making love until their passion was spent and sleep claimed them.

The next day Anna came by, both excited and worried. "What is this I hear about David going back without you?"

"It's true, Anna. It has to be that way."

"But it would be to your advantage, even your safety, to go to New York City with him."

"I agree, but I'm a ballet dancer. I don't want to be anything else. Lapin has made me first soloist and that's a good climb upward."

"It's only below prima ballerina. Is that why you asked Heidi to go with David?"

"No. It so happens Heidi is exactly right for the part.

How did you learn all this?"

"I stopped by the theatre in case you were there early, as you often are. I was told by a dozen dancers of this sudden change."

"It's not a scheme on my part to get Heidi's role. I would prefer to be with David, but I had to make a choice. The ballet must come first. David agrees with me."

"What if there's more trouble? If he is not here to protect you?"

"We were attacked two nights ago when we left the ball. Four men set upon us. They beat David severely, but did not hurt me. One of them held me, fondled me a little, and he said something strange. I didn't even remember it until now. He said he would like to have me, but his orders forbade it."

"Did you tell David?"

"No, I don't want him to worry. Nor do I want to have to worry about him being attacked a second time."

"Why would they want to hurt him?" Anna wondered.

"No doubt because they already know I love him. I'm a public figure, just as he is. It's an easy matter for those bullies to keep track of us. They probably make a point of knowing about every facet of our lives."

"Yes," Anna agreed.

"Also, I want David to leave as quickly as possible to prevent another attack. The next time they may kill him. I couldn't bear it."

Anna regarded Nicola worriedly. "Are you forcing David to leave while you deliberately remain here and expose yourself to greater danger?"

"I am not forcing him to leave. His profession forced that. I don't want him further endangered."

"What about yourself?"

"I'll risk anything to reach the peak of my career.

That is my only reason for remaining here. You know how much I love David."

"He loves you to the same degree. I had hoped you would leave with him. Has he proposed marriage to you?"

Nicola nodded. "I accepted, but my career comes first."

"Has Lapin given you any encouragement?"

"Not much," Nicola admitted.

Anna's brow furrowed. "Do you suppose he will ask you to his apartment for the usual reason? If so, will you go?"

"I will," Nicola smiled mischievously, "with you as my chaperone."

Anna laughed. "Poor Lapin. He's no match for you. Your papa would be proud of you. I am already and I am trying to take his place. I must, because you may not be out of danger yet. I think that what happened two nights ago proves it."

"I'll do my best to shut them out of my mind. Knowing I have your friendship will help. Also, it has done a great deal to ease my loneliness. After David has gone, I will have only you."

"I'll not fail you, my dear," Anna said. She bent and touched her cheek to Nicola's. "Good luck, my child, and for God's sake, if possible, avoid danger."

"I will, though I won't think of it. Perhaps, the more famous I become, the more fearful those ruffians will become, and will think twice before harassing me again."

"I'll pray to God you are right, but I will come by frequently. Also, as you say, you are a public person. If I should hear anything worrisome, I'll be at your side as quickly as possible."

"Thank you, Anna. Don't worry about me. I believe things will work out. They have already."

"I hope so. I must go now. Remember—send for me if you are threatened in any way. We will go to the police and see that you are given some sort of protection. If you are unable to contact me, go yourself."

After getting a solemn promise from Nicola to do so, Anna left.

# Ten

Heidi's last dance was in *La Sylphide*, a romantic ballet which she had performed many times before, but there was general agreement that she'd never been better than in this final performance before going to New York.

And Nicola, as first soloist, was regarded as perfect. Both shared in the final curtain applause, after which Heidi had to leave the theatre promptly to pack and join David early in the morning.

Nicola, in her dressing room, was far more aware of her loneliness than her triumph. It was as if David and Heidi had already sailed. She tried to be gracious to several admirers who had managed to get backstage and knocked on her door, but for once her heart wasn't in it. Only Tonio saved the day for her by coming to talk about what was now going to happen.

"Lapin has been scouting around looking for a prima ballerina, but I don't think he's had much luck," Tonio said. "At least, that's what I hear. I guess his reputation as a slave driver and a seducer has become common knowledge and he can't get anyone."

"I doubt that," Nicola said. "I don't like him. I agree that he drives us to near collapse sometimes, but bear in mind that as a ballet master he never resorts to clichés, and won't use acrobatics except in the best taste. I don't think this company has ever given a mediocre performance under his guidance.''

"All right, give him his due, devil that he is. But if he does not find a replacement by day after tomorrow, he has to give you the lead. There's nobody else in this company who can do it as well as you.''

"I hope I get it, Tonio,'' Nicola said wistfully. "Maybe they'll think I'm selfish, and even that I managed Heidi's departure to better my chances, but that's not true. I stayed because my place is here. Heidi is nearly thirty and her days are numbered, but in this New York play she'll be as much an actress as a ballet prima and I'm sure she'll do as well at that as at her dancing.''

"All right, say you get her role. What's the ballet? *Giselle*? That's a tough one. What I want to know is whom you'll dance it with. Theodor or me?''

"I don't know. Theodor is a good dancer, but you're much better and I'll emphasize this to Lapin if he decides on me.''

"He listens to no one and never takes advice. Yet the last time we did *Giselle*, Theodor wasn't very good, particularly at the end where the dancing becomes frenzied as Giselle nearly dances him to death. I recall that Lapin gave him hell for sloppy work.''

"I remember. I think he was angry with Heidi that night. Tonio, I want nobody but you to dance with me.''

His somber expression softened and he managed a smile. "Thank you, Nicky. You have no idea how much that means to me.''

She turned away from him. The way he spoke and looked at her revealed he was still in love with her.

"Don't be frightened, Nicola. I know who has captured your heart.''

"I'm not frightened, Tonio. You are a gentleman."

"As for *Giselle*, I'm going to practice the role anyway," he said. "You never can tell."

"True," Nicola agreed. "So will I."

She was late leaving the theatre and there were very few people about and, of course, no one to see her home. She opened the door to an apartment that seemed unusually empty and still. It affected her to such a degree that she inspected every room and closet for fear of an intruder. Her heartbeat resumed its normal pace after she'd concluded the examination.

David had excused himself that night; there was so much for him to do. She went to bed longing for his closeness and his tender kisses. She slept badly, but was up early to get to the depot to see them off.

They were waiting for her when she arrived, standing beside a mound of baggage. David reached for her as she broke into a run when she saw them. He embraced and kissed her a dozen times, like a man long starved for love.

Heidi moved up beside them. "I'll see that he behaves himself," she told Nicola. "After seeing you two, and listening to him rave about you, I don't think he'll need watching. Nicky, I want to thank you again for the opportunity you have given me."

"To be frank," Nicola said, "I did it more for David because I knew he needed someone with the kind of talent you possess."

"I hope I succeeded in returning the favor. I talked at length with Lapin. Has he done anything about my part in *Giselle* yet?"

"Not that I've heard. I haven't seen him to talk to."

"Remember, I tried very hard, but Lapin is not a responsive man. He likes to make up his own mind."

"If he doesn't give Nicky that part, he doesn't have a mind," David observed. "Good luck, Nicky darling."

"Thanks, David. I'll send you a cable if I do." She glanced at the watch attached to a waist-length chain. "It's almost time. Remember, my dearest, I love you."

"Maybe once I get the show set, I can find someone to understudy my role. If I do, I'll surprise you. If not, remember I love you too. Be careful, darling, and promise me that if anything happens to frighten you, you'll send me a cablegram. I'll come to you, show or no show."

They clung tightly to each other for a final kiss. "I'll be careful," Nicola promised. "And I'll be working as hard as you. The harder I work, the sooner I'll achieve my goal. I believe that once I've accomplished that, I'll be impatient to go to you."

She watched the train pull out of the station and then slowly walked along the platform to the exit. She continued walking, trying not to think. Yet she couldn't shut out David's face or the fact that he might be gone a year, perhaps two. But she reminded herself their separation had been of her own choosing and insistence. She was young, there was so much for her to do, and her ambitions lay here in Vienna—at the Hofburg with the Austrian Royal Ballet.

She felt pangs of hunger and remembered she'd not taken time to breakfast. She stopped at a small coffee shop, drank coffee and ate a very light meal. It was now mid-morning and she realized that to dance *Giselle* tomorrow night, she would have to prepare herself, because this ballet called for the most intricate footwork imaginable. At the end of the ballet, as Giselle, she would awaken from her grave to take Albrecht, the hero, in her arms and dance him to death. She recalled Theodor's interpretation of the role a month ago and shuddered to think of dancing the role with him. She hoped Lapin would remember how poorly he'd danced. If she were ordered to perform with him, she would, but she dreaded it.

At the theatre she found half a dozen girls at the *barre*, raising a sweat. She was not to join then, for the man at the stage door informed her that Lapin was in his office. She was to see him the moment she arrived.

"You're late," Lapin grumbled as she entered the office. "You've kept me waiting, and this is a time when we cannot delay."

"I'm sorry," she said, "but I was seeing Heidi off."

"And your lover, no doubt."

"Yes, the man I'm in love with, M'sieur Lapin. Please do not make light of it."

"Sit down. Don't be so testy so early in the morning. I do not have good news for you. I have found a prima ballerina to take Heidi's place, but you will continue in the first solo part."

She had steeled herself against this, so she was able to accept it with grace. "I'm glad you did find someone. I know that you do not believe I am ready for such a part and I bow to your judgment, *M'sieur*. I have to admit you seldom make a bad decision."

"Now, that's very nice of you to say that. Very nice. It was my wish to find out what you think of my decision and I can see you do agree with me. Well, I was testing you. I like testing people. It brings out their true nature."

"Testing?" she asked. "What do you mean?" Her hopes began to soar.

"I mean that you will be prima ballerina of the Royal Ballet. At least for one performance. If you do well, the position is yours. However, I do have a condition."

"*M'sieur*," she said in a worried voice, "if you mean a repetition of what happened at your studio. . ."

"No, I don't mean that at all, though I can't see why you made such a big thing of it. What I mean is this. If you draw the Emperor's favor again, I wish you would put in a good word for me. He acted as if I were a neophyte in the corps."

"I shall do my best. May I ask whom I will dance with? As you know, I prefer Tonio."

"I know that, but you'll take Theodor."

"Do you recall the way he danced the part last month?"

"Very well, and if he does it again, I'll kick him out. But he knows the part. It's too intricate for a newcomer like Tonio."

"I will not defy you," she said. "I only wish it could be Tonio."

"It won't be and that's that," he said. "You can go now. Remember, you will give a stunning performance, or you will go back to the corps."

"I will remember," she said.

She sighed deeply. She was gratified that she had the part, though she knew very well it was only because the lack of time precluded his finding anyone else of star quality.

She changed into her heavy practice clothes and studied the script of *Giselle*, though she knew every movement in it. More and more she distrusted Theodor's ability to take the leading role.

Magda was waiting on stage impatiently. She ran up to Nicola, wiping perspiration off her face and neck with a heavy towel.

"What did he say? Do you have Heidi's part?"

"Yes, I have it."

"With no fuss? No compromise?"

"He knows better. Oh, he made me sweat. He told me he had someone else and then said he was only testing me to see if I agreed with him. I don't like that man, Magda, but he is a great ballet master for all of that."

"Monster! That's what he is. A devilish monster. Who dances with you?"

"His choice is Theodor. That's how it will be."

"Damn him! Theodor stinks! All he's got is a fine figure and a pretty face. Heidi once told me she was afraid of him."

"Well, I'm not, but that doesn't help poor Tonio. He'll be heartbroken."

"You'll rehearse this afternoon, won't you?"

"Yes. Tonio said he'd be here, but he needn't have bothered. I hate to tell him the news."

"I think Theodor just went right into Lapin's office. I just had a glimpse of him. . ."

"I'll be civil to the man. He is part of the Royal Ballet and he can dance well when he wants to. There are times when he looks bored and that's when he becomes a sloppy dancer."

Nicola went to the *barre* and began her warming-up exercises. She was still at it when Theodor arrived. And right behind him came Tonio, looking downcast.

Nicola greeted Theodor civilly, but went by him to reach for Tonio's hands and hold them. "I'm so sorry, Tonio. Lapin insists it must be Theodor."

"I know. Lapin told him. But it doesn't matter so long as you got the lead. I'll be cheering for you."

"You'll cheer for some other ballet company if you waste our time," Theodor said curtly. "Come along, Nicky. If you're ever going to learn this dance, it had better be before the performance."

"I know the dance," she said. "As well as you do. I suggest we start with the *pas de deux* in the first act."

"As you wish."

"Aren't you going to spend at least a little time limbering up?" she asked.

"I don't need it. I keep in trim. A waste of time as far as I'm concerned."

"Then I suggest we begin."

Tonio walked over to the *barre* and leaned against it

166

to watch. The *pas de deux* was fairly simple at the start. It was a romantic dance, but as the first act continued, Giselle was to discover that the man she loved was an imposter and she would then dance, as in a dream, the same steps she'd dance with him when she discovered she loved him. At the end of the first act, she would dance this dream sequence as madness possessed her, and she would finally drop dead at his feet.

It was a ballet based on a German legend and the most popular ballet in Germany and Austria, if not all over Europe. They agreed to perform their parts in the first act.

The dancing went well, even while done in practice clothes and not the airy-light costumes of the performance. Theodor seemed to be trying very hard. Nicola grew more and more confident that he would show improvement over the last time he danced this part.

She danced to the end of the stage. Then, *en pointe*, she began to run toward him. At the last moment she became airborne expecting to be deftly caught, but as she flew toward him she saw him stagger back a step or two as if he were suddenly uncertain of himself. He reached for her and missed. She struck his shoulder and sent him reeling, but she landed on the stage floor with a crash.

She was unable to move; she was sure she'd been badly injured. Performers were running toward her, but it was Tonio who reached her first. He gently turned her over, then raised her carefully. She was finally able to stand. Both her knees were bloody, and her right elbow felt as if it were broken.

"Can you walk?" Tonio asked.

"I. . .think so. I want to try."

He put his arm around her waist to steady her. She took a few tentative steps and was relieved that no bones had been broken. She was sore from head to foot and would be in pain by morning.

"I'm all right, I think," she said. "Just what did happen?"

"He lost his nerve. He stepped back and then he wasn't ready when you were on your way. It was outright carelessness. In fact, you'd almost think it was deliberate."

Nicola felt those old quivers of terror flash through her. Tonio was right. It did seem a deliberate act, allowing her to fall and certainly guarantee she would be injured. There had been many instances in ballet where a dancer who missed being properly caught was so badly injured she would never again dance.

Nicola deliberately shook off Tonio's supporting arm at her waist. She rose *en pointe* and danced her way to the *barre*. There she did leg and neck exercises to make certain there was no injury which had so far not manifested itself.

Lapin was there now, having been summoned from his office. Theodor stood alone, gazing at everyone, looking for some consolation. Lapin wanted to know what happened and there were a dozen people to tell him in their own way. Lapin strode up to Theodor.

"Well, what's your excuse this time, you dumbhead?"

"She didn't aim herself. . . ."

"She did!" a dozen voices cried out. "You stepped aside. You wanted her to fall."

"I did not!" Theodor shouted. "I swear I did not."

"Well, whatever your excuse, you may consider yourself no longer a member of this company. You've been careless and lax once too often. Tonio, rehearse the part with Nicola. Theodor, get out of this theatre and don't come back. You almost ruined the only chance we have of putting on this performance. Get out!"

"If you don't feel like going," Tonio said harshly, "I'll be glad to help you."

"You stinking Serbian," Theodor shouted in wrath. "You'll never be as good as me. Who ever heard of a Serbian ballet dancer? All you people are good for is raising pigs."

Tonio took a few rapid steps forward and Theodor promptly fled. The tension lessened and finally someone began laughing at Theodor's indignified departure.

Nicola led Tonio to the row of hard chairs. They sat down and Tonio's face broke into a smile. "He did say I could have the part, didn't he?"

"That's what he said, and it makes me very happy. Tonio, do you really think Theodor deliberately let me fall?"

"It seemed that way to me. Maybe he was mad because you wanted Lapin to use me instead of him. He always was a sorehead."

"Tell me, Tonio, are you really Serbian?"

He nodded and his smile faded. "Yes. Tonio Seville is a name I made up. My right name is Michael Sandovic. I always wanted to be a dancer, but it would never happen in Serbia, so I went to Italy and studied there. I took an Italian name because. . .well, you heard what Theodor said. Whoever heard of a Serbian dancer? He's right too."

"It doesn't matter where you came from," Nicola said. "And stage names are more often used than not. What does matter is that I know you are a fine dancer and when I got airborne I know you will be there to receive me. We're going to dance a *Giselle* they've never seen before. We'll put everything we have into it and force Lapin to admit we're so good he has to make me prima ballerina and you *premier danseur*. Then we'll be on our way."

"It will be exactly as you wish it to be."

Nicola got to her feet. "Then if we're going to be the talk of the ballet world tomorrow evening, we'd better set about getting ready for it. We'll repeat the *pas de deux* in the first act, just as Theodor and I tried it."

"I'll be in my practice clothes in five minutes," he promised, and ran across the stage to the dressing room area. Nicola returned to the *barre*. Magda joined her.

"That was close," she said. "You could have broken your neck. It wasn't your fault. We all saw that your approach was perfect. He should have caught you with no difficulty."

"I wonder why he didn't?" Nicola asked.

"He's mad at the world. Maybe he figured he'd be fired after the performance. I can tell you now that when he danced with Heidi, she carried him. He'd make all kinds of mistakes, and she'd cover them up by her superior dancing. Maybe he thought you wouldn't and that he might as well leave the Royal Ballet with his head up, saying you were too clumsy to dance with. There had to be some reason for his behavior."

To Nicola, there was nothing silly about it. Theodor had deliberately let her fall. It was true she could have been killed, more likely crippled, but whatever it was, she'd have to end her career. This could be another attempt by the friends of Sander, the assassin, to inflict their revenge on her.

This thought brought more than the delay of her energetic work at the *barre*. She wished David were back. If they were striking at her again, she would need his strength and courage. She was a fool not to have married him.

She raised one leg to the *barre* and the other almost crumpled. She cried out in pain. Magda grasped her waist in time to keep her from falling again. She helped Nicola back to the row of chairs. The rehearsal was postponed. The doctor for the Royal Ballet was called and made a careful examination.

"No bones broken," he reported. "No sprains, just a lot of swelling from the impact of the body with the floor. There will be contusions, black and blue marks."

"I can't dance that way," Nicola said sorrowfully. "I'll look a mess."

"Now don't you believe that," the gray-haired doctor assured her. "You may find you'll have a very sore back, but if you can stand it, you can dance. You're also just short of having a shin splint and that may give you pain, but no loss of ability to perform. As for your knees and your elbow. . .there is magic. Something in my medical bag. Take off your leotard and heavy sweater. I'll be at your dressing room in a few minutes. Magda, you go with her."

The doctor's magic was displayed for the benefit of Magda and Nicola a few moments later when he applied a tight bandage of exactly the same color as her skin. It was so thin it could not be noticed from a distance, and it eased most of the pain.

Nicola arose and kicked, went *en pointe,* pirouetted and sat down with a satisfied sigh. "I can do it. Thank you, *Herr Doktor.* You are a magician."

"One more thing," the doctor said. "Before you perform, warm up some. After the show, warm down. Be sure of that so you don't stiffen up for days. You'll be all right, Nicola. I'll be on hand tomorrow to replace the bandages."

When she got home, she removed the restraining bandages as the doctor had suggested, and she applied hot cloths to the affected parts, and even took a very hot bath which made her feel a little better. She was in nightgown and robe when Anna arrived.

"What happened?" she asked, staring at the swollen elbow.

Nicola showed her the even more swollen knees. "I

dance *Giselle* tomorrow," she explained. "This afternoon Theodor and I were rehearsing and when I flew, he didn't catch me."

"The clumsy idiot! Have you seen a doctor?"

"Yes, the company doctor treated me and said I could dance tomorrow night and rehearse all day tomorrow. He used some kind of bandage that's so thin and matches my skin in color so effectively it can't be seen and keeps down the swelling. I'm quite all right, but I'm worried too. I wonder if Theodor let me fall on purpose."

"For what reason? The man must have. . ." Anna stopped short and nodded. "I know what you mean. He was paid or intimidated into trying to let you get hurt. Those people who killed your father. . ."

"It is possible. I think you'll agree to that."

"With them, it seems anything is possible."

"David thinks they are going to make my life a living hell up to the time when they plan to destroy me. Anna, I'm afraid."

"You have reason to be. But if that is their intention, the moment of real fear won't come until they are ready to finish it. Everything else will be preliminary, not fatal, but painful. Perhaps you have just had an example. Try to hold up, Nicky. We'll have done much to find out who they are and have them punished for it long before you will reach the peak of your career."

"The trouble is, I know what the peak is, Anna. And I think they may have guessed it."

"To dance at the Schönbrunn Palace? You did mention that before."

"It's what I aim for. After that, I can gracefully retire if I choose. Perhaps I will, because while I love the dance, I know now that I love David even more."

"It will be a long time before Schönbrunn, dear Nicky. As I said, time enough for those terrible people

172

to be found and disposed of. I intend to take it up with certain police officials. It will all be done quietly. There is no point in making this public. That might damage your career, I'm sure. You concentrate on your career. I'll concentrate on ferreting out those scoundrels who attacked you."

"I hoped you'd say that, Anna. I'm going to be on my guard every moment from now on."

"Of course you know how proud I am about your rise to the prima ballerina place in the Royal Ballet. It's something girls train for many more years than you had to. But you are exceptional, and don't say I flatter you. It's the opinion of everyone."

"I still have to prove myself. If I don't give an exceptional performance, Lapin will find someone from another company somewhere. And I'll be just filling in."

"Did he say that?"

"Not in so many words, but I know how his mind works. This is my one chance. I can't say I never had one, so I will dance well."

"The *Giselle* ballet can make or break a ballerina. I've seen it many times and I always enjoyed it, except for one thing. The ballerina appeared exhausted when she took her bows."

Nicola laughed. "She probably was and I may be also, but I'll try not to let it show."

"Well, I'll be on my way. I work for a living too, and with all this intrigue going on these days, messages flying back and forth, the cipher bureau is a busy place. Besides, you need all the rest you can get tonight."

"I'm going to write David before I go to bed."

"The man won't be in New York for days."

"He'll get the letter right after he arrives."

"Nicky, are you going to let David know you think there was another attempt to—well—punish you?"

"No," Nicola replied promptly. "He needs to concentrate all his thoughts on a new show. Besides, I'm not sure anyone paid Theodor. . .oh, something else. Sit down again if you have a moment. I'm to dance with Tonio, of course, now that Theodor has been dismissed."

Anna resumed her chair. "Tonio is a fine partner," she said.

"His name is not Tonio. It's. . .I think the first name is Michael, but I'm not sure. However, I am certain of his last name. It's Sandovic."

Anna waited a moment, puzzled. "Well?" she said.

"He's Serbian. He admitted it to me. He wanted to dance. Because there are no facilities in Serbia for a dancer to study, he went to Italy and took an Italian name."

"But what has that to do with all this trouble? I'm confused, Nicola."

"The name of Papa's assassin was Sander. Tonio's real name is Sandovic."

Anna exhaled sharply. "Oh, I see what you mean. They might be related. There's a chance, I suppose. But hasn't Tonio been very kind and thoughtful as far as you are concerned?"

"He's in love with me. At least he said he was. I never gave him encouragement. And, of course, once he saw me with David, he knew it was hopeless."

"Don't give him an opportunity to mention it. And be careful around him. I'll see if I can find out anything about the man. We do have some connections that are useful for getting information, especially about someone from Serbia. I'll let you know."

After Anna left, Nicola wrote her letter, telling David she would dance *Giselle* the next evening and how pleased she was. It was a happy letter and she hoped it would reassure him that all was well with her and, as

Anna had said, leave him to concentrate on his show.

She took the time to apply hot packs to her knees and elbow. They were still swollen, but she was certain the injuries would not affect her dancing.

Before she slept, she thought of David and of the dance and the applause she hoped for. And she thought about the theatre at Schönbrunn Palace. When the social season began and the Emperor and Empress invited guests to the theatre, if her luck held she would be on the palace stage.

That was her dream. And, she thought with a mild shudder, it might be a dream suddenly cut off.

# Eleven

The poster was there at the front of the theatre, proclaiming that tonight Nicola Maneth, *prima ballerina,* would dance *Giselle.* Nicola wished her father could have been with her to see it. Even so, she was filled with pride and a savage determination to make that performance the best one of her life. The only moments of doubt she possessed were the thoughts that those people who had vowed to torture her in revenge for sending Sander to his death might find some way to interfere.

However, this depressing feeling left her as she applied her makeup. There was great excitement on the part of everyone, especially Lapin, who was in a state of perpetual motion, shouting orders, making suggestions, pleading for a good performance, but with no one paying the slightest attention to him. He was so highly agitated he didn't even realize it.

The overture was playing when Nicola reached the wings where Tonio awaited her. He extended his hands and she placed hers in them. She was trembling slightly, partly from nervousness and partly because the occasion would be a test for both of them. He squeezed her hands gently and his eyes revealed an awareness that he knew what she was thinking.

He spoke in an undertone. "This will be our night, Nicola. We will let nothing spoil it. Promise?"

"I promise," she whispered.

There was no time for further talk as the curtain rose to a packed house and the dancing began. On stage, Nicola quickly becme Giselle and forgot her nervousness. Her miming, when she first met the man she fell in love with, was perfect. Their *pas de deux* in the first act went off without a flaw; the applause attested to that. In the final scenes of the ballet, however, the dancing became more intense, growing faster and faster until it reached a peak of excitement. Nicole and Tonio acquitted themselves well. They received nine curtain calls.

To her amazement, when the curtain fell for the last time, Lapin rushed onstage and embraced her. She made no attempt to fend him off, for it was his way of expressing his gratitude for her performance. Her dressing room was banked with flowers, but the bouquet she pressed to her bosom was one which had been placed on her dressing table. It was a small bouquet of violets edged in real lace, with David's card attached. His note stated he had ordered them before he left. Nicola was almost reduced to tears, except that a packed dressing room wouldn't allow her to opportunity to indulge in them. She set the flowers back in their box and turned to receive the accolades, some of which were being shouted to her from the corridor because there was no room for anyone else to enter. Milling about were famous personages who, after praising her, pressed her with invitations to parties which would be given in her honor. She expressed her thanks without committing herself. She hoped Tonio was being honored in the same manner.

Finally, her dressing room was cleared and she changed, with the help of a maid, for the party which was to be given for the cast at one of the opulent hotels. Both she and Tonio were to be the honored guests. Carriages were provided for them and a special one for her, Lapin and Tonio. Lapin couldn't keep the smile off his face. He was happy for both of them, and for the future of the company.

Nicola said, "You look pleased, M'sieur Lapin."

"Why shouldn't I be?" he replied, still beaming. "You surprised me beyond my wildest expectations."

"We may have surprised you, *M'sieur*," Tonio said, his manner superior, "but we knew we would not let you down."

Lapin laughed. "Tonight you may tease me all you wish. It may sound insane, but I feel like I've had my first triumph. I must admit you dance superbly together."

"Thank you, *M'sieur*," Nicola said. "Praise from you everyone cherishes. You drive us hard, oftentimes cruelly, but there is no one in all of Europe who is your equal as a teacher."

"I agree," Tonio said. "And when we reach the party, the entire cast will toast you to show their appreciation."

Lapin smiled self-consciously. "I didn't think I could be modest. I know I am a hard driver. Sometimes unfair. Sometimes cruel. Temperament, I suppose. But always, the ballet is my love. So I force you to work so hard, you hate me. Also, my behavior is not always what it should be. I know my weaknesses. Teaching ballet is not one of them. Now I have said enough. Besides, we are here. Enjoy this evening. The party has been given in your honor."

"It is for all of us, *M'sieur*," Tonio said. "And you

—our dedicated teacher."

"No more compliments," Lapin said good-naturedly. "Enjoy the evening."

Nicola insisted Lapin give a little speech first, after which she and Tonio thanked the entire cast and Lapin. The champagne flowed freely, though she was careful to restrict her drinking to three glasses, none of which she finished. The party lasted far into the night and she smiled gratefully when Tonio offered to see her home.

"I know your happiness tonight isn't complete without David," Tonio said once they were settled in the carriage. "I just wish he could have seen you dance tonight. However, I can't help but say I am happy you allowed me to be your escort. You know how I feel about you and you know I will behave. I promised."

Nicola smiled gratefully. "It is lonely without David, but the choice was mine. He wanted to marry me and bring me back to America."

"You did Heidi a favor," Tonio said. "She was delighted at the opportunity."

"Her reputation was already established," Nicola said. "I have yet to establish mine. And I lived for the ballet all my life. I couldn't turn my back on it without having achieved the peak I have worked so hard for."

"You have already achieved it," Tonio said. "Every nuance of your performance tonight was perfection."

"Yours also, Tonio. We work well together, but we must take nothing for granted. We must not neglect practice, we must watch our weight and above all, we must be aware of Lapin. He will watch us constantly, looking for something in our performance to criticize."

Tonio laughed. "Lapin seemed transformed tonight. I felt like pinching myself, wondering if I was awake or dreaming, he was so magnanimous."

Nicola added agreement. "Things have gone well for us since the Emperor and Empress paid us the honor of viewing our performance."

"We owe them eternal loyalty," Tonio said with a happy sigh.

He rested his head against the upholstered side of the carriage and closed his eyes. Nicola knew he was as happy as she and just as exhusted. Fatigue was overwhelming him just as it was her. She was glad. It would keep her from lying awake, her body aching for David's. She hoped he would be so busy he wouldn't miss her in the same way. She had no right to expect faithfulness from him. After all, he was a man. She would be satisfied if only he would continue to love her. She pressed the bouquet of violets she was holding to her cheek, then to her lips.

Tonio chose that moment to open his eyes. Lucky David, he thought. He was glad Nicola couldn't read his mind. It wasn't easy controlling his emotions when the girl he loved was so close. He wanted to reach over, take her in his arms, rain kisses on her face and bosom, carry her into her apartment and possess her. Thank goodness, their dancing was so strenuous it demanded complete concentration. He insisted on accompanying her to the door of her apartment. He kissed the palm of each of her hands, bowed and bade her good night. She was so touched by his gentleness that she kissed him lightly on the mouth, turned, quickly unlocked her door and went inside. She had to, for his arms raised to embrace her.

She had meant the kiss only as a gesture of gratitude for an evening that was a triumph, but when she saw the quick look of desire with which his eyes regarded her, she knew she must not do that again. At least, not when there weren't others around. The kisses of people in the theatre had no meaning other than to express appreciation for a favor, or the thrill of having given an excellent performance.

Also, she dismissed the thought of Tonio having anything to do with the group who had assassinated her father and who had threatened to destroy her when she reached the peak of her profession, a success which was coming much faster than she had dared hope for.

Tonio, she realized, could no more indulge in intrigue than David. He was as honorable as David and she believed he was just as protective of her. Even if Tonio's surname resembled that of Sander, the man who had murdered her father, that was no proof that they were related. She trusted Tonio and felt disloyal having such thoughts of him. She resolved not to think of him again as possibly being involved with those who had terrorized her.

The next day found Nicola restless. She performed some household chores, went to the store to make a few purchases of food and returned to the emptiness of her apartment. There would be no more performances for a week, and while she would report each day for practice, there was neither the pressure nor the long hours as when a performance date was close by. She felt stifled in the apartment. The silence started her mind working and served to bring back those terrifying moments of her father's assassination. She snatched her handbag from the chair where she had tossed it, went into the hall where her hat graced the small table below a mirror. She paused only to put it on and slip the hatpin through the straw crown.

Outside, she headed for her favorite coffee shop a block away. She frequently dined there because they catered to the needs of her diet and were quite proud that she would favor them with her business. She was beginning to realize that she had suddenly become a well-known and somewhat important person.

She was just beginning her meal when she saw a man enter and look about inquiringly. He seemed familiar, but she wasn't certain of his identity until he saw her, smiled in recognition and came to her table. It was only then she realized this was Leopold Kramer, the lawyer who had been passing by when her father was shot and who had testified in court as to what he'd seen.

"Fräulein Maneth, may I sit with you?"

"Of course, Herr Kramer. I've never really had the opportunity of thanking you for helping convict my father's murderer."

"It was my duty. I must say that I'm glad that man was executed. He was a menace, from what I have heard."

"I agree. Have you experienced any trouble because you testified?"

"None whatsoever. I know they subjected you to some very serious harrassment. You were courageous to stand up in court and tell what happened. It's a shame it did happen, but I think you nullified any benefit they hoped to get."

"Please, Herr Kramer, couldn't we talk of something else?"

"Forgive me, *Fräulein*, and allow me to congratulate you. You are the talk of the city today. How sad your papa couldn't have seen your triumph. I won't dwell on that part. I must say that the newspapers have given you glorious reviews. I'm honored to be sitting here with a young lady who has beauty, talent and intelligence."

"Thank you, Herr Kramer, but you are the intelligent one. An attorney commands much more prestige than a ballerina."

"That might be true in some cases, but not where you are concerned."

"I disagree."

"That is because you are not aware that there are too many lawyers in Vienna. It is a constant battle to get clients. Not a healthy situation for any profession."

"I'm sorry to hear that. I hope you don't have that problem."

"Regretfully, I do. It becomes very frustrating waiting for clients."

"I can well imagine it does."

"Is there something I can do about your father's estate? I mean, some way of being useful."

"I wish there was, Herr Kramer. But Papa had his own lawyer and the will states that this attorney must handle everything."

"I see. I suppose you make a great deal of money."

"Not as much as one would think. I'm quite new at this business and I haven't the reputation that insures large salaries. However, Papa left me enough to take care of my needs."

"I'm glad to hear it. You'll have even more when you reach the top of your profession."

"Well, I hope so."

He pushed his chair back as a waitress approached and he signaled her that he was not going to stay.

"It has been a pleasure, *Fräulein*. I hope we shall meet again."

"I hope so too, Herr Kramer. Good bye and good luck."

He nodded, turned and walked toward the door. A frown touched Nicola's brow as she watched him exit. She wondered what that was all about. It seemed to her that he was sounding her out for some purpose and she thought he came very close to asking her for money. If he had, she'd have given him what she could, for she was indebted to him for his help in convicting the murderer. Still, there seemed to be something strange in the way he'd approached her. Perhaps he'd even followed her from the apartment house. How else would he have known she was inside, for her table could not be seen from the street. He could not have been just passing by and happened to catch a glimpse of her.

There were no logical answers to these questions and she shrugged off the whole thing as a coincidence. Yet the questions remained with her, and when Anna came to visit Nicola described the encounter.

"He wanted something," she told Anna. "I've no idea what it was, but I do believe he was sounding me out. Probably for another approach. He said his practice was not good and he seemed distraught. Do you think he needs money and was hinting about it?"

"What else? It's true that there are too many lawyers in Vienna and only a few at the top make much money. It isn't strange that he feels in need of financial help, but why didn't he just come out and ask? After all, he did help you in a time of great crisis."

"I may look him up and put it up to him frankly," Nicola said. "I am in a position to be of moderate help, and I'd not like him to think I was utterly unresponsive."

"Stay away from him," Anna advised. "If he wants something bad enough, he'll come back."

"He hinted that he might. Well, I can't dwell on his troubles. I wonder how David and Heidi are enjoying the voyage. They should be in the United States in another day or so, I think."

Anna regarded Nicola with affection. "I suppose you've written to him every day."

"Yes, I address my letters to the theatre where he is to perform. I hope I'll hear from him one day soon. He must have had time on his hands during the voyage."

"Which is still going on," Anna said. "You will have to be patient. And hope Heidi is loyal to you or at least turns to unattached gentlemen who are also making the voyage."

"You are trying to frighten me," Nicola said, her face shadowing.

184

"No," Anna said kindly. "Just teasing. You have nothing to worry about. David loves you too much to philander."

"It wouldn't be philandering when I sent him away. I hope he will be faithful, but he is a man. I know last night my body ached for him."

"Ah," Anna said. "You have known the fulfillment of love with him."

Nicola colored slightly, but she eyed Anna directly as she spoke. "Yes, Anna. I am a complete woman, thanks to David."

"I knew the wonderment of it with your papa. I suppose those two times you walked in on us—much to our embarrassment—have more meaning to you now."

"Both meaning and understanding. I know the hopeless ache you must be filled with, wanting Papa close to you again. That is what I am experiencing now. And reaching out with my hand for David's."

"Please don't." Anna eyed Nicola sorrowfully. "My grief is too fresh."

"Forgive me. I will one day have David again—I hope. You will never have Papa. I am as thoughtless as Herr Kramer. I begged him to stop talking about Papa. I couldn't bear it, thinking of what happened."

Anna nodded somberly. "I know. I didn't mean to be rude. It was just that we were both grieving for our loneliness. Never mind. You will soon be busy."

"Yes," Nicola agreed. The ballet season starts this weekend and I'll be so busy I won't have time to be lonely."

"I'm proud of you, as you know," Anna said. "The city is buzzing with talk of your performance. Yours and Tonio's, but especially yours. The newspapers have stories of you. It is as if you had a fairy godmother who waved her magic wand and you immediately reached the top of your profession."

"If only it hadn't begun with Papa's death. His murder. I would still be content to be a member of the *corps de ballet* if it would bring him back."

"It won't, my dear. We know that. Concentrate on the present and your future. Stay busy. Take advantage of every opportunity."

"I intend to. Perhaps next year my dream will come true. I'll be invited to perform at the theatre in Schloss Schönbrunn. The annual event takes place in February at the height of the social season."

Anna nodded somberly, but didn't speak.

"Why so glum?" Nicola asked.

"Have you forgotten that prophecy or threat that those animals made? That harm will come to you when you reach the pinnacle of your success?"

"I haven't forgotten. It worries me when I think of it, but it won't stop me. That's why David didn't want to return to New York City."

"Whatever may happen won't happen at the palace," Anna reasoned. "It's guarded like the treasury vaults. These are not quiet, sensible days, Nicky. There's war in the air. I come across the symptoms almost every day in my work. Everybody is mad. War mad. Russia hates Germany and has a pact with France. Germany hates France and has big forces in readiness for trouble. England is on the sidelines, but will jump in against Germany if there is war."

"Papa used to be concerned about it too. Where does Austria-Hungary stand?"

"With Germany. Our ties are too close to abandon the Kaiser. We'll be in it very soon after anything starts."

"I hope it does not start. However, now that you mentioned it, I do recall seeing more military uniforms than ever."

"Oh, don't think too much about that. Franz Josef

adores uniforms. All kinds. I've got faith in our Emperor. I regard him as a level-headed man who doesn't advocate war."

"I think of him as a kind and gentle man," Nicola said. She recalled her intimate night with him, and the covert ways in which he seemed to have helped her out of difficulties.

"He's that without question," Anna agreed. "I'd best be going home. All this talk about war makes my department so busy I have to work all hours. But I'll not miss your performances, Nicky. Not a single one."

"Thank you. I'll see that you receive good tickets. It will inspire confidence to look out and see someone I love in the front row."

"I'll also applaud the loudest," Anna promised with a smile. "Keep well, Nicky. Be careful at rehearsals. Don't overdo it. As if you'd pay any attention to that."

"Good night, Anna. Thank you for coming by."

"As you know, a person can grow lonely. So you may be assured I come here to enjoy your friendship as much as to help you with any problems. I'll see you tomorrow evening."

"We could go out to supper."

"I'll look forward to it. Good night, Nicky."

Nicola closed the door and locked it, shot the bolt she'd had installed and went back to studying the choreography of the next ballet they were scheduled to do.

The first night was a tremendous success. The gentlemen in evening dress escorting beautifully gowned ladies whose sparkling jewels added to the glamour of the evening. Heavily ornamented carriages pulled up, from some of which exited members of Franz Josef's court, all of whom arrived early. Most exciting of all, the Emperor and his Elisabeth were to be on hand. The royal box had been redecorated for them and the gilded chairs were waiting.

The excitement backstage was even greater than that in the audience. Lapin, no longer worried about Nicola and Tonio giving a lackluster performance, concentrated on shouting at the first soloist and the *corps de ballet.*

Once again, at Nicola's insistence, she shared her dressing room with Magda who had, by some lucky chance, been given the second solo part and was as excited as Nicola had been only a few days before, when she'd danced *Giselle.*

The repertoire consisted of a series of well-known ballets with several performances of *Giselle.* Nicola looked forward to them, because in that ballet she was able to generate the greatest applause.

"The monster seems more tolerant all of a sudden," Magda commented.

"He always was mostly bluster," Nicola said.

"You didn't think so when he was on the verge of firing you," Magda reminded her.

Nicola gave her a fond glance. "One does forget so easily. Yes, he was abusive and big-headed. I suppose to someone new he still is. We're just used to him."

"Forget him. What do you hear from Heidi?"

"I haven't heard a word from her. Not even from David. I've read every newspaper I can get and I've found nothing about a storm at sea to have delayed them. David's show is to open in two days. I don't know what's wrong, but something must be."

"Put yourself in their place," Magda said. "Two days to the opening of a new show. I'll bet they're both so busy they've not eaten or slept except in snatches. We've been through that."

"I've thought of that too and it's kept me from worrying too much. I certainly hope they'll let me know how it goes over."

"You can bet they will. Heidi told me it was the best

script she'd ever read and excellent choreography. You surely gave her a golden opportunity. The rest of us will be out of the picture when we're her age. Careers die young in the ballet.''

"When I dance at Schönbrunn, I will be satisfied if I never dance again. It's crazy, but ever since I grew interested in ballet as a little girl, I made that my goal.''

"I hope I can see you there. We ordinary mortals don't get into the palaces.''

"I've never been there, of course. They do say it's like a fairyland.''

Magda turned her back to the maid who buttoned her up. With a last look in the mirror, Magda was on her way to the wings. Nicola, with a little more time, concentrated on her makeup. When she opened the door, Tonio was waiting for her and they made their way to the stage. The curtain had already parted and the *corps de ballet* were dancing. From the edge of the stage where they were well hidden, Nicola and Tonio studied the packed house.

"There must be fifty million florins in diamonds out there,'' Tonio said.

"And a fine audience. I can see they're already enjoying themselves. We'd best get set now. I'll not stop the dancing to take bows so we'll proceed right through. Ready?''

They went onstage to a flurry of applause, but when the dancers didn't pause to acknowledge it, the audience settled down to enjoy a performance of a lesser-known ballet, but one no less effective than the standards. Ballets were being written in great numbers these days, but few of them reached the Burgtheater.

The evening was over before they knew it and once again they were applauded beyond their expectations. Tonio and Nicola faced the royal box and paid their respects. Afterward, Tonio escorted Nicola to her apartment. He informed her he would continue to do so during performance weeks.

"You told me you hadn't heard from David or Heidi," he said. "Was there anything today?"

"My mailbox was empty," she said. "I'm beginning to wonder too. But then, they have much to do. Also, letters from overseas are slow. A great many things can delay them."

"Of course," Tonio agreed. "Give them time."

"Thank you for seeing me home, Tonio."

"I wish we could enjoy coffee shops and restaurants like normal people. Putting an end to an evening like this by just going home seems a waste."

"You wouldn't think so tomorrow night if you galli-vanted all over Vienna tonight."

"It's not the gallivanting I look for. Only an honest, filling supper."

"The day will come soon enough when we can indulge. I think we have the shortest career—in the number of years we can perform—of any of the theatrical professions."

They were standing before her door and he had caught her hands in his. He raised them to his lips.

"You were magnificent tonight, Nicky," he said.

"So were you," she replied.

"Nicky." His voice was tortured as he spoke her name. Before she could protest, his arms enclosed her and he drew her close. He bent her back slightly and his mouth covered hers. She tried to push herself free of him, but his mouth was tight against hers, his arms holding her so close she couldn't make use of her own. She was well aware of the passion she had stirred within him. His mouth left hers and he rained kisses on her neck. He pushed the collar of her dress aside with his chin and his mouth moved down to her chest. A few of the buttons of her bodice came undone, revealing the

190

cleft of her breasts. He moaned softly at sight of them, bending her back further, making them more available.

All the time she kept pleading with him, begging him to let her go. Finally she lifted her foot and gave his ankle a sharp blow with the heel of her shoe. He cried out from the pain, but the act caught her off balance. One of his hands lowered to her derrière and he pressed her tightly against him.

When her pleas were to no avail, Nicola tried something else. "I'll scream, Tonio." It was difficult getting the words out because he was holding her so tightly.

"Let me come inside, Nicky, please," he begged. His hand was busy, trying to excite her.

"No, Tonio. You promised. You promised. I don't love you."

"You're lonely, just as I am," he argued huskily. "Give me your key. I'm facing the door. I'll open it and carry you in."

"No!" she exclaimed. "I'm not strong enough to fight you, but I'll not give in to you. If you take me, it will be rape. You know that."

He released her reluctantly, holding her gently until both her feet were on the floor and she had regained her balance.

"You broke your word," she said severely. "I never want to see you again."

Tonio's breath still came quickly. "I'm sorry for what I did, Nicky, but I couldn't help it. I know what I promised, but I hold you at each performance, our bodies touch, and it is all I can do to control myself."

"Then it would be best if we did not dance together again," Nicola said stiffly.

Tonio's breathing was becoming less labored. "Please, Nicky. Give me another chance. I'm no saint. In my mind, I have possessed you many times. I just lost my head, went crazy."

"You certainly did." She fumbled for her key in her handbag, thrust it in the door, turned the lock and went inside. She closed it without even giving Tonio a further glance.

"Nicky." His voice, now under control, penetrated the door. "I beg forgiveness. Please—give me a second chance. I would never do what you said it would be. Never. No matter what. Just say we can still dance together."

"I'll say no such thing." Nicola spoke through the closed door. She moved quietly into the darkened parlor and sat down. She was deeply shaken herself and angry that it could have happened. Obviously, Tonio was experienced in the art of lovemaking, for he knew exactly how to arouse her. But she was also angry. Angry that she hadn't sensed what he was about to do. Angry with herself for not going with David. It was David's arms she wanted around her, caressing and fondling her, David's voice she wanted to hear, whispering endearments and speaking of his love. *David, David, David*. It would always be David. She realized suddenly she was whispering his name over and over.

She sat there for half an hour, not moving, lest Tonio still be outside her door and hear her. When she was certain he had left, she walked slowly into the bedroom, unaware of her bodice, still in disarray. She lit the gas light, undressed, bathed and sat at her writing desk, her thoughts still of David. She couldn't understand why no letter had come from him. There had been time, yet not even a cablegram had arrived. She took paper from her desk, picked up her quilled pen, dipped it in the crystal inkwell and started to write. She asked why she had received no word from him and begged him to try and find the time for even a brief letter.

She was tired, yet felt she was partially guilty for

192

Tonio's behavior. He was fully aware that she missed David and thought, perhaps in her loneliness, she would turn to him. She thought also of Kramer, the attorney, and wondered again why he had sought her out in the restaurant. Could it be he'd had something on his mind, or was it pure coincidence?

Lying in bed, she realized she would have to excuse Tonio. They danced too well together. She felt he would not try to force his attentions on her again. He knew she had no desire for him to make love to her.

The next day he was at the rehearsal hall before her. When she appeared onstage, his eyes sought hers. She gave a brief nod of her head, signifying forgiveness. His face lit up and he came to her.

"Thank you, Nicky. It won't happen again."

"If it does, it will be the last time I'll dance with you." She spoke with quiet firmness.

"May that day never come," he said penitently.

Every day of the week was a repetition of this one—rehearsals, warm-ups and warm-downs, then dancing to an appreciative audience. The Burg Theater was making a great deal of money these days and her salary had been substantially increased. She was now a true prima ballerina and there were no longer any threats, open or implied, that she would be sent back to the *corps de ballet* if she failed to put on a good performance. So it was work and dance and directly home after a light supper at a coffee house. And no letter from David. She'd sent him two cables. One yesterday, another this very day. She was now growing more and more worried that something had happened to him. Her mind conjured up all sorts of things, from sickness to the failure of his show.

By the end of the week, on Saturday, a cable addressed to the theatre was delivered and she realized something was wrong with the mail delivery, that

David had not failed to write. The cable stated in the usual scarcity of words that he had written every day and added that the show was a success.

Nicola didn't comment on this cable to anyone, but the next day she dressed early and seated herself on the first flight of steps in her apartment building. From there, she could see the mailboxes without being readily seen herself.

The mail usually came late in the morning. The mailman made his delivery, locked the boxes and departed. Two minutes later, she saw a boy of about twelve saunter into the lobby. At first, she thought nothing of it until the boy's manner grew furtive. Unaware that he was being watched, he took a key from his pocket, stepped to Nicola's box, unlocked it and removed the single piece of mail.

He stuffed this under his shirt, closed the box, withdrew the key and turned around to find Nicola standing right behind him. He cried out in surprise and sudden fear as he made an attempt to dodge around her. But Nicola blocked him, seized him by one arm, tore open his shirt and snatched the letter from under it. She raised it to read the inscription and for a second relaxed her grip on the boy. He tore himself free and raced for the door before she could stop him. He cleared the outside stairs in one long leap and was gone.

She made no attempt to follow him. The letter was of far more importance to her. She sat down in the lobby, opened the envelope and removed the two-page letter. She relaxed and enjoyed every word.

*Darling Nicky:*

*Is anything wrong? I have your letters so faithfully written, but in those I sent you I've asked several questions you have never answered. I get the feeling you are not receiving my letters. If I don't get any answers to those questions in a few days, I shall send you a cable. I cannot believe all my letters have gone astray. But we'll come to that later.*

*For now, I'm happy to report that the show is shaping up as something quite out of the ordinary. Rehearsals have gone remarkably well after several postponements, which is usual, and Heidi is a prize. She took to this new form of entertainment as if she'd been born in a stage trunk. She will be toasted and partied all over the city and will become world famous. She sends her love and she means it, for she feels indebted to you for giving her this opportunity.*

*I hope that your full week is as great as was your special performance in* Giselle. *I knew you were superb. I only wish I could have been in the audience.*

*I am, well, a bit tired as I imagine you are. This theatre business is an exhausting and exacting profession. Of course, going on stage to say a few lines and sing a few songs is nothing compared to the kind of dancing you do. I've wondered if the Emperor has attended any more performances.*

*And how is Lapin behaving these days? He ought to be a very happy man. By the way, there was a good-sized article on your dancing in a New York City newspaper, complete with a sketch of your beautiful face that made me tie myself down so I wouldn't take the next ship to Europe.*

*Please answer my questions so I'll know you are getting my letters. How were you received, what ballets are you dancing? How does Lapin treat you now? Has anything out of the ordinary happened since I left? Anything!? If so, please, darling, send a cablegram. I worry constantly about you. I'll come at once. I have trained an understudy to step in if I have to leave suddenly, so there won't be any interruption of the show. I'll hold my breath until I hear from you, but I wish it was you I was holding instead of my breath. I love you dearly and forever.*

She cried a little, but then composed a cablegram, telling him she had received only this one letter. Then she sat down and wrote a long letter, answering his questions, and relating how a boy had apparently been supplied with a key to the mailbox and had been systematically stealing his letters.

Her encounter with the boy left her unnerved, but she sent the cablegram and mailed the letter. At least she knew David hadn't failed to write and that he was in fine health and spirits and his show should be a success. And, best of all, he still loved her.

That night she saw Anna in the audience, as usual, and she sent a messenger to her with a note asking that she wait for her after the show. She instructed the same messenger to bring her a glass of cold milk after each performance from now on.

"It relieves the pangs of hunger," she told Magda. "I don't have to go out of here almost at a dead run for something to eat. And I'm less tempted to overindulge."

"I like overindulging too much to be satisfied with a glass of milk," Magda said. "Next morning I sweat out at the *barre*, but the day I quit ballet, I'm going to eat ten meals and stuff myself at every one. My lieutenant says I'm getting to look like a scarecrow I'm so skinny. He likes his women soft and round. But he shows up every night, so I guess until he can see clear through me like a pane of glass he'll keep coming."

The performance went very well and, as usual, to a capacity audience. The glass of very cold milk was delivered as she returned to her dressing room and she sipped it and enjoyed it. She was glad she had thought of the idea.

She excused herself to Tonio because she was meeting Anna. "It's important I talk to her," she explained to him. "She works all day and sometimes into the evening, so our hours conflict. I'm sorry."

Tonio looked concerned, but nodded. He'd been the perfect gentleman since that night he'd forced his atten-

196

tions on her. She was pleased to see Anna waiting at the door. She had a carriage at the curb.

"What's happened?" she asked as they walked to the vehicle.

"A strange thing. I don't know what to make of it and I had to talk to someone about it."

"That's what I'm here for. We'll stop at a coffee shop. I know you have to eat. . . ."

"I've something waiting in the icebox. I want to get this off my mind. When we get home, I'll tell you. Otherwise, have you been well? I've not seen you in. . ."

"Forty-eight hours," Anna said with a smile. "I've been at the theatre each night, but I'm just too tired to go around to the stage door. They're driving us like slaves at the office. And you, Nicky? There's no need for me to ask how you feel. Someone who can dance as you did tonight has to feel well. Have you heard from David?"

"That's what I want to talk about when we get home."

They talked of the performance, the audience, any bit of trivia that came to mind until they were in Nicola's apartment. She hung up her coat, helped Anna off with hers and lit a fire in the fireplace. The nights were cold now and the heating system was not functioning as its best. She set the table and placed salad and sliced cold cuts on it. She brought the pot of coffee to the table and they talked while they ate.

"I received a cablegram from David. In it he said that I had not answered questions he'd put to me in his letters."

"How could you when you hadn't received any?" Anna spoke as she helped herself to a generous portion of salad and several slices of meat.

"Exactly," Nicola said. "I'd not received even one

letter. Yet, from the cablegram, I knew he had written me. So this morning I posted myself on the stairs where I had a view of the lobby and mailboxes, but I could not be seen.''

"Was this before or after the mailman came?''

"Before. Though just minutes before he came and put the mail in some of the boxes, including mine. Almost immediately after he left, a boy of about twelve ambled into the lobby, looked about and then opened the box with a key. I slipped downstairs noiselessly, seized him, tore open his shirt and got the letter, but he managed to escape. I didn't try to follow him. I couldn't have outrun him. Anyway, it was the letter that concerned me. It was from David and it was a long one. In it he revealed he had written letters aboard ship and after his arrival in New York City. Obviously, every one of them was stolen after having been delivered here. I don't know what to make of it other than it is another way of harassing me. That band of ruffians know I love David. Naturally, not hearing from him would upset me, interfere with my performances.''

"They want to make as much trouble for you as they possibly can. They'd like nothing better than to break it up between you and David.''

"What a day that will be! They must be very ignorant people if they think they can do that. I'm afraid they're getting ready for some kind of mischief and they don't want David back here. They assume I'll believe he lost interest.''

"It's quite possible. However, I doubt they have anything more drastic in mind than stealing your letters for the reason you mentioned. These days you are far too prominent for them to try anything on a larger scale. For instance, if you disappeared, there'd be one massive hunt for you and I doubt there are many places in Vienna where they could hide you. You're too well known now."

"They won't be satisfied with that," Nicola said. "I think they are up to something far more sinister."

"I hope not, but we can't do much about it unless you will let me hire a detective to watch you. Or assign a government agent."

Nicola sighed. "If they are planning anything, no detective is going to stop them. Besides that would be calling too much attention to myself. I prefer to take my chances."

"If so, be doubly watchful. Does Tonio still escort you home each night?"

"Yes."

"Good. I think you should take a carriage to the theatre each night. And no matter where you are, make certain there are people around. In a restaurant or coffee shop, choose a table in the center so you will be surrounded by others and also be readily seen. I can't think of any other precautions you can take."

"I can't either. Thanks, Anna, for your concern and help. I feel better for just having someone to confide in. Thanks for coming."

"It's little enough. I'll keep in touch with you. If you are even suspicious of someone, send for me. I'll come at once."

Anna retrieved her coat and Nicola helped her into it.

"Oh, I almost forgot," Anna said. "Remember telling me of the lawyer, Kramer, who sought you out in the coffee shop?"

"Yes."

"He committed suicide last night. Hanged himself. His body was found this afternoon."

Nicola sat down slowly, her brow furrowed worriedly. "How dreadful. It puzzles me and yet I had the feeling once I thought over the few minutes he sat at my table and conversed with me, that he had deliberately sought me out.''

Anna looked puzzled. "For what purpose?"

"To tell me something. I don't know if he refused because he was afraid, or because he wanted money. He made several ambiguous remarks that led me to believe he was in need of help, but he didn't have the nerve to ask me for it. Now he's dead.''

Anna nodded slowly. "If he did have something to tell, it's too late now. But the police say it was suicide, or so the newspapers indicate.''

"It could have been, of course," Nicola granted. "It could also have been murder and made to look like suicide. If there was something he wanted to tell me, or information he wished to sell me, it would be against the people who have been harassing me all these weeks. I believe it's more than possible that he was murdered. They found out he knew something, or he approached them to sound them out for money, to have them pay for the information. I think this is a most serious event, Anna, and I'm becoming frightened.''

Anna sat down again. "Who can blame you? Yet what could Kramer have known? I can't even venture a guess.''

"The only part he took in all this was to be passing by as the murderer fired at Papa. He must have seen something. But what could it have been that I didn't see?"

"I wish I knew the answer to that. Of course you're not even certain he knew or saw anything. You did tell me he complained of a lack of clients and money. He might have killed himself during moments of despair.''

"It's too coincidental, Anna. I feel there is more to it.''

"You could be right. And while we're on the subject of suspicious people, what about Tonio?''

"What about him?"

"He seems to be a very well-bred young man and a fine dance partner for you, but there is this question of his hiding his Serbian nationality. I think his reason for doing so is a little flimsy—the fact that Serbians are not noted ballet dancers, the fact that he became an Italian by changing his name. That just does not ring true."

"I trust him, Anna."

"Quite likely you have every reason to. Yet, his Serbian name is so close to that of the assassin who killed your father. I don't know about Tonio. I like him. He is very solicitous of you, but that could be a mask for his real intentions toward you. Also, I checked and learned the assassin has brothers."

"No, Anna, I can't believe that about Tonio. If he wanted to harm me, he had many an opportunity to do so."

"Just the same, I'm getting as concerned about your safety as you are. I shall attend the theatre every evening that I can possibly make it and I shall come backstage to your dressing room just to be certain you are safe and that nothing more has happened to give you cause for further anxiety. If Tonio isn't there to take you home, I shall do so."

"Anna, I can't let you do that."

"If your father had lived another twenty-four hours, I would have been your stepmother. I consider myself responsible for you."

"Thank you," Nicola said softly. "I appreciate your solicitude and I shall never forget what you have already done."

"Now I'd better get out of here before I roast in this heavy coat and go outside to freeze in it. I won't budget from outside your door until I hear the lock click. Be very careful about that. And promise never to open the door to anyone you don't know."

"That's a promise easy to make. Good night, Anna. Thank you for listening to my woes. I feel guilty bothering you, but I've no one else."

"You'll find my shoulder strong enough to support you no matter what. I'll see you tomorrow night. And don't feel any guilt. I'd believe I failed you if you didn't turn to me."

Nicola closed and locked the door securely. She looked out of the window a moment later to watch Anna cross the street below, looking for a carriage.

Nicola sat down and concentrated on the problem of what Kramer could have seen or known. Moments before her father was killed, Kramer had walked by and her father had mentioned him as a lawyer. Then the killing took place. Kramer had turned around as the shots were fired. He had testified to seeing Sander with the gun, seeing her father fall and then watching Sander begin running away.

But that was what she too had seen. How could there be more? What could have happened that Kramer saw and she did not? And if there was something, why did Kramer hold back? Because he thought this information might be useful in seeking money? It was possible, though she believed he'd never shown any inclination toward this kind of blackmail. Certainly, he'd testified honestly at the trial. She had thought of him as an ambitious lawyer without the personality or drive to make something of himself.

She was by no means satisfied with the manner of his death, but there was no clue she could uncover to explain it. As always when she was troubled, her thoughts turned to David. If only he were here so she could discuss this latest tragedy in the events which surrounded her and the reason for it. Still, she determined not to mention it in her letters to him. She knew he would instantly leave his show, close it if need be, and come to her. She doubted there was any emergency sufficient to necessitate that.

# Twelve

Nicola was at breakfast the following morning when she answered a knock on her door without opening it.

"This is the police," a man's voice called to her. "Let me in, please."

She hesitated a moment, wondering if this could be a ruse, but decided she had to take the risk. She opened the door to face a tall, heavy-set man who promptly showed her a badge.

"Inspector Reikert, Fräulein Maneth. May I come in?"

"Of course," she said. "I'm having breakfast. Will you join me in a cup of coffee perhaps?"

He smiled. "You are asking a coffee-lover, Fräulein Maneth. I would be delighted."

He was also amenable to accepting a few of the biscuits Nicola had made, though she nibbled at only one. He was an amiable man, a lover of ballet who felt especially honored to be dining with the prima ballerina. But when breakfast was over, he became the policeman and she soon regarded him as a very capable, shrewd man.

"I am here about the death of a lawyer named

Leopold Kramer. Did you ever have business with him?"

"Not business, *Herr Inspektor*. However, if you recall, a man named Sander was tried for the assassination of my father. Herr Kramer was a witness to the crime and testified for the prosecution."

"I'm aware of that," the inspector said. "Was that your only contact with this unfortunate man?"

"There was one more time. I was having lunch in a coffee shop recently when he entered, came to my table and asked if he could talk to me."

"You did not invite him to meet you?"

"No, *Herr Inspektor*. I don't even know how he was aware that I was in the coffee shop. I was seated near no window so I could not have been observed from the street."

"Then it may be assumed that he followed you there."

"Unless he just happened to be in the vicinity and saw me enter."

"What did he wish, Fräulein Maneth?"

"I honestly don't know. He told me his practice was not very good. He hinted that he was low on money, though he did not ask me for any. Our talk mystified me, for I knew of no reason for it. He suggested my using his legal services. I declined. I do not believe it was merely a chance visit. Thinking back, I sense he was a little distraught. That's why I'm of the opinion he went there to solicit money from me in exchange for information, but lost his nerve or became frightened."

"Of what, *Fräulein*? Or of whom?"

"I don't know. I wish I did. Are you conducting an investigation of his suicide?"

"It was not suicide, Fräulein Maneth."

Nicola inclined her head briefly. "I suspected as much when you came calling, *Herr Inspektor*. I wish I could help you."

205

"The arrangement of the rope, a chair. . .several other things indicated it was murder and not suicide. What's more, Herr Kramer was known to be in arrears in many bills and was regarded as a bad credit risk. But the day he was supposed to have killed himself, he made the rounds of his creditors and settled with them in full, much to their amazement—and mine—I must add. We also discovered a sizable amount of currency in his room."

"In other words, someone paid him a large sum of money."

"Precisely. We would like to know what for."

"I can help you in but one way, *Herr Inspektor*. Herr Kramer and I saw my father assassinated by a man named Sander. Before his execution, I was kidnapped and both raped and threatened with more trouble if I did not amend my testimony. This I did not do."

"A brave defiance of this assassin and his friends. I, of course, know about that."

"I think all of Vienna did. I have no proof of this, not even a glimmer of proof, but Herr Kramer must have seen something I did not see and it meant he had dangerous information. What it was, I don't know, and I cannot understand how he saw something I did not at the time of my father's murder."

"We more or less agree with that premise, Fräulein Maneth. We have tried to determine where Kramer went the day before his death and the day it happened. We attempted to trace the money he so mysteriously obtained somewhere. No luck in either case. So there seems little we can do about it except keep a watchful eye out."

"I am troubled by these threats made to me, *Herr Inspektor*. The death of Herr Kramer assures me those people are desperate or ruthless, or both. They killed Papa and still pose a threat to me, and now an even greater one after Herr Kramer's murder."

"Sander, I have learned from the foreign office, would have eventually become the revolutionary ruler of one of the Balkans. He'd been working toward it for years, but your father came upon the scheme, also discovering the plot against the Emperor, and wrecked it. Sander is dead, but he made many friends who would have surely profited if he ruled an entire country. You were responsible for Sander's execution, and there is no doubt but that they are not inclined to be friendly to you. Now if they attempt any action against you, please let me know and I shall do whatever I can."

"Thank you, *Herr Inspektor*. I'll remember that."

"You understand we do not know the identity of those who worked with Sander here in Vienna. The people taken into custody in Budapest did not talk. It is still a mystery and a dangerous one."

She saw him out, closed and locked the door again, debating with herself whether or not to let David know. She needed him. Yet she could not bring it upon herself to interfere with his career at this important stage of it, though since talking to Inspector Reikert, her fears were now compounded.

The theatre had a calming influence on her, even while it was empty and she was exercising at the *barre* along with many of the *corps de ballet*. Here there was no talk of death and threats. The beauty of the ballet brought another world to her, where she felt safe and comfortable.

There would now be a full week of ballet. A different one each night, which required a great deal of rehearsal, so she was going to be kept extremely busy. The nights she dreaded, even accompanied by either Tonio or Anna, for they finally left her alone in the too empty apartment. By day, and in the evening, she was surrounded by music, lights, people she loved, and an audience that approved of her by compelling her to take many curtain calls. Then by night she lived in a state of near terror. The death of Kramer only intensified her fears. If they had arranged his death, most certainly they would not hesitate to arrange hers too. It was promised her when she reached the peak of her success, but how could she know how they'd decide when that peak was? Becoming prima ballerina fulfilled almost all of her dreams. It was a position not easily attained, but she had reached it and was now secure in her role. That could easily be considered the brightest peak of her career. Yet no sign of violence had occurred.

David's letters finally began to arrive with regularity, now that they were sent to the theatre. Each morning when she reported for exercise, she entered the theatre eagerly, and each day she was rewarded with an envelope addressed to her in his handwriting.

He asked, in each letter, if she were in need of him; if things seemed to be closing in on her; if she were harassed by anyone or if something strange had happened to frighten her. In her replies, she went to great lengths to assure him that all had been going well with her and that she was receiving his letters at the theatre.

She was glad she hadn't troubled him, for she finally received a letter from him telling of the successful opening of the show. He enclosed some clippings of the excellent reviews of the critics. Heidi had gained immediate acceptance, her talent praised in glowing terms. Nicola even felt a pang of envy, though quickly dismissed it.

By the end of the week, the staggering load of being featured in seven different ballets had exhausted her. She wondered if that was why she kept her dressing room door locked, though seeing Anna in the audience at each performance was reassuring. The thought came to Nicola, when the curtain came down for intermission, to send a note to Anna asking if she would come backstage after the final curtain if she weren't too tired. Nicola wanted the companionship of a woman.

She finally had to lock her door, because too many people were coming in to congratulate her on her performance or to relate a bit of gossip.

Without rhyme or reason, she started to cry. Perhaps they were tears of fatigue, but Nicola told herself they were also tears of happiness because the week had been so successful. She felt a sense of relief that nothing had been done to frighten her to the extent that her performance suffered.

She opened her door following Tonio's knock and his request to enter, only after she had hastily doused her face with cold water and removed all traces of tears.

One look at her face assured him something was wrong. "Are you ill?"

"Just tired, Tonio."

"I'll take you home immediately."

"No, thank you. Not tonight. Anna will be here shortly."

"Then she will be with you."

Nicola nodded. "Thanks just the same, dear friend."

"Get rest," he counseled. "You're pale."

"I'll be all right."

"I know how exhausted you must be. Every muscle in my body aches. This week was too much for anyone to bear. Lapin is merciless. He'll wear us out in a season."

"We won't let him," Nicola said. "Thanks for supporting me so splendidly."

"We're heading for the Schönbrunn theatre," he said with a smile. "No question about it. Want to bet?"

"No, Tonio. We'll know soon enough now. The social season at the Schönbrunn Palace begins in February and that's not very far off. We can hope and pray.''

"Good night. Get all the rest you can. If you need me, send a messenger. I'll come promptly. Promise?''

"I promise.''

While they talked, Tonio moved around the dressing room nervously, an indication of his own fatigue. Anna arrived soon after he left.

"I met Tonio outside. He told me you wouldn't be with him this evening.''

"I'm tired, Anna. All I want to do is finish removing my makeup, dress and get some sleep.''

"Good. You look exhausted. I'll take you home—after you've eaten.''

"I'm too tired to eat. I'll be content with my glass of milk. I do want to talk with you though. I'll wait here until you get something to eat. Don't hurry. I'll take my own good time. And if you're too tired, you needn't see me home. I'll take a carriage.''

"*We* will take a carriage," Anna corrected her. "I'll go to the coffee shop around the corner. Give me half an hour or so.''

After Anna departed, Nicola locked the door, then drank more milk, removed her makeup and arose from the dressing table to take off her dancing costume. A wave of dizziness overcame her, sending her reeling against the wall.

It had been too much, this solid week of dancing. She decided to lie down until Anna returned. She lowered herself onto the small couch carefully; she felt as if she might suddenly faint. The mirror lights were too bright and her eyes pained from them. She got to her feet again, staggered somewhat, but managed to turn the lights off. In the dark, she retreated to the safety of the couch and lay down. It was good to get off her feet. She felt warm and comfortable. It was like heaven.

Then she recalled that Anna was coming back, but the

door was locked. She managed to rise to her elbows in an attempt to get up, but she fell back and remembered nothing until she awoke with a start and didn't know where she was.

Gradually her eyes grew accustomed to the dark and she realized she was still in her dressing room. She sat up, waited until a wave of dizziness left her. Then she managed to reach the gaslights at her dressing table. She found a lighter, pressed it to create the necessary spark and the gas flamed instantly.

She would have to hurry now, because Anna would come back very soon. She had no idea how long she'd napped. She looked at her lapel watch and was astonished to learn that she'd slept at least three hours. It seemed impossible.

She stood up, steadied herself, unlocked the door and stepped out into the corridor between the dressing rooms to find everything in total darkness and a complete silence. The theatre was empty. She couldn't hear a voice or a footfall. She was alone in the vastness of the big building.

Anna must have come, decided Nicola hadn't waited and left. Everyone else must have believed the same thing. There were no watchmen in the theatre, and no one prowled its darkness by night. She took off her dancing costume and hung it up.

She put on her street clothes, found a button hook to button her shoes, picked up her coat and turned out the gas. She was now in total darkness and she suddenly felt the first twinges of fear running up and down her spine. She had a strange feeling that she was not alone. Pausing just outside the dressing room door, she listened. There was no sound, yet she seemed to sense the presence of another person. She had an urge to go back into the dressing room, close and lock the door and stay there until morning. She held her breath, because it seemed to her that she could hear the sound of breathing from someone not far away, but thoroughly concealed by the darkness.

"Who is there?" she asked. "Who is it?"

There was no reply. She decided the best thing to do was to make a dash down the straight corridor to the stage door. Before she reached it, there would be four steps to climb to a small platform just inside the door, but she knew where that was. If she were unlucky enough to injure herself moving too fast in the dark, that was better than standing where she was, or even retreating to the dressing room.

She took a few steps down the corridor. She could see nothing and she guided her way by keeping one hand against the wall to her left. She began to regain some of her confidence and decided the sound of breathing, which had frightened her, simply did not exist except in her tortured imagination.

Suddenly there was movement and someone near the stage exit shouted. Footsteps followed. Nicola turned and fled back to her dressing room. She knew where it was and she seized the doorknob, but the dressing room door was locked. She hadn't locked it. Someone else had.

"Please," she called out, "whoever you are, what do you want?"

"You!" a man's voice said softly somewhere behind her. This was not the man near the stage door who had shouted. This was someone else. There was more than one man here.

"What do you want?" she called out again. "Who are you?"

"Remember the room at Sander's house? Remember being in bed with a man? Remember, *Fräulein*? I remember and those with me were jealous of me that night. We have come to enjoy ourselves—with your

212

body. Your lips, your breasts, your legs—all of you. That's what we want."

"You're insane," she called out. "Mad! Keep away from me!"

"We shall have you," the same voice threatened. "There are several of us, all eager to possess the prima ballerina. It would be well to let us have our way. If you do not, you may be badly hurt. Do you understand, *Fräulein*?"

She had quietly managed to bend down, tear open the buttons of her shoes and slip out of them. She held one in her hand and threw it in the direction of the stage door.

At the same time, she flattened herself against the wall. Someone went by her, moving carefully because of the dark.

"Do you hear her?" he asked.

The man at the stage door was uncertain. "I don't have her in my arms, but she's not far off. I heard her stumble, or fall. . .something. . ."

Nicola was by now moving on stockinged feet along the corridor in the direction of the stage. She was terrified, but she managed to keep her head and not give way to hysteria. They'd made it plain enough as to what they were after and also equally clear that they were members of the band that had threatened her before. The fact that they knew about the incident in the Sander house the night she'd been kidnapped was proof of that.

She was in the wing now, moving through darkness, but in a fairly familiar place. There was a clear path to the stage. If she could reach it and then descend to the audience section, she might be able to make her way to the door leading into the lobby, and from there to the street exists. They'd be locked, but she could pound on them, even break the glass in one if she could find some weapon to use for that purpose. At any rate, she would create so much noise, it was bound to be heard and these men would have to get away quickly.

She brushed against one of the curtain ropes and it snapped back, not noisily, but in this intense silence, loud enough to make her wince.

"She's near the stage," someone called from the stage itself. She wondered how many of these men were there. She froze in place and let them make the next move.

They were coming from the dressing room corridor, making all the noise they wished, because there was no longer any reason to be silent. Besides, she was outnumbered. Nicola was still holding one shoe and she didn't dare set it down for fear of creating even a slight sound that might give away her location. The only friend she had was the darkness and her familiarity with the layout of the theatre.

Those from the corridor were coming closer. She began to cross the stage, as lightly as she had danced over it, making no sound. If she could reach the opposite wing, she might be able to dodge behind scenery and retreat the way she'd come, back to the stage door which was probably not guarded now that they knew her location.

"I hear her!" a man shouted, almost in her ear. He wasn't a dozen feet away. Terror now made her lose some of her better judgment. She began to run. The man was close enough to step out. She collided with him, creating as much surprise in him as in herself.

A hand grasped her by the shoulder. She had inserted her right hand inside the shoe she carried so that it acted as a glove and she swung this as hard as she could, aiming for a target hidden by the dark, but measured by the closeness of the man who held her. The heel of the shoe struck a vulnerable spot on the man's head or face. He gave a cry of pain and let go of her.

She moved to the edge of the stage, bent down and located the gas footlights with her hand. Using it as a guide, she followed the lights to the end where she knew she was close to the steps leading to the aisle.

"She's not near us," someone called from one of the aisles. They were behind her and ahead of her. She had no idea how many were in the aisles, but the man who spoke had used the plural so there must be at least two of them. They'd be waiting in the orchestra pit perhaps. She might run head-on into one of them again if she attempted that route of escape. She felt safer on or near the stage. She straightened, moved a few steps toward the wing she hoped was not under guard.

Then, as she was frantically seeking somewhere to hide, or a route to the stage door, there was a flash of light. One of the men had found the control for lighting the mirror-backed gas footlights and the rapid series of flames made her turn away from them because of the brightness after the inky dark.

She was at the north end of the stage. Slowly she backed and sidestepped to the center of the stage. She looked about. There was one man standing in the north wing, two men blocking the south, and three of them standing before the orchestra pit, wrecking all means of getting off the stage for a run to the back of the theatre.

They were not masked or hooded, but they were wearing black coats with collars large enough to be raised to cover their faces. They also wore the popular hats with large turned down brims so she was unable to recognize any of them or to store in her mind a description of them. Perhaps that would be easiest to do if they pinned her down and carried out the awful threat she knew they were well capable of.

They began to move slowly toward her. She backed up a few more steps. They had their arms straight out as if to enfold her as soon as she was within their reach.

Nicola threw back her head and screamed as loudly as she could. She kept on screaming and they kept on approaching her. Apparently they knew her voice would not reach the street. Even if it did, there'd be precious few close by to hear her.

"You're all mad! Crazy!" she cried. out. "Let me alone! Go away! Please go away!"

"We shall go away after we have had what we want," one man said. There is no use in fighting us. We'll kill you to get what we're after. If you value your life, do not resist us."

She screamed again. Suddenly the footlights dimmed and went out. Once more, she was in darkness, standing there in the middle of the stage waiting for eager, strong hands to tear off her clothing, to throw her to the stage floor and ravage her at their will. She raised her hands to her face and tried again to scream, but she couldn't bring forth a sound. She was about to turn to the left and run through the darkness, hoping to avoid them somehow. She took a few steps. Nothing happened. No one seized her. No hands came out of the gloom. She stopped and listened. The great theatre was silent. It was as terrifying as the intruders.

She wanted to call out, to hear an answering voice, even if it came from the lips of one of those horrible men. But again, she had no voice. She could only stand there, frozen in fear, moving her lips, as in some of the miming she often acted.

It was worse than when she could see them. Now she didn't know what to expect, or from where they would come. She stood fast for five full minutes and yet nothing happened, nothing broke the silence.

She disengaged the shoe that was still on her hand like a glove and threw it to her right. The shoe landed on the stage floor and sounded like a battery of cannons.

There was no answering sound. She now took a few

steps in the direction of the stage door. No one intercepted her. Suddenly she realized that she was alone. They had gone, vanished as quietly as they had entered. This had been only a means of intimidating her, terrorizing her, leaving the final acts until later. This had been a warning of what was to come, and it was performed in the cruelest way possible without resorting to violence.

She was in the dressing room corridow now. By counting the doors, she came to the one which led to her own room and which had been locked. It was now unlocked and she went inside, somewhat fearfully. They may have arranged this and were there in the dark to greet her with pawing hands.

She moved slowly across the room. Familiarity with it enabled her to reach the dressing table. Now she managed to light the gas at the sides of the mirror. She turned around fearfully. No one was behind her. The dressing room was as empty as the theatre.

She quickly locked the door and then dropped onto the couch to bury her face in the pillow and sob uncontrollably. She had no idea how long she remained there, but finally she sat up, used a towel to dry her tears and went to the sink to splash cold water onto her face.

On her way back to the dressing table, she noticed that the glass which had contained her milk was gone, and she realized that the deep and overwhelming sleep must have been caused by some drug covertly placed in the milk. For some reason, she thought of Tonio, moving restlessly about the dressing room, but she threw that idea out of her mind. He wouldn't be so cruel.

She was feeling better now. The realization that all of this had been meant only to terrorize her gave her some confidence that she was safe, at least for the time being. She saw that her stockings had been torn and were ragged around her feet. She found ballet practice slippers and put these on. Then she went to the stage door and lit the gas light there. Returning to the dressing room, she turned out the light, made her way along the now dimly illuminated corridor. The stage door was bolted, but she turned this, put out the light, went out into the night and closed the door. Not having a key with which to turn the bolt back into place, she was compelled to leave it open.

It must be near dawn, she thought. The streets were deserted. She walked quickly along the sidewalk. Once she saw a watchman and she ducked into a doorway. She didn't want anyone to question her, touch her, talk to her. The terror was still there, and it would overwhelm her if anything happened to frighten her again.

She reached her apartment house. By then, the ballet slippers were in tatters because it was some distance from the theatre. She let herself into the lobby, sat down for a few moments in the dimly-lighted entrance, then went up the stairs to her apartment.

Once the door closed behind her, she felt safe. Her tense muscles relaxed. The terror left. She was home. Here, they couldn't get at her, threaten her, frighten her half to death with their tricks. She sat down slowly on the couch, automatically loosened the thongs of her slippers and removed them. She'd lit one lamp and now lit others until the entire apartment was well illuminated. She went to her writing table and composed a brief letter to David, writing of what had just happened and begging him to come to her. She addressed an envelope, read the note again and then tore it into shreds, dropping the pieces into the wastebasket.

She was beyond any more tears. A slow anger was taking the place of the fear. She would go to Inspector Reikert in the morning and ask his help. But she knew she couldn't do that. She'd endured enough publicity.

Any more might be apt to damage her career.

Sitting there at the desk, alone, as dawn began to filter through the windows, she reviewed her career in her mind and resolutely planned to make it even better. There was a goal, represented by the Schönbrunn theatre, which she was determined to reach. Not even something was horrible as this business tonight would stop her. If those people were trying to break her by this kind of terror, she'd show them she was stronger than they.

A sudden thought occurred to her that there was one other thing she could do if it became necessary. She could visit Franz Josef, explain to him what was going on and seek his help. He was bound to answer her with forces that would crush those who sought to finally kill her. It was a last resort, and she disliked reminding the Emperor of that night so many months ago. However, if it became necessary that was what she would do. It was time to fight back. They were certainly her enemies. They'd murdered her father and they had promised her death also, but not with the suddenness with which they'd attacked her father.

She was still awake when Anna knocked and called out, her voice raised in anxiety. Nicola arose, moved to the door and turned the bolt, her gestures mechanical.

Anna came in, closed the door. "What in the world happened last night? Why didn't you wait for me? I came back. . .they said you must have gone home alone."

"I was not alone," Nicola said, her voice a monotone.

Anna saw her bare feet, the torn stockings and paled as she took another look at Nicola's face. "Nicky, what is it? What happened?"

"Sit down, Anna. I locked my dressing room after you left and I waited for you, but someone had managed to place a sleeping potion in my glass of milk. That had to be it. The glass was removed so there would be no proof."

"You were drugged? Why would they do that unless someone wanted to kidnap you—or worse?"

"Nothing makes sense, yet everything was done to terrify me. It was a nightmare. I could never have imagined anything like that happening to me."

"Were you hurt? You know what I mean. You look numb."

"I should," Nicola replied dryly. "However, they scarcely laid a hand on me. I woke up in the dark. The theatre was pitch black. Everyone had gone. I was quite alone—at least that is what I thought. I got dressed, started to leave the theatre heading for the stage door when someone blocked my way. Someone else locked my dressing room door so I couldn't retreat. Not that it would have done me any good. There were six of them, Anna. Six. . .well muffled in coat collars, the wide brims of their hats turned down so their features were in shadow. I could never identify even one of them. They told me they were going to take me—as I had been taken before. They threatened to hurt me if I did not give in."

Anna listened, her features expressing the horror Nicola had felt when confronted by her assailants. Then she frowned. "You said the theatre was in darkness."

"It was until they lit the footlights."

"Six men? Nicky, are you sure they didn't. . .I mean, before you wakened."

"I'd have known. Anyway, my dressing room door was locked."

Anna nodded. "I know you locked it after I left. I listened to make certain."

"Anyway, I told you they scarcely laid a hand on me. One man tried to in the darkness on the stage and I struck him with my shoes."

220

Anna regarded Nicola as if she were bereft of her senses. 'How did you manage that?''

"I was carrying my shoes, trying to keep my whereabouts secret so I could gain the front of the theatre and escape."

"Did you hurt your assailant?" Anna asked.

"I must have, because he cried out. That was done in total darkness. Then they lit the footlights, brightening the stage. That's when the six of them started to come toward me. I was hemmed in on all sides. There was no way I could escape them. Even if I jumped off the stage and tried to run up the aisle they could stop me, because three of them guarded the aisles. As they came closer, there was no doubt as to what they meant to do. Then, suddenly, the footlights went out. I stood there for heaven knows how long. Nothing happened. They had gone—vanished. It was like waking from a nightmare. But this was real."

"Thank God, they didn't harm you. It seems incredible they let you go."

"They were sent to frighten me. To reduce me to a state of panic and they almost did. I think if they had seized me, tried to carry out their threats, I might have lost my mind. But they didn't want that. I have the feeling they're saving me for the final act, whenever that will come."

Anna embraced her. "Oh, Nicky, how awful that must have been. Will you listen to what I have to say? I want to suggest something."

"I've always listened to you, Anna."

"Then listen well and do what I say. Send David a cablegram."

"No, I will not take him from his success."

"I didn't mean that. Go to him! Cable him you are coming. Then get on the first ship. . . ."

"If I do, they'll only follow me. These savages have

all kinds of resources. I believe now they fully intend to kill me—or make me wish I were dead. I will not expose David to this violence. But I'm not going to just sit here and let it happen again."

"What can you do, for God's sake?" Anna demanded impatiently.

"I'm angry. They terrified me last night, but they won't do it again. I intend to find them, expose them and see they are properly punished, even if I have to risk my life doing it."

"Nicky dear, you're talking recklessly. What can you do?"

"I don't know, but there must be some way to find out who they are, where they are. If I do nothing, they'll just bide their time until they are ready to kill me. I'll not just sit here and wait for that. If they can think of such schemes, I can think of some too. If my career as a dancer is ruined because of this, that is how it must be. They're certainly going to try to destroy me one way or another."

"Nicky, have you forgotten something?"

"What?" Nicola demanded.

"Dancing at the Schönbrunn Palace."

"I'll dance there if I am invited, but meantime I am devoting myself to the task of searching for these people."

"Why not let the police. . ."

"No," Nicola broke in before Anna could finish the sentence. "I've already told you why I won't."

Anna nodded. "You're still distraught, poor baby. You need sleep. You got none last night."

"Yes, I did," Nicola said. "Don't forget. My milk was drugged."

"That's not the right kind of sleep. I'll stay with you. Please forget your anger and go to bed. I'll not leave this apartment until you waken."

Nicola sighed. "What about your job?"

"That will be waiting for me," Anna assured her.

"I feel guilty taking up your time, but I need you. I'm grateful, my friend. And I am tired. I'm a bundle of nerves."

"That's apparent. So is your fear, though a few moments ago your anger dominated."

"I don't know what I'd call it, though I meant it. But I don't want to think of it now. Please don't let me sleep all day. A few hours will do."

She got up wearily. Anna was at her side in a moment and had an arm around her to help. In the bedroom, Anna helped her undress, slipped Nicola's nightdress over her head. When she had settled down, with the covers over her and her head nestled in the pillow, Anna bent and kissed her cheek.

"Sleep now, my child." She straightened and placed a hand on Nicola's brow. "Your brow is so hot I'd swear you have a fever."

"Just nerves," Nicola said, her voice already blurred with sleep.

Anna nodded, though not too convincingly.

"Good night," Nicola said, without a thought that it was already daylight.

# Thirteen

Someone shook her, trying to waken her. Nicola opened her eyes and looked up into the face of Anna.

"I'm sorry, Nicky. I wanted you to sleep all day if possible, but Lapin sent word."

"Lapin?" She sat up, wondering who Lapin was. Her mind seemed to have gone blank. Then suddenly remembrance came. "Lapin? What does he want?"

"There is to be a meeting of the entire company at two. No one is exempt. The messenger he sent said it was very important."

"What time is it now?"

"Noon. You don't have much time. I'll prepare something to eat for you while you bathe. While you're eating, I'll get a carriage."

"Thank you." Nicola got out of bed and went to the bathroom. Suddenly all the terror of the evening before came back with a rush that set her hands shaking as she prepared a bath. She made it hot and soaked in it to relax her muscles. Gradually, the vivid memory of the night left her. She hastily dressed, did the best she could with her hair, ate hastily with Anna standing by. Nicola looked up at her with a smile. "How I wish you had married Papa years ago."

"If the choice had been mine, we would have. Don't remind me of it, Nicky. I think about him all the time. Right now you'd better get down to the carriage. It's been waiting for half an hour, I think. You know Lapin. If he says it's an important meeting, he begins it right on time and if you're not there, he goes for your heart."

"I'll make it. I can't think what he wants us for. We've finished a week of dancing. We all need a rest and besides, the ballet season is waning. Still, he does get ideas. We'll see."

Prodded by Anna she made it to the theatre just in time. Everyone else was there and Lapin cast a baleful eye her way, but he didn't say anything.

"Children," he said, "I have good news. The best possible news. In two weeks, on Saturday, we are to put on a special performance of *Giselle* for the Emperor, the Empress and. . ." he paused for the effect, "the Kaiser and the Kaiserin. They are coming to Vienna on a state visit. Now you know how much the Germans admire *Giselle*. It is, after all, based on a German legend. I know it is not the easiest ballet in the world, but it is effective and very colorful. We shall have a much larger orchestra and brand new sets which I have already arranged for, and I shall add eight more to the *corps de ballet*."

"Will Nicola and I dance the leads?" Tonio called out.

"If you maintain the skills you have shown so far. Remember, I want no dallying. Every day we shall practice and rehearse all the time. You will report at nine and stay until I tell you to go home. That, I warn you, will not be early."

"*M'sieur*," Nicola said, "it was my impression that we have done an outstanding job on *Giselle*. You make it sound as if the performance needs a great deal of work."

"There is always room for improvement. I have seen better *Giselles* danced, but the one you will dance for the Kaiser will be the best that has ever been done or I'll have your hides. You may take this day off. Tomorrow, be here at nine. Bring extra exercise clothes. You will soak more than one outfit with your sweat."

He moved slowly around the room, twirling his gold-headed cane which he was never seen without any more. He looked like an animal on the prowl as he moved slowly among the dancers, studying their figures, their postures, looking for added ounces.

"Are there any questions?" he asked, apparently satisfied.

"We realize what a great honor it will be dancing for such important royalty," Nicola said. "You may be assured, *Monsieur*, the dancing will be perfect."

"I expect it to be. There will also be a generous bonus for each of us if there are no flaws. Every duke, arch-duke, duchess and archduchess will be present at the affair. No more illustrious audience can be imagined. From this we shall gain the reputation of being the best ballet group in the world. That is all."

Tonio moved over to Nicola's side. "I don't know why he will try to perfect something that is perfect already. We could put on that ballet tomorrow and it would not be flawed."

"I know, but he is the ballet master and the responsibility is his to see that a performance worthy of such royalty is guaranteed. And I don't mind the rehearsing and practice. It is a difficult ballet, especially for you and me. We can always learn something more."

"I'll go along with it. Nicky, you don't look well. Are you ill?"

She chided him with a look. "Certainly not. I lack sleep and I'm going home and get as many hours of rest as I can."

Her light manner didn't fool Tonio. "You don't look yourself. Something happened, didn't it?"

She glanced at him somewhat sharply. She didn't think either her fatigue or nervousness was that obvious. "How did you guess?"

"Your hands are shaking. You're pale. There are dark circles under your eyes. Also, they lack sparkle. I was fearful Lapin might notice."

She managed a smile. "He's too excited about our command performance."

"That might well be," Tonio agreed. "Though it still doesn't lessen my concern for you."

"Do you recall after last night's performance, you were in my dressing room?"

"Yes. I was going to take you home, but you turned me down for Anna."

"What made you so nervous last night?"

"Was I nervous? I don't know. I had no reason I can think of. It was the end of a strenuous two weeks of shows. That's enough to tire anyone. Why do you ask?"

"I have to be honest with you, Tonio, but here on stage is not the place for it. Let's go down to my dressing room."

She closed the door and sat down opposite him. "I'm ashamed of myself, Tonio, for what has been in my mind. I was thinking that what happened last night may have been at your order, that my refusal of your advances angered you."

Tonio's features revealed his puzzlement. "My order? The only orders I know of are those I take. I've given no orders. What's troubling you, Nicky?"

She told him in detail of her experience in this darkened theatre in the middle of the night. He sat in growing horror at the story and before she was done, the horror had left him for a full measure of anger and hatred.

"I swear I had nothing to do with it. I don't blame you for suspecting me. I could have drugged the glass of milk. I must have passed it fifty times. Yes, I was nervous. I'm always that way because I've reached a point in the world of ballet I aspired to, but never thought I'd make. Thanks to you, I have, but I'm a worrier at heart. As my success grows, so do my worries."

"Did you notice anyone else near the glass of milk, Tonio?"

"Nobody in particular. There were times when I thought the whole ballet company was in your dressing room. I came to your door three times. The fourth time it was closed. I knocked. Even Lapin was in there once. The second time I looked in, I believe. Even Anna was there. At least, she told me she was taking you home."

"She intended to. My nerves have been ragged lately and, after last night, I'm beside myself with fear. I'm afraid of the dark, afraid of being alone. I see people on the street and wonder if they are watching me. If it continues, I feel I might go mad."

"Of course you won't. You're far too level-headed for that. As for being alone, I'll stay as close to you as I can, whenever I can. And you have Anna. What you should do is send for David. Or go to him."

"Anna said the same thing. I disagree. Things are going too well for him. He can't afford to leave. Besides, if he came back they'd probably try to harm him—to get even with me. They're so filled with hate and revenge, I don't know what to do."

"Do nothing. You won't have the chance anyway. We start rehearsing tomorrow and every day until the show. You won't have time to worry. You'll just work, starve yourself and sleep. I'll see you home each day and when you leave your apartment in the morning, I'll be waiting.''

She arose, went to his side, bent down and kissed his cheek. "I'm thoroughly ashamed of myself for even thinking you had anything to do with what happened. Very well, Tonio, we shall give them a *Giselle* they'll remember. This is the one company that can do it. Our corps works well together. Even Lapin will have to admit we could not have done better. Nor would any other company in the world. I'll be ready at eight.''

On the way out she found a letter from David in her private letter box. She tucked it in her handbag, saving it to be read when she was home alone, and prepared to enjoy it. Tonio walked with her and they chatted amiably, mostly about little chnages in the dance. Before they entered her apartment house, they were as enthused about the prospect as Lapin had been.

The letter was not long this time. He was busy, he wrote. The show required a few small changes that turned out to be more difficult than he had believed. Heidi was rapidly becoming the toast of New York City and was besieged with stage-door admirers. She was keeping her head, however, and David had nothing to worry about with her. He asked again for reassurance that she had not been subjected to further harassment or danger. He declared his love and utter devotion to her and stated he looked forward eagerly to when they could be together again. He even suggested she take a vacation from Lapin's shows and come to New York.

She was as tempted to take him up on that as she was determined not to write a line about the episode in the theatre. With enough time she wrote a very long letter and poured out her lonely heart to him, at the same time begging him to stay with his show and make it the full success it deserved to be.

She would mail it in the morning. For now she intended to prepare a snack, lie down and catch up on her sleep. She felt sorely in need of it, especially since Lapin was going to be extreme in his criticisms to get the most out of all his dancers.

She was washing her dishes when Inspector Reikert arrived. Her face lit up at the sight of him, because she had made up her mind to enlist his active help before the situation grew so bad she'd suffer more than an attack of nerves from it.

"Before you tell me why you wish to see me again, *Herr Inspektor,* may I tell you what happened to me last night?"

"Of course. Does it have to do with the other troubles?"

"Definitely yes." She related the story again in detail while he listened, and his somewhat heavy jowls moved as he set his teeth in high anger.

"Fräulein Maneth, I had no idea it has become as difficult as that. You should have sent for me. Do you suspect anyone?"

"No. If I were a suspicious person, I would suspect everyone. How can I tell you who drugged my glass of milk? There were so many in and out of my dressing room. I can't even prove the milk was drugged because the glass was taken. I cannot point to a single suspect. That why I ask your help."

"You shall have it. Tell me what you think of your ballet master, Philippe Lapin."

"Is he involved?" she asked in surprise.

"We do not know. That is why I ask questions. What about him?"

"He is a slave driver, but he is the best ballet master in the world, in my opinion, and the company concurs in that. If he weren't, we would have rebelled long ago."

"Is he a wealthy man? Does he make a great deal of money?"

"I can't answer that. You could probably get that information better than I."

"Were you aware that Herr Kramer, who is supposed to have killed himself, and Lapin were acquainted?"

"No, *Herr Inspektor*. I never saw them together. Though I see Monsieur Lapin only at the theatre."

"We have been digging deeply into the movements of Herr Kramer just prior to his death. The day before he died, he visited Monsieur Lapin at his private studio. He stayed there for about half an hour. Before I question Monsieur Lapin, I wanted to know if you knew anything about that pair."

"I suppose someone like Lapin does require the services of a lawyer, but I don't think he would go to such a one as Herr Kramer, who was an admitted failure."

"We don't know, but we think he may have gone to Lapin for money."

"What on earth gives you that idea? Lapin is a tight-wad. Never one to be free with money."

"Because Lapin, a few days before Kramer's visit, had drawn a considerable sum of money from his bank. Now we can only hazard a guess as to the amount Kramer had, but it would be, roughly, in the amount Lapin drew out."

"I don't see how there could be a connection between Herr Kramer and Monsieur Lapin. He has no political connections, *Herr Inspektor*. I doubt he knows anything about politics, especially those involving foreign countries. And he has caused me no trouble, done nothing to upset me at rehearsals. He's even praised my performance."

"Tomorrow I will ask him. I want you to be there. You know him and you can tell better than I how he reacts to this. Of course, the whole thing may be just a coincidence. In police work, we find that it usually is, but we have to examine everything in detail. As for you, I shall assign a man to keep guard over you."

"Please don't," she begged. "Please, *Herr Inspektor*. For the next two weeks we are rehearsing to put on a difficult ballet for the Emperor, the Empress and the Kaiser and his family. It must be perfect. If Lapin sees one of your men watching me, he will be very angry. That is the way he is. He will feel a guard present will unnerve the corps and he could be right. It might do the same thing to me."

"Are you protected in any way?"

"My male partner comes for me and brings me home. I have a good friend, a lady who would have married my father if he had lived. She works for the government. She has taken me under her wing. I feel that I am amply protected."

"Very well. But if any more of these vicious attacks are made on you, I would suggest that you let us keep a surveillance around you."

"If it happens again, I'll accept your offer of protection because I don't know how much more of this I can stand. I may as well tell you this too. They have warned me that when I reach the very apex of my career, they will kill me. They blame me, as you know, for Sander's execution."

"And this apex of your career will happen when, may I ask?"

"This ballet, which we are to do for royalty, will be attended by some of the most important people of the continent. It is so important that I fully believe this would be the crowning glory of any prima ballerina's career."

"Are you afraid?"

"Terribly. I know what they are capable of."

"I will see you tomorrow at the theatre then. You shall have all the help my department can give."

"Thank you, *Herr Inspektor*. But no guard. At least, not yet."

She let him out and locked the door, wondering how much longer she would have to live in constant fear. Yet it bothered her. As the day progressed she grew more and more worried. If she were right, if dancing before royalty meant she had reached the zenith of her career, then she would have to expect the final blow.

She picked up the sealed letter to David and weighed it in her hand as she weighed it in her mind. It took only moments to put aside the thought of sending a cable-gram asking him to come back. If he did, it was quite likely he'd be harmed too, and she knew of no way he could help her when nobody had the slightest idea of who led these people, or even who they were. It would be both an act of danger and foolishness on her part.

Anna came that evening and listened to the story of Inspector Reikert's visit. She grew more concerned than ever at Nicola's reaction.

"You're not yourself, Nicky. You talk too fast and you stumble over some of your words. You must rest and stop this ceaseless worrying before it affects your dancing, especially now that you will likely perform the greatest ballet of your career. If those important people like you as much as Emperor Franz Josef did, you will be hailed as one of the best prima ballerinas in the world. Have you thought of that?"

"Constantly. I'll try to behave myself. I know I'm nervous and ballet dancing has to be done without a trace of nervousness. I have almost two weeks. By then I'll be myself again."

"I hope so. You should have accepted the Inspector's offer of a guard."

"It would upset the corps, Lapin would be furious

and I would be responsible. I feel I am safe until after the command performance."

"Let us hope so. Go nowhere and see no one except those at the theatre. Take not the slightest chance. If you grow frightened on the street, find the nearest policeman and ask him to notify Inspector Reikert. Do not panic. Think of the fact that you will be protected. And remember all the while, there is more than a chance that those responsible for your trouble will be identified and caught. Inspector Reikert is working on that now."

"If they wished to punish me for refusing to save Sander's life, they have succeeded."

"That is something they must never find out. Do you have enough food in the house?"

"I don't know. I've been so distraught I haven't even looked."

"Well, I will right now and whatever you need I'll go out and get. You are not to do any shopping. Stay away from crowds. In fact—stay off the streets."

"I know. I'm going to shut out all thought of danger. I realize what it can do to a dancer, especially a prima."

In the morning, Tonio, faithful as always, waited in the lobby for her and a carriage was at the curb. On the way to the theater, she told him about Inspector Reikert's visit.

"You should have accepted his offer to protect you," he said. "That's the most important thing of all, even way above the success of the dance. If you feel you are not up to these rehearsals, we'll tell Lapin we don't need that much training. And to be truthful, we don't. We've mastered that ballet, difficult as it is. Lapin is just exerting authority and probably looking for publicity."

"No matter what his motive is, we must bend to his will. In a way, I'm glad. I'll be busy and with the corps. I'll not have time to think."

In their practice clothes, Nicola and Tonio began to

rehearse the second act. The ballet boys and girls worked at the *barre* again in a warm-up and soon the stage was alive with dancers going through their routines. All of them realized the importance of this special production of *Giselle* and that a huge success would provide work for as long as they were able to dance. There would be a great deal more money and travel all over the world. It was a ballet company's dream.

Lapin arrived somewhat late, but immediately began his everlasting criticism. Brandishing his cane, he went from one group to another, shouting, exorting, sometimes even pleading for perfection.

Inspector Reikert, true to his promise, arrived just before noon and presently Lapin sent for Nicola. In his private office, with the door closed, Inspector Reikert continued the questioning he had begun before Nicola's arrival.

"Now my dear Monsieur Lapin, in Fräulein Maneth's presence I wish to ask more questions."

"What has she got to do with this?" Lapin demanded. "Nicola, have you been telling lies to this policeman about me?"

"I have said nothing about you, *M'sieur*."

"Then what are you doing here in my office?"

"Inspector Reikert sent for me, *M'sieur*," she replied. "Please ask him."

"You will see why in a moment," Reikert assured him. "First, please be reminded that every answer you give me will be thoroughly checked. It would not be well to catch you in a lie. Do you understand?"

"I don't understand anything. I have no idea what this is about and I think it's the underhanded work of Nicola, and if it is. . ."

"A few days ago," Reikert said, "you were visited by a lawyer. May I ask what his name was?"

235

"What lawyer? I have no business with any lawyer. . . ." He paused, looked sharply at Reikert. "Do you mean a man named Kramer?"

"Answer the question, please."

"We he really a lawyer? Yes, such a person came to see me."

"What was his business, please?"

"Why don't you ask him? I'm sure he's better prepared to answer that question because all he did was confuse me."

"He is dead," Reikert said. "Under suspicious circumstances. What did he want with you?"

Lapin glanced at Nicola. "He swore me to secrecy, but I know now why you are here, Nicola. The questions he asked me were about you."

"About me?" Nicola asked in dismay. "What sort of questions? And why?"

"He told me he was connected with a law firm that is handling your father's estate and he wanted to know how much you were earning as prima ballerina of the Royal Ballet."

Reikert nodded and smiled at Nicola. "We are getting somewhere. M'sieur Lapin, what did you tell him?"

"I told him it was none of his business and if he wanted this information, he should ask Nicola, not me."

"Thank you, *M'sieur*," Nicola said.

"Did he ask you for money?" Inspector Reikert asked.

"Of course not. Why should he? I couldn't believe he was a lawyer even if he did give me his professional card. He didn't have the air of confidence a good lawyer has."

"One more question," Reikert said. "You drew a considerable amount of money from your bank

236

recently. It is important that you tell me what you did with it. If you consider this none of Fräulein Maneth's affair, she will withdraw."

"I have no secrets! You are making me sound like a criminal. Yes, I drew a considerable sum from my bank. I withdraw as much as I can spare every four or five months and I send it to Paris. Or did you think because I am a ballet master, I do not have a wife and children?"

"I see. You have a copy of the draft, perhaps?"

"I have. It's at my studio, not here. If it is of such importance, I will fetch it."

"It is not necessary," Reikert said. "I appreciate what you have told me and be assured you will not be bothered again."

"I send my money out of this country because I don't think conditions here are stable and something is going to blow up. In these Balkan countries every nation hates the other and it's one long squabble that is bound to result in war one of these days. Austria will be involved because she is the center of all the trouble and they hate her too. If they thought they had a chance, and if they were sure Russia would back them up, I think they'd declare war. Of course the Kaiser and Germany have something to say about it too. Why did you think the Emperor has invited the Kaiser here? To demonstrate that Germany will defend Austria if there is war."

"Of course, my dear sir," Reikert agreed. "Thank you once again. You will understand that Fräulein Maneth is a strictly innocent party to what is going on. Also to what I am trying to investigate. She has given me absolutely no adverse criticism of you, sir. Nicola, I wish to talk further with you."

They left a mystified Lapin and went out into the alleyway at the stage door. Reikert removed his hat and wiped his brow.

"You keep it very hot in there, *Fräulein*."

"Lapin insists we are more limber when everything is kept warm. I'm afraid we didn't get far with Lapin."

"He shows a remarkable knowledge of what is going on," Reikert observed. "He is no amateur in reasoning what may happen in the Balkans. For a ballet master, I think that might be considered unusual. However, we know now why Kramer went to see him. Of course you can guess the reason."

"I think so. Perhaps you'd better make it clearer in my mind."

"Kramer went to Lapin to find out how much you were paid, so when it came time to ask money for what information he had, he could determine a sum you might consider."

"Then why didn't he ask me?"

"There is the other side—Sander's people. If he thought they would pay more. . ."

Nicola nodded her head slowly. "Yes, I understand, *Herr Inspektor.*"

"He went to these other people, made his demand and got his money. Then, when he thought he was quite safe, they killed him."

"What could he have known? From what Papa said just before he was killed, he knew Kramer casually. I doubt he ever had any business with him. So whatever Kramer knew and was paid for in return for his silence, was something that must have happened during those few seconds before and after Papa was shot. Yet I was there too and I saw or heard nothing. I find it perplexing, *Herr Inspektor.*"

"We have to search for the answer, *Fräulein.* No doubt I will call upon you again. At least we have absolved Lapin—to a degree. I found his opinion of the political situation, intriguing. We shall see."

He raised his hat and walked down the alley. Nicola returned to the stage. Tonio left the *barre* to go to her side and they resumed their practice.

"May I ask what that was all about?" he asked.

"Someone, involved in a matter which the inspector is investigating, came to see Lapin, but it was on an altogether unrelated business, so the matter is now dropped."

"I hope he scared some sweat out of Lapin. Let's begin with the entree again right up to the coda. I think we might find a few more places where I can show you to your best advantage."

"You are kind, Tonio."

"I could not be otherwise with you, Nicky. And you know why."

"Yes," she said, "I know, and I appreciate your keeping your emotions in check."

"Let's go," he said tersely.

# Fourteen

The rigors of constant rehearsal kept her so busy she had no time to worry. Her concentration was in her dancing. She and Tonio remained even after the cast and Lapin had left, striving for absolute perfection.

The day after Inspector Reikert visited Lapin, she noticed that there always seemed to be one or two men not far away whenever she was outside. She'd refused to remain confined every hour she was not at the theatre and she resumed walking and dining out, sometimes alone, sometimes with Tonio or Anna.

She knew these were Reikert's men and she felt that she was being adequately protected. Perhaps some of this guarantee of her safety also came from the Emperor. How he knew about her troubles she had no idea, but then he seemed to have had knowledge of other incidents when she needed help.

For three days she felt more at ease than at any time since David had left. His daily letter was the high point of her day. She eagerly looked forward to it and rejoiced that his show was hailed such a success. One phase sharpened her loneliness, his comment that it was bound to be around for a long time. That meant they'd be separated at least until late winter, because even after the ballet honoring the Kaiser, she and the company would have to wait for a formal invitation to dance at Schönbrunn Palace in February. After that, the ballet would suspend for a few weeks and she would be free to travel to the United States. She found the thought exciting.

Her life had resumed a normalcy she'd not thought possible. At least, as normal as could be the life of a ballerina who adhered to the strict discipline demanded of her profession. The fear that had been with her was completely dissipated. She knew it was due, in large part, to the men who followed her. She felt quite safe with them as her shadows and even went out one evening to take a brief walk. She was pleased to regain the tranquility of her apartment, not because of fear but because she was not used to being unescorted. However, one thing did unsettle her, but only slightly. Her silver-backed hairbrush, which she always kept on its tray with matching comb and mirror, was on her night table instead of her dresser. She frowned as she picked it up and regarded it, then shrugged. She was tired, and it could well be she had laid it there in the morning without thinking.

A few days later she found other items which were not in their customary places, and which couldn't have been moved by her. She wasn't that fatigued. She mentioned it to Tonio first.

"What kind of items?" he asked. "You know you're tired and it's possible your mind is still in the theatre rehearsing. That could account for your misplacing them."

"I thought of that," Nicola said quietly. "Especially when it was my hairbrush, or my soap dish which I use each day. But I found two porcelain figurines in the kitchen, my silver hand mirror on the couch in the parlor, and my silver shoehorn in a kitchen cabinet. It's beginning to make me wonder if I am losing my sanity, or if fatigue has made me absentminded.''

"Neither," Tonio assured her. "Who has a key to your flat?"

"The manager of the building and Anna."

"Does Anna come in to clean?"

"Nothing other than wash and dry the few dishes we use when we have a snack."

"Could someone have stolen her key?"

"I would be the first to know," Nicola replied.

"Perhaps she isn't even aware it's gone," he reasoned.

Nicola thought a moment. "It could be. Recently, either I've been here when she came, or she returned with me from rehearsal and I used my key."

"Is anything missing?" Tonio asked.

"Not that I know of. I think it's more of the same type of harassment. I'm not going to let it upset me though, and for a very good reason. We are giving a command performance. I doubt my enemies would do anything to interfere with that."

"Nothing more than a wish to upset you, so you would not do your best. However, I'll say one thing. It has not interfered with your dancing."

Nicola smiled. "That's a relief to know."

"Anyway, now that we're here, I'll go in and check the rooms and closets."

"I doubt anyone is in there waiting to do me harm."

"I'll make certain there isn't. If I'm outnumbered, scream. Help will come soon enough."

"I'm certain of that," Nicola said, thinking of the men Inspector Reikert had assigned to guard her. "I know for certain I'm a good screamer."

"It's the best weapon a woman has," Tonio spoke as he preceded her into the flat. Nicola lit the gas light and Tonio paused to look around, then checked the bedroom and bath. He retraced his steps after he had checked the closets and looked into the kitchen before returning to the parlor where Nicola sat.

"I lit the gas light in the other rooms," he said. "No one is in here. Did you look around while I was checking for intruders to see if anything has been placed other than where it should be?"

"Yes. I'll look in the bedroom."

"Check each room."

Nicola did so and returned to find Tonio stretched full length on the couch. When he became aware of her presence, he jumped to his feet.

"Would you like some tea and biscuits, Tonio?"

"Yes, but not tonight. You look exhausted and I am exhausted."

"Yes," she agreed, "but it's worth it, don't you think?"

"I do." He placed his hands lightly on Nicola's shoulders. "Even when you're exhausted you look beautiful."

He bent and kissed her brow. "Don't worry. I'm too tired for anything more. And I won't break my word. You have enough on your mind."

"We both have." Nicola kissed his cheek. "Thanks for being my trusted friend."

"Since I can be no more," Tonio's smile was regretful, "I will be that."

"I'll walk you to the door. Go home and sleep."

"It's all I'm good for these days. I'll stand outside until I hear you turn the bolt."

Nicola did so and listened as Tonio's footsteps retreated to the stairway. She was famished and would have found drinking a cup of tea relaxing, but once she was in her bedroom, the bed looked far more inviting. After putting out the lights in the other rooms, she undressed and was in bed and asleep in minutes.

Anna stopped by late one afternoon when Nicola and Tonio were rehearsing. Nicola was delighted to see her and suggested they go for a walk as soon as she had changed to her street clothes.

"Delightful," Anna said. "Tonio can keep me company until you're ready."

Nicola ran to her dressing room, overjoyed at the sight of Anna. It had been some time since they had been together, but Tonio had faithfully walked Nicola home, sometimes coming in for tea and biscuits. She had noticed nothing further amiss in her flat until last night. It so happened he hadn't come in, and Nicola decided not to mention it until she had talked with Anna.

Once they reached the street, she did so, relating what Tonio already knew and adding the fact that she had found the remains of some brandy in a glass on a table in the parlor.

"Were you in my apartment, Anna?" she asked.

"No." Anna's astonishment was evident both in her voice and her face. "Why didn't you let me know?"

"I told you what Tonio did. And still does on some evenings. Nothing happened since then, until last night when I found the glass."

"Tonio should not have left you alone. Or at least he should have gone to Inspector Reikert and reported it."

"He was gone before I noticed."

"Then you should have gone."

"Perhaps I should have," Nicola mused, "but I felt there was no need for it."

"The last time I was in your apartment, we were together."

244

"I know," Nicola agreed. "But you do have a key."

"What about it?" Anna seemed puzzled.

"Do you still have it?"

"So far as I know." She opened her handbag and took out a key which she held by a braided section of yarn which was looped and knotted at one end. "Who else has a key?"

"Only the manager. Tonio thought yours might have been stolen from your handbag."

"No," Anna said somberly. "Did you check with the manager of the building to see if he had been asked to allow anyone entry?"

"No," Nicola admitted.

"Then you must do so when we reach your flat. This news has upset me."

"That's why I didn't tell you." She didn't remind Anna that keys could be easily duplicated. It would only increase her worry.

"Please tell Inspector Reikert."

"I'd rather not. Let's look in this window. I love the wood carvings."

"They're the best in the city," Anna said. "But I have more than wood carvings on my mind."

"So have I. It was just a ruse so you would see the reflection of two men standing across the street."

Anna raised her eyes from the carvings and said, "You are also followed?"

"They follow me everywhere. I have gone out at night alone and they are there. They keep their distance and pretend they're not even aware of my existence."

"Nicola, you must be out of your mind."

"I am quite safe," Nicola replied. "Calm yourself. They are protecting me."

"How do you know?" Anna said.

"They've been following me since the day Inspector Reikert came to question Monsieur Lapin regarding the

245

murder of Kramer."

"What would Lapin have to do with it?"

"As it so happened, nothing. Kramer wanted to know what I was paid." Nicola shrugged. "Lapin apparently satisfied Inspektor Reikert; he hasn't put in an appearance at the theatre since."

"Nicola," Anna scolded, "after what happened to you, how can you be so trusting? What proof do you have that these men across the street are guarding you?"

"I already told you. I went out alone at night and walked and though they followed me, they never molested me in any fashion. Now let's pick another subject. You see how upset you get? That's why I don't like to mention anything of a suspicious nature to you."

"Whom else could you tell?"

"Only Tonio. And I really shouldn't bother him."

"Why not? He's a friend and would be more, I believe, if you would have let him."

"Have you forgotten David?"

"Not for a moment. I wish you would send for him."

"That's out of the question. Besides, I have made up my mind that I will go to him after the command performance."

"I'll be glad when it's over and you are away from here. I only hope those people don't follow you."

"Stop worrying. Let's stop at a coffee shop. I can't eat but you can."

"That's my problem," Anna said, relenting. "When I worry, I eat. I have put on weight since your papa died. My life has become dull and very sedentary."

"Pehaps you will come to New York City with me," Nicola said hopefully. "It would be such fun to have you for company. I would have lots of time on my hands, since David would be giving daily performances."

Anna looked pleased at the idea. "Thank you, Nicky,

but I doubt I could get away.''

"Think about it, will you?''

A smile crossed Anna's somber features. "Yes. That I promise.''

They visited a coffee shop, but Nicola ate more sparingly than ever, and Anna berated her for this.

"But Anna, if I put on six ounces, it will slow me down. This presentation of *Giselle* must be flawless, better than any we've done so far. Nothing in the world must impede that, because if it comes off as we hope it will, we are bound to be invited to dance at Schönbrunn and you know that if we are invited it will be the most important event in my life.''

"No doubt you will be invited. Even without the command performance, I think it would happen. But if you please the Kaiser, Franz Josef will be forever indebted to you. Austria needs German help if anything happens.''

"Do you think it will? Soon?''

"I hope not,'' Anna said. "But only God knows.''

"You're in the code bureau. All kinds of messages go over your desk. Papa used to say so and regarded you as a very important person in the foreign office.''

"The letters in code that pass over my desk sometimes tell Franz Ferdinand, the Emperor's next in line, to make his wife show more respect for the royal court. Or an ambassador writes his wife to sell their wolfhound. The vital messages don't come to me. I'm not that important. I'm glad. If trouble is brewing, I don't want to know about it.''

"Well, what would be your guess that nothing will happen in the line of warfare until after the social season?''

"I would bet one hundred percent that there'll be no war. It's the social season all over, and the men who make wars are too busy lining up for the grand march at

247

some uniform-riddled affair. Besides, everything is knee deep in snow. However, I'll be honest. I do fear trouble. If this were spring, I'd make no such bet."

"It seems that Papa's beliefs are slowly coming true. He always said there would be a great war because the big powers are going to be dragged in."

"Your father was wiser than most of the foreign office officials are now. So I suppose it's coming, but not yet. Not quite yet."

Anna walked back to the apartment house with Nicola. At the door she paused and turned casually. "Yes, you are followed. Those two are across the street, a short distance behind us."

"At least, now you know why I'm not worried."

"I'll know better tomorrow after I speak with Inspector Reikert."

"That isn't necessary."

"I disagree. I'll come upstairs with you."

"No, please. I don't wish to be rude, but I am tired. I need all the rest I can get."

"Suppose we go in and speak to the manager to find out whether he let anyone in your apartment, perhaps someone who said he knew you."

"Not tonight, Anna. I'll do it tomorrow."

Anna gave a despairing shake of her head. "Please do."

Nicola kissed Anna's cheek. "Good night, Anna. It was pleasant being with you."

"And with you. Do be careful."

Nicola had her key out of her handbag by the time she reached her door. When she unlocked it and stepped inside, she cried out in alarm. Chairs were misplaced, and a stack of music for the ballet was scattered on the floor. Nicola closed the door gently, ran down the steps and was in time to call to Anna who had not yet reached the corner. Anna ran back.

"Someone is either in the apartment or has been there. I didn't wait to make certain which. I'm afraid to go in."

Anna looked around. "Where are your bodybuards? We'd best try to get word to Inspektor Reikert."

"Anna, please don't. No unsavory publicity, please. The newspapers will blow this all out of proportion and the performance may be cancelled. Please come up with me."

"There may be men in there. Those same ones."

"We can scream."

Anna eyed Nicola unbelievingly. "We could be murdered."

"Don't be a coward."

With a resigned sigh, Anna led the way up the stairs. She used her key to unlock the door, threw it wide and they stood there listening. There were no sounds. This gave them some added courage and they ventured into the parlor. Room by room, they searched everywhere. There were many signs of an intruder having been there, especially in the room Nicola's father had occupied. Drawers had been carelessly examined, and clothing she had not yet found the courage to dispose of had been roughly handled. But there was no one in the apartment.

They sat down with a sense of relief. After awhile, Anna arose and went to a sideboard where she poured a small amount of brandy into two glasses. They sipped the liqueur slowly and tried to analyze the reason for the ransacking.

"I wonder what they were after," Nicola mused. "Certainly, the search was thorough. I'm beginning to think there is more to this than merely getting revenge against me. That's included, no doubt, but there has to be more. They must be seeking something of importance.

To them, at least."

"Someone knows when to burglarize the place," Anna agreed. "Some one or more persons thoroughly familiar with your work schedule."

"I intend to remedy that by asking the landlord to put new locks on the door. If he refuses, I'll do it myself."

Anna finished her drink, set down the glass and went to one of the front windows. Without turning around, she said, "Those two men who followed us—the inspector's policemen—they're out there now. When we needed them, they weren't in sight, but one of them's there now. Nicky, I better stay with you tonight."

"Go home," Nicola said. "I'll push that heavy chest of drawers in front of the door. If anyone breaks in, I'll raise a window and scream for the guards across the street. I'm not giving in to this. At the moment, I'm more angry than frightened."

Nonetheless, it was difficult for Nicola to get to sleep that night. The lightest sound awakened her. She got up twice to make certain there'd been no evidence of the chest being shoved aside so the front door could be opened.

She slept later than she wanted to, because Lapin was driving them harder than ever and was easily aroused to anger, especially if anyone came late. She dressed quickly, taking time only to drink a cup of black coffee. On the street, she was in such a hurry to find a carriage that she didn't even think of looking around to see if the police were still guarding her. Also, she had not checked with the manager to learn if anyone had asked to be let in to her flat.

She arrived five minutes before Lapin stormed through the stage area watching the warm-ups, looking for any signs of weakness or exhaustion. Soon they would begin rehearsing to music, and it would become more and more difficult and tiring.

Added to this, Nicola hadn't received a letter from David, and this upset her. She was tempted to send him a cable of inquiry, but decided against it. More than a week would have to go by before she would resort to that.

One thing in the company's favor was that time was passing so fast the dancers had no opportunity to disobey Lapin's strict orders to get all possible rest. Nicola was so busy she didn't even have time to worry about no longer receiving a daily letter from David. And Lapin paid special attention to Nicola and Tonio. When they rehearsed their *pas de deux* he was always on hand, stopping them if they made the slightest error, even those no audience could possibly be aware of.

"Your elevations are bad," he complained to Nicola, and as often to Tonio. "You are supposed to come down quietly. You sound like a milk cart. Try it again and again. Elevate higher. You can get higher. No. . . no. Again you have made too much noise when you come down. You must be light. . .so light you think the weight of a feather sounds heavy. Again, Nicky. Now again. Both of you. . .up. . . use your leg muscles. Tonio, *entrechat* means change position of your feet at least eight times. I counted only four."

They retreated to a bench and sat down when Lapin finally went off to bother someone else.

"I wonder what they pay a *premier danseur* in New York—or even Singapore," Tonio said wearily when he got his breath back. "That man is going to kill us. I don't know how he can hear your slippers hit the stage when you're practically in my arms and I can't hear it. I think he's faking, just making it hard for us."

"He's never liked me personally," Nicola admitted, "but when he criticizes our dancing, it's not personal. He's trying to get the very best out of us. Give him his due. He's succeeding."

Tonio wiped sweat off his face and neck with a towel. "Nicky, don't get angry at what I'm going to say."

She gave him a startled look. "What could you possibly say that would anger me?"

"You aren't quite yourself. . .that is, your timing is off a little. Lapin hasn't noticed it yet, thank heaven, but I'm afraid he will. I don't know how to describe this . . .it's not sloppy dancing, but it's as if you're too tired. Your muscles don't respond as well as they should. Possibly it's your nerves."

"I wasn't aware of it," Nicola said. "Thank you for telling me. I'll try to find out what's wrong."

"Of course we know what's wrong. You're being subjected to harassment. They search your apartment to frighten you, to throw you off. What they're trying to do is get you into a state where you can't dance well. And you must, because everyone at the theatre that night, including the Emperor and the Kaiser, are balletomanes and you know how critical they are of mistakes. They'll spot them every time."

"You're right, Tonio. I don't get the amount of sleep I should. Too much has happened. I have tried to remain calm and thought I was doing well, but apparently I haven't been."

"Will you accept a piece of advice from me, Nicky?"

"Yes."

"Don't be in a hurry to leave the theatre when the day is finished. Stay in your dressing room and after everyone is gone, lock yourself in and lie down. Sleep as much and as long as you can."

Nicola regarded him with dismay. "Tonio, surely you remember what happened to me right here on this stage."

"Of course I do. Only this time nothing will happen. I will leave the theatre as usual, but I'll return without being seen and I'll spend the night close by your door. With a gun on my lap."

"It would help," Nicola agreed. "It might work. It's certainly worth a try. I appreciate your concern."

"If only I could . . ." he broke off the sentence. "Let's start with your airborne jump. I want to perfect that catch, but I hope we don't have to practice it so much you become black and blue. When you fly into my arms, you have to be caught in a strong grip. I hope I don't hurt you too much."

"You haven't yet. Well, Lapin is looking our way and sending a message that we have loafed long enough."

Tonio's idea seemed very good, but it had one hitch. A cup of black coffee was Nicola's breakfast. They didn't take time off for a noon meal and after the rehearsal day was over, she was famished. If she was to stay all or part of the night, she had to arrange for something to eat. Tonio did his best to take care of the problem, but the food he brought was not the kind that nourished an exercise-worn body without adding too much weight.

They slipped out of the theatre before dawn. Tonio got a carriage and they were driven to Nicola's apartment. Once she stepped on the sidewalk, she felt afraid again.

"Why did you let the driver go?" she asked.

"It's not far to my flat," he replied.

"Walking will only fatigue you more."

Tonio smiled at her concern. "Perhaps, but aren't you afraid to go upstairs?"

"A little," she admitted, "but not if you'll come to the door with me and wait until I turn on the gas light."

"I intend to."

Upstairs, he entered the apartment and again searched it. Nicola removed her hat and dropped it onto a chair. She smiled when he reentered the room.

"I take it all's well," she said.

"It looks that way," he said, then muttered an oath.

"What is it?" she asked.

"Look at this." He picked up an ashtray on which rested the well-chewed end of a cigar. He went over to the window, opened it and tossed the cigar out of the window.

"Someone was here again," Nicola sighed. "Whoever it is, he comes and goes as he pleases. If this keeps on, I'll have to live in a hotel."

"They'd likely get in there too. You need more sleep. Go to bed. I'll use the couch."

"No, Tonio, I can't allow you to do that. It's just as important that you dance as well as I do. In four or five hours we have to be back in the theatre. I'll be all right. There are two policemen outside, I think. It's so dark I can't see them, but they have been there right along."

"Why not report this to Inspector Reikert before you go back to the theatre? Maybe he can devise some plan to make certain no one else gets into your apartment."

"I'll do that. I must. Go home now."

"One thing more. You haven't mentioned getting a letter from David lately."

Nicola smiled. "Like us, he is probably tired. Please go home, Tonio."

She lay down on the couch in the parlor, meaning to stay there until she relaxed. When she did, sleep overcame her.

She awoke, still dressed. She bathed and dressed quickly, breakfasted and went directly to police headquarters, hopeful that Inspector Reikert would be in his office.

He welcomed her in his usual gentlemanly manner and listened as she told him about the illegal entries to her apartment. He made notes, shook his head and offered little more than consolation.

"We can guard your apartment day and night, I suppose, but if they can't torment you there, they will find other means which may be even worse. So long as you are not bodily harmed, so long as no one waits for you to come home, I suggest you try to realize what they are doing is trying to break down your nerve. You must be strong enough to resist them."

"Thank you. I'll try to be strong. Besides, there are your men who follow me. . . ."

"What men?" Reikert asked as he leaned forward in fresh concern. "I have no one with orders to give you personal protection."

What courage Nicola had managed to gain evaporated in a second or two.

"There is always one man watching. Most of the time there are two. They follow me wherever I go. I've seen them several times. Not always two, but there is always someone."

"I'll surely look into that, Fräulein Maneth. Perhaps they have made their first mistake and we can arrest one of those men. That will help us."

"I hope so."

"Can you identify them?"

"No," Nicola said forlornly.

"Never mind. We'll get them. How is our friend, M'sieur Lapin, behaving?"

"Well enough, except that he's driving us harder than ever."

"For the command performance. I tried to get a ticket, but then in my position, it was impossible."

"If I can locate an extra one, you shall have it, *Herr Inspektor.*"

"Thank you. It may be of interest for you to know

that Lapin lied about sending money out of the country."

"He did? Is he then under suspicion once more?"

"Not exactly. We discovered where the money went. It seems he brought a well-known dancer here from Berlin, and she discovered he was not half as interested in her dancing as in her body. He made a mistake. She gave up a lucrative assignment to come here and dance, so Lapin had to make a very healthy payment to keep from being sued and brought into court. It would have been the end of him if he had. The Royal Ballet is Franz Josef's favorite and you know how much he hates deceit and. . .flesh mongering. I have made no report. Creating this trouble for Lapin now would be inadvisable."

"It would be a catastrophe," Nicola agreed. "I have to run or I'll be late."

Tonio, in practice clothes, was waiting for her and followed her into her dressing room.

"Anna came by to make sure you were safe. I told her about the cigar butt. Also, you were to see Inspector Reikert on your way to the theatre to inform him about it, and to thank him for the guard and to ask it be made more secure. That pleased her."

"Tonio, those men watching my apartment and following me, weren't Reikert's men. He had assigned no one to keep an eye on me."

"The man was one of those who assaulted you?"

"We have to assume so."

"Tonight," Tonio said, "I'm going to try and catch him. Believe me if I lay my hand on him, we'll get some information."

"Reikert is going to try the same thing. Excuse me now. I must change."

"If you're going to look for a letter from David, there isn't any."

Nicola sat down slowly. "I had hoped. . .I'm growing anxious about him. He may be ill."

"Heidi would have let you know. You've not the slightest cause to worry about David. You'll see."

"Thanks, Tonio. You're probably right."

"Change, get at the *barre* and sweat it out. Before Lapin comes."

She closed and locked the door after Tonio left. It was getting so she automatically locked every door, something she had never done before. She got into leotards, a heavy shirt and leg warmers. On stage she rehearsed every part of the dance which was her responsibility. She also made suggestions to some of the ballet girls, points by which they could improve.

Lapin didn't arrive until afternoon, which made everyone happy, but when he did come, he was in a sour mood and took it out on the dancers by shouting commands and making them repeat exercises until they were dizzy. Nicola and Tonio were no exception. She had an idea Lapin's contact with the dancer from Berlin must have been an upsetting one.

She gave up trying to get rest in the theatre. It was as difficult there as anywhere, and all she did was give way to the fear she was trying so desperately to conquer.

There were two more days of rehearsal which, she knew, would intensify even from the hours and effort they put in it now. When she was dancing, she felt confident, but alone in her apartment she was beginning to feel a lack of confidence. She doubted her courage, her talent, even her desire to dance.

If they were going to make their prophecy come true, it would be at the height of her glory and that would come when the final curtain came down on *Giselle*. It was then that full recognition would come to her, when she would be toasted as the best ballerina in Vienna. Then she would be a candidate for the title of *prima ballerina assoluta.*

She was totally unable to enjoy dreaming of those moments when royalty would come backstage, when there would be a reception that would glitter like diamonds, when she would be congratulated on every side.

All she could dwell upon was the fact that at this particular moment, someone would be plotting her death and be prepared to carry it out. She would surely not be allowed to enjoy her fame and success.

She cried a little and felt painfully alone. Tonio had gone home to rest. Anna was working overtime. David was in New York and from him came only a silence difficult to understand.

# Fifteen

The day came far too soon. Nicola, despite weeks of rehearsing, felt she wasn't ready. Now there would be only a few hours in which to rehearse before the curtain went up and she would face a glittering, critical audience. There would be no rehearsal until the middle of the afternoon when the final dress rehearsal would be held. Then a rest for three or four hours, and the moment they'd all worked so hard for would arrive.

Nicola indulged in a long, hot bath to relax her. She was surprised at how much better she felt.

She went to the small coffee shop she favored, though she ate very sparingly, just enough to keep her from total starvation. Two heavy-set men entered and occupied a table close to hers, directly in front of her. At first she paid no attention to them, but then she saw them smiling at her and nodding somewhat vaguely. These were not admirers of hers. Their smiles were more like leers, as if they were suggesting something immoral and evil. They would bend their heads close together while their eyes were upon her, and they would whisper and laugh until Nicola felt as if they were undressing her.

She could make no complaint. They were doing nothing illegal and if they were questioned they'd deny their behavior or even that they knew her. She paid her bill and got out of there. She looked for a carriage, but could see none. She began to walk to the theatre.

At an intersection she stepped off the curb. A man very close to her brushed against her and his right hand lightly touched her on the thigh. An unobtrusive gesture, but a deliberate one. Before she could do anything about him, he had vanished around the corner. Two blocks farther a man was looking into a store window. As she came by, he suddenly turned to walk in the same direction and collided with her. Again hands touched her suggestively and a man leered at her before he also walked swiftly away.

It happened a third time, fairly close to the theatre. The same sort of thing, except two men were involved and for a few seconds she was pinned between them. Again it was done cleverly so that no one else on the street noticed it. They vanished like the others, but by then Nicola was in a state of near panic. She wanted to run the rest of the way, to scream if another man approached her.

By the time she was in her dressing room, she was trembling visibly. She sat down and tried to steady her nerves, and recalled that she'd been in such a hurry to reach the privacy of her dressing room that she'd not even stopped to see if there was a letter from David in her mailbox. She hurried out, hoping one would be there. Even a brief note from him would have helped her tremendously, but there was nothing.

She returned slowly and dejectedly to the dressing room, closed and locked the door and lay down on the sofa. She told herself over and over again that if she gave way to the ingenious torture of these people, she would be playing right into their hands. It was even possible that they were endeavoring to create in her such terror that, if she did dance, it would be far below the standard of what was expected of her in skill and grace. In a state of nerves such as she now had, it would be all but impossible to put on a good performance.

She needed steady hands and a clear head. Her flying leaps required a precision and skill that must not be impaired by a case of nerves. Tonio would help her, possibly even shield her mistakes if he could, but if that happened, they'd both reveal their mediocrity. Somehow she had to put everything out of her mind except the dance. Possibly, if she'd not been molested on her way to the theatre, she might not have been so afflicted by fear.

Resolutely she arose, put on practice clothes and went out to the *barre*. It was still so early that only three girls were warming up and they were too busy to even greet her. She began her exercises and, while they helped, it was no cure. Many of her practice steps and pirouettes were slow and clumsy. She felt as if she were out of shape and had not danced in days. She berated herself for being a fool, for being so weak that she had succumbed to the efforts of her enemies to make her look like an amateur when the curtain rose. Anger did help, but again, not enough. There was that same uncertainty, an apprehension that something else would happen to totally wreck her career.

By the time the whole troupe arrived and Tonio was at her side, she was not much better than when she'd been alone. He noticed it at once and quietly led her to the rear of the stage, behind some of the scenery. He put his arms around her, holding her close.

"You're in a sad state, Nicky. Cool off here for a few minutes. Tell me what's happened to you."

"I've been molested, nudged, leered at. I've read suggestive words on the lips of men staring at me. It happened in the coffee shop and on my way here. I was frightened enough before that happened. Now I'm ready to. . .to. . .just sit down and cry."

Some of the cast were eyeing them as if they suspected the two stars of the show were secret lovers. Tonio led her to the very end of the *barre*. They began routine exercises, but went on with their low-voiced conversation.

"In less the seven hours," Tonio warned, "the curtain is going up. You have to be ready, Nicky. You can't fail!"

"I'm going to try, but I'm not sure I can do it, Tonio."

"It's not only for yourself. It's for me, the whole cast, the people who produce this show. Your responsibility is to a great number of people. The whole show rests on your shoulders."

"I know that." She looked in the mirror behind the *barre* and saw how strained-looking she appeared. Scraggly too, for her hair, done up on a knot for practice, had not been well arranged and lacked the perfection expected of a ballet dancer even at practice.

She left the *barre* and assumed the attitude position standing on one leg while the other was extended to the back with the knee bent, with one arm raised, the other extended from the side. It was a graceful, beautiful pose. Nicola loved it and had perfected it. Now her extended arms shook visibly and she was unsteady on that one leg.

Tonio hurried to her side, put an arm around her waist and made the assumption to a normal position look like part of the dance. Lapin had arrived and was watching them. Apparently he saw nothing wrong. Not yet.

"Thank you," she whispered. "You see how I am. How I will be."

"I don't believe it," he said. "You may be nervous now and with good reason, but once the music and the lights and the audience become part of you, you'll steady yourself because you have the strength to do it, to overcome what these people are trying to do to you."

Nicola disengaged herself from his dancer's embrace. "I want to try flying. Please, Tonio, don't let me fall."

"Have I ever?" There was anger in his voice now. "You're letting yourself get even more upset and you are upsetting me. Go ahead, dance. Get rid of all this fear."

She glided across the stage and leaped into his arms. It was done with grace and polish, but in his arms Nicola clung to him in an entirely ungraceful way.

He set her down. Lapin was approaching, walking fast, pounding the end of his cane on the stage floor with every step.

"What's the matter with you, Nicola? That was the clumsiest piece of business I have ever seen. You're letting Tonio cover for you. Maybe the audience won't notice, but I will. Now you try that again. Try it a hundred times if you have to, but get it right. And I'll stand here to see that you do."

Nicola fought back tears. She crossed the stage, went through the routine again, forcing everything out of her mind but the fact that she must be perfect. She was. The leap had all the polish required, but Lapin was not satisfied. She performed the leap three more times until he nodded and walked away without another word. Nicola sought one of the hard chairs and sat down. Tonio handed her a clean towel and she mopped the perspiration from her face and neck.

"You did much better," he said.

"Only because Lapin stood there ready to fire me if I

263

missed. But he won't be on the stage, Tonio. I'm still unsure of myself.''

"Listen to me, Nicky. Lapin won't be at your side, but right in front of you will be several hundred people watching every move you make. They are the severest critics a dancer can have, and a good dancer responds to this and becomes perfect. You will become great. Once you look out beyond the footlights, all your troubles will vanish because there won't be any, expect your duty to dance to the very best of your ability, plus your love for ballet.''

"Of course I'm going to try," she said. "I only hope I won't disgrace the whole troupe and the reputation of the theatre. I do feel better.''

"You must not tire yourself. Practice when Lapin is looking. Otherwise find ways to rest. At three, we have the dress rehearsal. Getting ready for that will take your mind off everything that worries you.''

She found a brief opportunity to lie down in her dressing room. When it was time to dress for the final rehearsal, she felt ready to face it. Now there was a full orchestra and nothing was different except that they played to empty seats. The theatre had been elaborately decorated with the flags of the Austro-Hungarian Empire and the flag of Germany. Bright bunting was in place, there were flowers in the boxes, everything was in readiness.

The rehearsal went off in a manner which even satisfied Lapin. When it was over, he stood at the footlights and spoke to the assembled dancers.

"If it has not yet occurred to you, the future of this troupe depends on what happens tonight. If this comes off as a lackluster dance, we are finished. If it comes off with the perfection I demand, you will all find it profitable, worthwhile, and you will have your dancing years assured. When those days come to an end, you will still be part of ballet—all of you—for you will be remembered as the ballet that entranced much of European royalty. There can be no halfway measures tonight. Be perfect or be prepared to accept the circumstances that will follow if you fail. You may rest now. No food and precious little water. When the performance is over, we shall go to the Adler where the chefs outperform those at any other dining room. You will be allowed to eat all you like, to dance with royalty, and be sure to bow or curtsy when you are praised. I will not instruct you again today. It is now up to you."

With this last sentence he directed a baleful glance straight at Nicola. Tonio's arm around her waist tightened as if to lend assurance. She looked up at him and smiled.

Shortly after six, Anna arrived. She was allowed entrance denied to anyone else not connected with the troupe. She closed the door and sat down.

"You look better than I've seen you in some days. You must have found it possible to rest."

"I feel myself," Nicola lied. "I have made up my mind I am going to do well tonight. Because, dear Anna, if I do, I have triumphed over those who wish me to fail. I am concerned with what happens afterward, though."

"Are you talking of those monsters who have threatened you? Their final act of revenge when you are at the height of your success?"

"Yes."

"You will be protected, better than anyone has ever been. There is no need to be afraid, only careful and prudent. Stay with people, do not go off either alone or with but one person. At the reception, remain on the dance floor as much as possible. You'll find that not hard to do, for the gentlemen will vie with one another to dance with you."

265

"If only David could be here," Nicola said wistfully.

"It would help, but he has his show, Nicky dear. You are quite right in not asking him to come back. Everything takes time. It will be over soon. All this suspense and horror. I'll be in the audience, but in the balcony this time. The best seats are all reserved for the foreign royalty entourages and our dukes, duchesses and all the others who wear silk ribbons and diamond tiaras. I wish you the best of luck, Nicky. You will not fail. For my sake, for David's, make this the best presentation of all."

Anna kissed her and then left abruptly before the tears which threatened overflowed. Nicola was touched by her show of emotion. Once alone, a few minutes before the overture began and the troupe assembled, she still felt unsure of herself. Having those men leer at her, jostle her and paw her, however slightly and surreptitiously, had made her feel degraded. She was certain her life was forfeit. It was just a matter of when and where.

The troupe crowded around her when she emerged from the dressing room, to encourage her and to swear they would perform better than ever. Lapin grasped both her hands and looked deep into her eyes.

"Perhaps I have been troublesome and even cruel, Nicky, but it has been for your own good. I have made you one of the most respected and loved prima ballerinas in the world. Tonight you will prove that all my efforts, and all yours, place you in line for the title of *prima ballerina assoluta*. You are the finest dancer I have ever instructed or known. Think of me as an ogre if you will, but even so, make me prouder than ever of you."

She leaned forward and kissed his cheek. "I will do my best, *M'sieur*. And I do appreciate what you have done for me, even if it was done with a sharp tongue."

266

The assembled dancers laughed aloud. Tension was gone now. They were all at ease, ready for the show, knowing they were trained to perfection and only some accident could damage their performance.

Nicola wished she felt as secure as that. What alarmed her most was facing the audience, wondering if her fear would make itself evident. She made her way to the wings. The overture was playing. Tonio took her hand and led her to a small viewing aperture in the curtain. She stared at the glittering diamonds, the bright uniforms, the boxes filled with royalty. She could see only part of the orchestra, but what she saw unnerved her even more.

"They expect wonderful things of you," Tonio said softly. "If we are as good as we believe we are, we can expect great things of them. I have heard that in all Europe there has never been such a congregation of important people before. Germany is not the only representative of Europe. They are here from Russia, England, France, Italy. They have traveled great distances to see you dance. You, Nicola, for you are the most important dancer in this troupe. Now calm yourself, tell yourself that you are going to make these people stand up and cheer. Are you ready?"

"Yes," she said. "Thank you, Tonio."

Her anxiety was at a high pitch. So was her desire to please. Tonio's words had instilled a flicker of courage she'd forgotten she possessed.

Then the cue came. She danced onto the stage for a solo, a variation from the normal *pas de deux*. Usually the male and female leads danced onto the stage together, followed in strict order by the male variation, then the female variation ending in the coda, or display of virtuosity, the highlight of the dance.

Her part now was brief, wtih a *fouette*, standing on one leg and using the other to whip her body in a series of turns. To accomplish this without getting dizzy, she fixed her eyes on one spot while her body turned.

She was doing well so far, but there was little lessening of her anxiety. As she came out of the series of turns, her eyes descended to the audience and for a single moment she thought she was dreaming, or that this was an illusion created by those who hated her. In the front row center, sat David, looking quite handsome in evening dress. He was smiling at her. His head gave a brief nod of encouragement. It was all she needed.

Suddenly the anxiety evaporated, the fear was gone. She flashed him a look of recognition and she danced as she'd never danced before. The end of the first act brought so much applause it startled her. The second was as good, if not better. She was the prima ballerina now, nothing else mattered. She was dancing for David, whom she loved. Tonio whispered how great she was, how well everyone was doing. Her heart soared, not only with thoughts of David, but with love of the dance.

The final curtain resulted in many calls, but the last was hers alone. She held the bouquet of roses, bowed so many times her back began to ache, but most of the time her eyes were on David and her smiles were for him.

She curtsied to the boxes which contained royalty. The Emperor, the Empress, the Kaiser and the Kaiserin, and all the archdukes and duchesses—all applauded. To her it was unbelievable and yet, here she was, curtsying to them.

Then the final curtain came down and she fled from the stage, wiping tears of happiness from her eyes. She evaded Tonio, passed by Lapin and stood alone at the entrance to the stage from the orchestra. Everyone seemed to know whom she waited for and no one approached or left the wings.

David brushed aside the velvet curtains that concealed the entrance. Nicola had never danced as lightly as when she rushed into his arms. She was unable to speak. David murmured his congratulations, but she didn't hear him. She only knew that she was in his arms and she was safe, and nothing in this world could harm her now.

She finally drew back a little and he kissed her. Those who watched applauded with the same degree of enthusiasm as the audience had applauded them.

Nicola turned to face them, clinging to David's arm. "Thank you, all of you. The applause was proof we did well and it was due to cooperation on the part of every one of us. I'm proud to be a member of this company. Now I beg of you to excuse me . . . ."

"Not quite yet," David whispered.

The entourage of royalty streamed onto the stage from a side door. Franz Josef embraced her and kissed her cheek. She recalled the night she'd spent with him and wondered if he did. He gave no indication of it. She curtsied before the Kaiser, a stern man with a military bearing. He looked as if he'd crack in half if he bent an inch. But he was lavish with his praises and the Kaiserin added her own. She was a lovely woman who seemed badly matched to this austere man with the turned-up mustache.

It was over at last, and what Nicola had pleaded for came to pass. No one intruded when they entered Nicola's dressing room and closed the door. Once again she was in his arms, crying and laughing at the same time. She finally recovered her wits and sat down on the sofa, pulling him down beside her.

"How in the world did you know I needed you? When did you arrive? Why didn't you let me know? I had no word from you for days."

"I was aboard ship," he said. Then frowning, he added, "Of course you knew I was on my way."

"How could I have known? I was never so surprised

269

in my life. It was like a miracle. Kiss me, David.''

''Which do you want first?'' David asked, his smile teasing. ''Your questions answered or a kiss? No, don't tell me. I know what I want. I've hungered for you for too long.''

His mouth came down on Nicola's and he drew her close. His hands caressed her, just as hers did him. He pushed the straps of her tutu down as he kissed the long, swanlike line of her neck. His hand cupped one of her breasts and a soft moan escaped him. Nicola's passions were as fully aroused as his, but she knew they couldn't enjoy fulfillment now. There was the affair which they must attend. David probably didn't know about it, but he would.

''Please, David,'' she murmured tremulously. ''I am as hungry for release as you, but there is a reception this evening. Also, there is much I want to know.''

''Can't it wait?'' He knelt before her, his hands fondling the entire length of her body. He pressed his face against her breasts, then covered them with kisses.

''Please, David darling. Later. Please.''

She took a few quick steps backward and almost lost her balance, because she had no more control over her emotions than he. But now that he was here, she wanted answers to the questions she had asked.

His eyes rebuked her as he slowly got to his feet.

She took two more backsteps. ''Please, David, I want you as much as you want me. Perhaps more.''

''No more, Nicky,'' he disputed. ''And cover your breasts. I'm going mad looking at them.''

She slipped the straps back on her shoulders. ''Sit down, David. On the couch.''

''If I sit there,'' he said, ''I'll grab you and there'll be no questions answered.''

She nodded. ''It isn't easy controlling myself either.

Sit on that straight-backed chair. It's terribly uncomfortable."

"I come across the ocean and you invite me to sit on an uncomfortable chair." He sat down and winced. "It is. It really is."

"Now, David, how did you know I needed you?'

"I received your cable, asking me to come as fast as I could."

"I sent no cable," she said in astonishment.

"Someone did. I left the show an hour later and booked passage on the fastest clipper I could get."

"But darling, how did you get a front row seat if you only just arrived?"

"I don't know. Shortly after I checked into my hotel —the same one I lived in before when I was here—I was handed an envelope with this one ticket. Of course I knew you were dancing, but I arrived so late I was unable to get in touch with you. I knew better than to see you before the performance. You'd be nervous enough."

"David, how I missed you. And what you did for me when I saw you in the audience, so handsome, so wonderful. Up to then, I wondered how I'd be able to get through the dance. One sight of you and all my confidence was restored. I found I danced better than I ever had in my life." She paused, then added apologetically, "But I'd never have taken you from the show."

"But who sent the cable and provided the ticket?" David asked.

"Never mind that. You're here. I feel strong and gloriously happy."

"What's been happening? I know something has if you were that upset, or someone concerned about you believed you were and sent the cablegram."

"I've been harassed several times. There's been a

271

murder. . .I wrote you about the attorney Kramer.''

"Yes. I almost came back then except for your insistence in the same letter that I should not. You never revealed your fears. Or the danger you were in.''

"Up to then it wasn't too bad, but afterward they began a subtle kind of harassment.''

"I should not have left you.''

"David, you had to. Has your leaving affected the show?''

"I had a cablegram waiting for me when I checked into the hotel. It was from the producer in New York and what it contained didn't make me feel very good. He said the show was going just great and I wasn't even missed.''

"I'll bet that was only to reassure you.''

"I have a large financial interest in the show, so I was immensely pleased to know it could run without me. Even if it was forced to close, I'd have remained here. When I leave this time, you'll be with me.''

"Thank you, David. I know now I need you more than my career.''

"Thank God. That's what I wanted to hear more than anything. I was going to force your hand, my love. I couldn't go on with an ocean separating us.''

"It won't—ever again.''

"During the intermission, a gentleman came up and told me you are to be the honored guest at a banquet and dance. Also, that I was to be your escort—which was good news.''

"Who was he?''

"I don't know. I assumed he was someone connected with the ballet.''

"It doesn't matter. Now I must change. Don't leave

this room, please."

Nicola was already behind the screen which assured her privacy while changing into the gown she had chosen for the evening. It had been a gift from her papa, the last one he had given her. She had forgotten about it in the turmoil of rehearsals and fears. It was a pale blue tulle with wide horizontal bands of satin ribbon decorating the skirt to the hem. A spray of pink roses started at one shoulder and crossed the bodice, continuing to the hem. Her slippers were blue satin with pink rosettes. Her hair was frizzed across her brow, then drawn up in a topknot and surrounded with pink roses which also adorned the gown.

"Let me watch you change, darling," David called.

"No," Nicola said laughing. "If you did, we would never get to the Adler where the affair is to be given."

"I won't deny you your triumph this evening," David replied. "But I'll be watching the clock, impatient to take you in my arms again and relive our love."

Nicola stepped from behind the screen. David got to his feet slowly, his eyes marveling at her beauty, her poise, the loveliness of her gown. She went to him and he kissed her gently on the lips.

"My beautiful Nicola. You look like royalty."

She blushed with the compliment.

She opened a drawer in a chest and took a pair of blue silk gloves and a fan from it. She handed him the fan while she slipped on the gloves. He put out the gas light and they left the theatre. There were few sounds coming from behind closed doors, indicating most had already departed.

When they entered the huge, glittering ballroom, the music stopped and the dancers formed a line down which Nicola had to walk. She was kissed and embraced and complimented on her performance. The Emperor and the Kaiser made their entrance later and Nicola curtsied before them. Franz Josef took her hand and led her onto the dance floor.

He held her close and looked directly into her eyes as he told her how lovely she was and how exquisite her portrayal of *Giselle*.

"You are like someone I once met," he said with a smile. "She was a girl—beautiful, poised, yet unsophisticated. She both charmed and surprised me as she took the step from girlhood to womanhood. I will never forget the few, brief hours of pleasure she gave me. Once over her shyness, she allowed me to initiate her into the joys and ecstasy of love."

"I am sure, Your Highness, she remembers too."

"How kind of you to say that. Are you enjoying the evening?"

"Indeed yes. And very honored."

"You deserve everything you get. You have worked hard for it. I talked with Monsieur Lapin. He told me how dedicated you are."

"The entire troupe is. I'm proud to be a member of it."

"I find your modesty appealing. You're a gracious lady and with the years, you will become more so." He looked around at the other dancers, then turned his attention back to her. "Tell me, how do you like the Kaiser?"

"Must I answer, Your Highness?"

Franz Josef laughed. "He is a very rigid man. He does not dance because he considers dancing unmilitaristic. His wife is much different. She is warm and friendly and I intend to dance with her, though her husband will not like it. God be with you, my child. Enjoy your success to its fullest. You will be hearing from the palace soon. It was an honor to have a lovely young girl dance wtih an old man like me."

"I am the honored one, Your Highness."

She curtsied when he handed her over to David, who bowed, then guided Nicola onto the dance floor. Their eyes never left each other as they whirled around the floor, though David guided her skillfully around other couples. He was a superb dancer and they reveled in their closeness. For a moment she wondered if others might notice, then she discarded that worrisome thought. Let them. There was nothing wrong with love or the fact that their faces revealed their hunger for each other.

The evening was a long one and the affair didn't break up until almost dawn. Nicola and David snuggled close in the carriage. They were tired, but happy.

"Don't fall asleep on me," he pleaded. "I know how exhausted you must be, but I think I'll go mad if you deny me your body."

Nicola smiled up at him. "I would go mad if you denied me yours."

"I'm glad we're in agreement on that," he said.

"We're in agreement on everything. You are my man and I am your woman."

"I want you as my wife," David said quietly. "I didn't know I could be jealous, but all eyes were on you when you danced with His Highness. He was completely enchanted by you."

"He was enchanted by my performance," Nicola said lightly. She hoped no one knew of her liaison with the Emperor. She didn't like to hold back anything from David, but that encounter had happened before she met him. And Franz Josef had been gentle and understanding. What he said tonight proved it. She had learned from him. She would learn more with David.

The very thought of intimacy with him made her eager for the evening to end in the privacy of her flat.

As she had done each night, she entered her apartment with bated breath. David was aware of it and studied her worriedly as she lit the gas light.

"You have been through a time, haven't you?" he said, taking her in his arms.

"Yes. Someone has a key to this flat besides Anna. I never did check with the manager. I've been so busy and so tired."

"Tell me about it," he said quietly, his arms still around her.

She told him about the harassment and the recent embarrassment she had been subjected to. David's lips compressed tightly, but he didn't interrupt.

"I hope to meet the person who sent me that cablegram and thank him. If I'd known what you've been through, I'd have been back sooner."

"You're here," she sighed happily. "My worries are over."

David smiled down at her. "I've been here before. We're going directly into the bedroom and I'll undress you. Are you too tired for lovemaking? I can be patient."

"Please don't be," Nicola said, giving him a reproving glance. "It's the only way I will really believe you have returned. I want you to possess me. I need your body and your closeness to reassure me I'm safe now."

"Now and forever." David bent, caught her up in his arms and carried her into the bedroom.

Nicola pulled down the bed covers, then let David undress her. He lifted her again and set her gently on the bed.

"Don't move," he commanded. "I want to feast my

eyes on your beautiful body while I get out of my clothes."

After he undressed, Nicola raised her arms to him. He gathered her close and held her tightly. Nicola strained her body against his, then lay back, still scarcely able to believe her beloved was actually with her.

He covered her body with kisses. They murmured endearments as their hands caressed each other until their passion reached a fever pitch. She was ready to receive him when he covered her body with his. Afterward, still holding her to him, he turned on his back. Only then, did the exhaustion they were both filled with prevail, letting sleep take over.

# Sixteen

She awoke to find herself still in the position in which they had fallen asleep. David's hands were caressing her gently, his lips kissing an earlobe. She stirred lazily against him and pressed kisses against his chest.

"What a delightful way to be awakened," she murmured, feeling a rapturous stirring within her.

"It's my pleasure, my darling," he said softly.

"And mine also," she replied, letting her hands move lightly down his sides where her fingers lightly traced the outline of his hips. "Oh, David, I love you so."

"And I love you," he replied. "Let's spend the next few minutes proving it."

"You make the most beautiful suggestions."

She raised herself sufficiently so that their lips could meet in a kiss that further aroused their passion.

David held her to him and turned gently so that once again he covered her and the room was filled with sounds of their lovemaking. Afterward, they lay on their sides, holding each other close.

David broke the silence. "I certainly must find out who sent me that cablegram and thank him. I don't know how I endured your absence."

Nicola traced the line of David's jaw with the tip of her forefinger as she spoke. "I'm wondering if it might have been Tonio. He was very kind to me. He escorted me always, except when Anna was with me. I was seldom alone."

"Naturally it wasn't Tonio who informed me in the theatre lobby about the soiree last night," David said. "I know him. And I'm grateful he looked after you. I'll thank him for doing so."

She slipped free of his arms, and sat up. "I must bathe and dress. You rest a little longer."

When Nicola came out of the bathroom, he propped himself up on the pillows and talked as he watched her dress. "Did Anna mention sending a cablegram to me?"

"Yes. So did Tonio. I wouldn't let them." She put on her corset cover, buttoned it and raised the embroidered eyelet edge to cover her breasts. She felt no trace of embarrassment either at her nudity when she left the bathroom or the fact that David never took his eyes from her. She was pulling the narrow ribbon through the eyelet to hold it secure and make a bow when she drew a sharp breath and looked at him. "David, I wonder if it could have been those men or their leader who sent you the cablegram. You know the threat they made to me because I testified against Sander."

"I assume that threat would have been carried out last night," David said seriously.

"Yes." Nicola returned her attention to dressing, bowing the ribbon and going into the closet for a street dress. She returned with a rose-colored, fur-trimmed cloth costume.

"I'm not sure just how I fit into their plans," David mused.

"I think I do, though the thought is horrifying."

"Tell me."

"They mean to murder you just as they do me."

"You really believe that, don't you." He raised himself and swung his legs over the side of the bed, his manner thoughtful.

"I do, David. And I'm frightened. There are many of them."

"There's only one thing we have to fear—the ringleader. Whoever he is, if we destroy him the rest will fall by the wayside. We'll talk about it at breakfast."

They went out to have breakfast and Nicola, for once, didn't hesitate to order what she wished. It was a meal made all the more wonderful because David sat across the table. All of her loneliness had vanished.

She was now able to calmly relate all that had happened to her. David listened impassively.

"Don't you have any idea who is directing this campaign against you?" he asked.

"I thought of Lapin and for a little while it seemed he might have been involved, but Inspector Reikert more or less absolved him."

"More or less is not good enough for me. Who else?"

"I discovered that Tonio is a Serbian, the same as these people who killed my father and threaten me. Also that his real name is Sandovic, which is very close to Sander, and all along it has been my impression that the leader of those who hate me is related to Sander. Still, Tonio has been devoted to me. Even Anna could not have been more attentive. Tonio searched the apartment each night, did everything in his power to help me."

"It might be," David reasoned, "his protective attitude toward you, plus his help, is a cloak to cover his real intentions. Someone in his position would know every move you made."

"I realize it. And for a while, it troubled me. But not

now. I believe I have never met the person who heads up this group of spies, or whatever they are."

"He certainly seems to have taken some precautions against letting you see him, or even hear his voice. When you were kidnapped and brought before him, you said he occupied a high-backed chair in a room so gloomy you were unable to see him. Not even his profile."

"That's true. But whoever he is, he is brutal and Tonio couldn't never be that."

"I admit he doesn't act like someone capable of doing what was done to you. First, Nicky, we're going to the cablegram office and try to find out who did send me that message. I believe now, as you do, I was brought here for a purpose."

"Darling, they may be waiting for us outside. They may be on the next corner, anywhere. Perhaps even in this restaurant. I'm doubly frightened now because your life is in danger."

"This time," David vowed, "I'll do my best to run them down. There is a girl in the troupe. I met her. She shared a dressing room with you before you became prima ballerina."

"Magda? David, you don't suspect her."

"I don't know. There may be a chance she is unintentionally helping someone she thinks is a friend. She would know what you are doing and where you are most of the time."

"I would hate myself if I suspected either Magda or Tonio."

"It's no time to let sentiment cloud your mind, Nicky. Someone is behind this and we must find out who he is."

"If we're both not killed before we do."

"Let's walk over to the cablegram office and ask a few questions. Or are you too tired to walk? Or afraid?"

"With you at my side, I'm not afraid."

"Then it's the cablegram office next."

Obtaining the information was not difficult. David passed money to a clerk and a copy of the cablegram was quickly produced. The copy was filed and paid for by Michael Sandovic.

"It's difficult to believe," Nicola said. "Tonio was so kind to me."

"Let's ask him why he did it. Do you know where he lives?"

"Yes. . .it's not far. He has a small flat."

"Have you been there?"

"Never. Why do you ask?"

"Only because I'd like to know whether or not his place has a back door which would enable him to make a run for it if he didn't wish to see us."

"I can't help you."

"We'll just have to chance it."

David hailed a carriage. Nicola gave the address and they rode to a somewhat poorer section of the city. The apartment house was recently built and, though modest, was quite attractive. Tonio's adopted name was on the mailbox. They took note of the number of his apartment and walked up the stairs to the third floor.

"I don't know that I want to go through with this," Nicola said. "I mean it, David. There is nothing that can make me believe Tonio is other than a kind and loyal friend who has been a great comfort to me."

"I appreciate all he did for you," David said, "but I hope his motives were decent."

They reached the door of Tonio's apartment and knocked. There was no answer. David knocked again harder, but still there was no reply. He twisted the door knob and found the door unlocked.

Nicola said, "He might still be sleeping."

"With his door unlocked?"

"Possibly. I know he was tired."

"Stay here a moment," David said. He pushed the door wide and went in. Nicola, peering from the open doorway saw what must have been Tonio's parlor, stripped of everything to the bare walls.

David reappeared, looking puzzled. "He's gone! Cleared out. There's nothing in the apartment."

"That's strange," Nicola said thoughtfully. "Not at all like him."

"Unless he was other than you thought. If so, he might have realized his hope of avenging Sander's death was no longer feasible. Or he may have just moved because he didn't like it here. His prestige has risen too. This is the end of the ballet season, so if he had any intention of moving, this would have been the time to do it. We won't accuse him of treason yet."

"I hope your reasoning is correct. Perhaps," she added brightly, "he left an address with the man who manages the building."

"We'll see," David said.

They made their way to the lobby, located the office of the building manager and David approached the desk, where a rather formidable-looking woman sat.

"We are looking for Tonio Seville," David said. "It seems he's moved out."

"Gone since this morning. Just packed up and called a wagon and some men to help and he's gone."

"Do you know where he moved to?" David asked.

"If I knew, I wouldn't tell you, but I don't. He didn't give me any reason, didn't tell me where he was going. He just went."

"Thank you," David said.

He touched Nicola's elbow and they left the building.

Outside, they paused to consider the significance of Tonio's disappearance, but could reach no conclusion because they had nothing to base their suspicions on.

"I guess we'll just have to wait until he contacts us," David said. "If he ever does. I have a theory, however. Is he in love with you?"

Nicola's smile was a little self-conscious. "Yes, darling. But he knew it was hopeless. I told him I loved you."

"He sent the cablegram to bring me back because he knew you were in danger and that you'd never send it yourself. Now that I'm here, he knows I'll look after you. If he's the kind of man you describe him as being, that's exactly what he would have done. He knows this time I'll insist you return to America with me."

"And I will. But what about the dance at Schönbrunn! If he has gone away, I don't know what we'll do."

"Have you an invitation yet?"

"No, but one is coming. I'm sure of it. When I danced with the Emperor, he said as much. Something like—he'd see me later. I think he meant the annual festival at the palace."

"Then I'll bet all I own that Tonio will be back. If I were in his position, I think I'd have gone away too, because it would be heartbreaking to be around you and the man you were in love with. But Tonio loves the ballet, so I'm sure he'll be back in plenty of time."

"Perhaps he left word at the theatre, with Lapin."

"We can always find out. We're both at leisure now with all the time in the world."

"I hope you're right," she said. "There may not be much time if those murderers are waiting for the right moment."

"We'll face that problem when it turns up, Nicky. There's not much we can do until they show themselves.

When they do, we'll be ready for them. I have guns in my luggage."

At the Burgtheater, they found Lapin in his office, a tired man but a triumphant one. He came to his feet and seized Nicola in a tight embrace while he kissed her, not with passion, but with gratitude.

"She is the greatest ballerina who ever danced on the Continent, or any other place," he declared enthusiastically. "You have made the Royal Ballet a famous group. I have letters, sent by hand, from twenty of the most important people in the world, all congratulating me and calling me a fine ballet master. As if that meant anything without you, Nicky."

"I've heard," David said, "from many different sources that you're the greatest."

"He is," Nicola added with a smile. "Even though he drives us to near distraction. But you were right in doing so, *M'sieur*. We needed the discipline and hours of work you insisted upon."

"Thank you, thank you, dear Nicky. You know, we are sure to get an invitation to dance at Schönbrunn. That will insure our success. Top it off forever. There can be no more illustrious audience anywhere in the world than those who are invited to Schönbrunn."

"*M'sieur*," Nicola asked, "have you heard from Tonio?"

"No. Should I have?"

"We went to his apartment to talk about the dance, but he moved out this morning. We wondered if he might have left an address with you."

Lapin clapped both hands to his temples. "*Mon Dieu*, do you think he has run away?"

"After his success?" David said. "I doubt it. We thought he might have consulted you before he moved."

"I have heard nothing from him. Not a word. What do you think has happened to him?"

"*M'sieur*, you worked all of us very hard and Tonio, I know, was tired. Perhaps he went off for awhile, but surely he plans to return to the ballet. It's his life."

"What idiots some people are," Lapin declared irritably. "Now I have this to worry about. As if there weren't enough without that. Nicky, if we get an invitation to the palace, we shall rehearse for ten days. And if Tonio is not here, I'll damn him to hell. If you hear from him, tell him to get in touch with me."

"Surely, *M'sieur*," Nicola said. "Thank you again."

"We made quite a team, you and I. Right from the start, from the moment you walked into the theatre, I knew you were going to become the best ballerina I ever coached. I could tell from the way you walked and that splendid innocence about you. Yes, I knew. I never make a mistake."

Outside, Nicola laughed at Lapin's last sally. "He treated me as if I stumbled with every step and I was far too stupid to learn anything. He told me so a hundred times."

David said, "I wonder about him. I've done a little studying on the situation in the Balkans. If there is a war, France is going to side with Serbia. I don't think there's any question about it. Now a man in Lapin's position, a ballet master, who would be considered absolutely harmless, could be a spy working for France and Serbia. Who would ever suspect him?"

"David, his heart and soul involves only ballet. I don't think he could report even street numbers to some organization. You must be wrong."

"Maybe. Well, we've covered everything I can think of. What will we do with all this time up to the Schönbrunn performance?"

"I'm afraid of loneliness," she said. "It gives me too much time to think. David, I know I've been successful at last and I'm proud of it, but I remember all too well the night I was taken to Sander's home and. . .and. . .I was told that when I became successful, I would face the same fate as Sander, who was also on the verge of great success. They meant it. I know they did. I've reached that point now and I'm apprehensive. For me and for you."

"I know. We have to do something about that. Give me a little time, the rest of the day. I'll come up with something. My first idea is for us to get out of Vienna. Go somewhere secretly. Let no one know. Just slip out of town in the night, perhaps, and enjoy ourselves until Schönbrunn. You need rest. You must rid yourself of fear and tension."

"David, I could think of no better an idea. May we go tomorrow?"

"No reason why not. I don't have much to pack and you won't need many clothes if we can find a hunting lodge that we can rent."

"If we could only get away. Somewhere. . .a place nobody would think of. Where we're not known. . . ."

"I'll take you home, then see what I can do about finding a place. Pack some warm clothes. . .these isolated places are sometimes snowed in, as you know."

"Someone will have to know so if we are invited to the palace we can be reached in time."

"Lapin or Anna," David said promptly.

"Anna, of course. I still don't trust Lapin entirely. Especially after what you said about his being French. France would become an enemy of Austria if there is serious trouble."

"Anna then. I leave that to you. I'll come back as soon as I make arrangements."

287

He brought her home, searching the apartment before leaving, just as Tonio had. Anna usually came by before supper, but Nicola took no chances. She summoned a messenger from the apartment-house office and sent him with a note to Anna. While in the manager's office, she checked to see if anyone had been admitted to her flat on some pretext. The answer was negative.

David was gone all afternoon, but Nicola was in such a state of euphoria she barely noticed the passage of time and was mildly surprised when Anna arrived.

Anna needed but one look around the apartment. "You're packing. Where are you going, Nicky? And why?"

"Not I. We! Where, I don't know, but I'm going with David. We want to find a quiet place. We need rest."

"I approve of that," Anna said. "But what if something happens—like Lapin demanding your presence at rehearsal? You know there is a chance the ballet will be performed at Schönbrunn."

"Yes. As soon as we are settled, I'll send you a letter. I can't do better than that because I have no idea where David will take me."

"I don't like it. These sudden arrangements. There is a great deal to be lost if you miss that invitation, Nicky. Besides, have you forgotten Sander's men? You would be safer staying around people. In an isolated spot, you would be an easy target."

"Stop worrying, Anna. David knows better than to take me so far away I will be in danger or can't get back in time to perform at Schönbrunn. Oh, have you seen Tonio?"

"No. Why?"

"David and I went to his flat and it's empty. The owner either didn't know or wouldn't tell us where he had gone."

"That's odd," she said thoughtfully. "But then, David's presence was a surprise."

"A beautiful one," Nicola said. "I think I have Tonio to thank for that."

"You mean he sent a cablegram?"

"Yes."

Anna looked hurt. "Why did you let him and not me?"

"I didn't let him. He did it on his own. I even forbade him just as I did you."

"Has there been any more trouble?" she asked worriedly.

"No. That's one reason we want a hideaway."

"It will be something if Lapin can't locate either you or Tonio."

Nicola laughed. "Just as soon as I have an address, you'll receive it."

"Be assured you'll hear from me promptly once Lapin contacts me. Unless you prefer that he contact you."

"I'd rather he didn't have our address. We don't want anyone to know where we are. I know you won't bother us unless it's important."

"It is really serious between you and David," Anna said.

"Did you ever doubt it?"

"Will you marry?"

"We will soon. We are as good as married now. You know that. You're not condemning me, are you?"

"Hardly, my dear. It was the same with your papa and me, except he wouldn't marry me—that is, he didn't propose until it was too late. How soon will you depart?"

"As soon as David finds out where we can go. Anna, I'm the happiest girl alive. The success of the ballet,

David's return, the affair last night.''

"I attended your performance. You were superb. I cried, wishing your papa could have been with me." Her eyes were moist. "Yes, the best thing you can do is get away. You would be safer. I promise if there is anything of importance, I shall surely let you know."

"Thank you, Anna." Nicola embraced Anna and returned to her packing.

Resigned to Nicola's plans, Anna helped and didn't leave until almost supper time. Half an hour after her departure, David returned with luggage, including a gun case. And food for a simple supper. While Nicola prepared it, David told her their plans.

"There are a few hunting lodges near Klosterneuburg —that's about twenty-five kilometers from Vienna. My hotel cooperated very well and they are certain we can rent one for a few days with no trouble. Especially at this season."

"Wonderful. David, these tortes are going to be the death of me. You know I shouldn't have them."

"If you put on a pound or two, we'll walk it off before the ballet. I brought along a hunting rifle. We'll walk the woods and have the time of our lives. Just you and me."

"Anna came by. I told her what we were about to do."

"You didn't tell her where. . .of course not. You didn't even know. What of Lapin?"

"She will instruct him to contact her and she will get word to us. I will write as soon as we have an address."

"Good. The fewer people who know, the better. What of the men posted across the street? Have you seen any sign of them?"

"Not for some time now. I'm sure they no longer shadow me."

"I hope not, especially since they're not police. I have rented a closed-in surrey so we won't have to be riding in the open. And there's plenty of room for our luggage."

Nicola poured their coffee and they sat down to eat. "We should have two or three weeks," she said.

"It will be a sort of a pre-honeymoon," he said with a light laugh. "The real one will come right after Schönbrunn. Will you marry me at sea?"

"At sea?" She looked up in surprise.

"Certainly. The ballet season will be over here, but the theatre season in New York is never over. We'll be going there. You'll be safe and among friends. There'll be far less to worry about."

"David, I didn't dream of such a thing, but it is so romantic. Oh yes, I'd love that."

"We'll sail immediately after your performance at Schönbrunn. We'll be hiding out from now on until rehearsals. During the time that takes, I'll be with you every moment, and we'll have arrangements made to sail, perhaps the morning after the ballet. Or as soon afterward as we can find passage. I know the police and intelligence services are looking for the people who have threatened to kill you. I went there today. I feel that when we do return to Vienna for the new season, they may have rounded them up."

"I'll pray for that. Will you stay at my flat tonight?"

"Would you have it any other way?" he asked.

"No," Nicola said boldly. "You have no idea how safe I feel in your arms."

"You have no idea of what you do to me when you're in my arms."

"Of course I know. It enflames me just thinking of it."

"Let's finish eating," David said. "We've wasted

enough time.''

''Now?'' Nicola asked, her eyes an invitation.

''Now!'' he replied with emphasis. He was up and around the table in three strides. He swept Nicola off her feet and headed for the bedroom.

# Seventeen

An early morning departure allowed them to make an easy journey of it. The weather cooperated by being crisp but clear, and there were no signs of snow. They rode in a leisurely fashion out of Vienna. Once along quiet country roads, they breathed more easily, for here they could not be followed for long without becoming aware of it.

Nicola plied David with questions about life in America, theatrical people, where they would live, how they would share the theatrical seasons. They even considered the idea of maintaining two homes, one in New York, the other in Vienna. Financially they were secure. David's show was turning people away.

"After Schönbrunn," Nicola told him, "it will not be long before I may be declared *prima ballerina assoluta*. It is an honor one does not openly seek, but Lapin has given me to understand that it will be mine. That, and you, darling, will fill my life. I shall want no more, ever."

They reached a tiny country village not far from the Danube, but they might as well have been in another country, so far as Vienna was concerned. At the post office, where all business was apparently conducted, they paid for the renting of a hunting lodge. Nicola took time to write Anna, giving her the address of the post office.

This much done, they bought food and then, following simple directions, they drove into the beautiful forest country, along narrow dirt roads, between towering trees and a wealth of brush. The lodge was small, but snug and weathertight with a huge stack of cordwood for use in the two fireplaces which David had roaring half an hour after they arrived. David lounged in a large chair before it. Nicola sat at his feet.

"I'm sure we were not followed," he said, "so we can feel safe here. For a few days we should not have a worry in the world. We can make our plans, be lazy and get a much-needed rest."

"I'm good at that," Nicola confessed. "But didn't you forget something?"

"Did I?" he asked dryly.

"I shall expect you to make passionate love to me."

"My dearest love, I'll always do that. I need only to look at you to become thoroughly aroused."

"Oh, David, it's so beautiful here, I can't believe we're in the slightest danger."

"As I told you, the police and intelligence have begun a careful search for those men. If we can get through these few weeks and the ballet, and get aboard a clipper immediately afterward, I can just about promise that we'll outwit them. If intelligence does not find them, they'll force them to go so deeply into hiding that they'll never dare to come out again. It's only these few weeks where there might be some danger."

Nicola gave a relaxed sigh. "I feel so safe here. They can't possibly find out where we are, and even if they did, they'd have a hard time locating us in this wilderness."

"Just the same," David said, "I've placed my rifle near the door and we'll go nowhere without it. I also have a revolver and I'm good with both weapons."

"I wish you hadn't said that." She moved beside him in front of the fireplace. "I hate guns. I saw Papa gunned down."

"I'm sorry, Nicky. Let's try to forget danger and concentrate on enjoying ourselves."

The days passed swiftly for them. They hunted daily, mostly for the exercise, though David brought down enough game to keep their table supplied. They made daily drives to the village and the post office. There was never any mail. Only Anna had their address and she would not send a message to return until it became necessary. They grew to be favorites in the village, because Nicola had been recognized as the ballerina who had charmed the Emperor and the Kaiser. Sketches of her had been in regional newspapers and they were shown several articles written about her. It was presumed they were married and this was their honeymoon. If their arms weren't around each other's waists, they were holding hands.

Nights were crisp and cold, ideally suited to love-making. Nicola was so content she dreaded the thought of leaving.

"We've been here for quite a time now," David reminded her. "Nothing happened, no strangers have been prowling about. I consider it a good omen."

"I hope you're right, yet I can't believe those men have abandoned their mission. They were too determined. It's your sudden appearance that has caught them off balance. They are probably thinking of other tactics to use against us.''

''You forget that those people are now being sought. I have been in contact with Inspector Reikert and I know what I'm talking about. I don't care what tactics they use. They can't do to you what they did before.''

''It's you I'm worried about. Part of their strategy could be to harm you. They're merciless.''

''Nicky, you said yourself that your performance before that assemblage of royalty could never be duplicated in importance, and that it placed you at the top of all your hopes and dreams. They didn't try to kill you to prevent it from taking place. You've reached the peak of your success.''

''Not quite. There's Schönbrunn,'' she reminded him.

''How could they know that? It is not certain you'll get a bid. There are others competing for that honor. I say you'd reached the top, when you made your last curtsy before the Emperor and Empress at the final curtain.''

''You're right, David,'' she said. ''It does make sense —coming from you.''

He poked at the fire, stirring up the embers, then added another log. He turned and opened his arms to her. With her usual grace, she was on her feet instantly. Her arms went around his shoulders as he drew her close. They'd made love each morning they awakened and in the afternoons and evenings, yet it seemed their passion could rise at their merest touch. Without breaking their kiss, he held her close, lifting her sufficiently so that her feet didn't touch the floor and carried her over to the long divan. He set her down and lay beside her. His hands slipped into the front of her robe and slid down the length of the sleeves, freeing her arms.

"Now let me," Nicola whispered. She loosened the belt of his robe and slipped it off him. He pushed hers aside and they pressed close to one another.

"My love," David said huskily, "you're all flame and desire. When your body moves against mine, I feel as if I'm about to explode."

"You have the same effect on me," she assured him. "Kiss me again and again, then possess me. Afterward we will talk."

He obeyed willingly. Afterward, they lay in languorous silence, their arms still holding each other close, their eyes revealing their passion and their love. David put his arm behind him, his hand seeking his robe which had slipped to the floor. He found it and used it to cover them. Beneath its warmth, they drifted off to sleep.

Later, they talked of Nicola appearing in a New York musical. "I have an idea for another show," David said. "I've made copious notes and the lead is for a ballet dancer, even though it is a musical. I've already written some of the music and lyrics to accompany it."

"David," Nicola said excitedly, "I didn't know you could."

"I'm not particularly interested in the role I play before the footlights. I like the creative end of the profession. I always have."

"That sounds exciting. I'd love to do it."

"You shall."

The next day their dreaming came to an abrupt end. Their daily trip to the village and the post office produced a letter from Anna.

*My dears:*
*I have been informed by Monsieur Lapin that in two weeks the Royal Ballet has been selected to open the social season at the theatre in Schloss Schönbrunn. The invitation came from the Empress in her own hand.*

297

*Lapin will begin rehearsals in three days.*

*All is calm here. No one seems to be watching your apartment any more. Your few brief notes arrived intact and there seems to be a general feeling of peace and quiet here. Still, I would be most cautious and keep your movements as secret as you can. Your apartment will be ready when you return. I hope the hours you two have spent together have enriched your lives.*

*Anna*

Nicola folded the letter and stuffed it back in the envelope. "It's from Anna. The Royal Ballet has been invited to Schönbrunn. Oh David, I hate to return. Let's wait until the last possible moment."

"You said you'd need ten days of rehearsal."

"It's what Lapin wishes. Perhaps we do need it after those days off. Anna didn't mention Tonio."

"Then we'll leave tomorrow morning. And don't start worrying about Tonio. I want no one in this lodge but the two of us."

That night she was somber and worried. Not even the comfort of a roaring fire and David's arm around her served to alleviate her fears.

"I may as well confess, darling David, I am very apprehensive. I know we've been at peace here and those people don't know where we are, but that will end when we return. I fear they have done nothing, because the end of it all is planned for right after the Schönbrunn ballet."

"I don't agree. I told you they must have made up their minds the peak of your success came after the last ballet performance. They couldn't guess you'd be invited to Schönbrunn and, even so, why would they make up their minds that Schönbrunn was more important to your career than the last ballet?"

"I don't know. It's a feeling I have and it won't go away."

"It will vanish because right after Schönbrunn we will sail. A week later we'll be in New York as Mr. and Mrs. David Jackson. And that will be the end of your fear and worry. Forever."

"May that day come soon," she said wistfully. "Make me forget, David. Take me in your arms and make me forget everything but that we are in love."

He kissed her passionately before he picked her up in his arms and carried her into the bedroom.

They prepared to return the next morning. David's clothes were already packed and Nicola was still engaged in getting her possessions in order. David picked up the rifle.

"I'll take the surrey to the village and see if there are any more letters. No need for you to come with me. I'll make it a fast trip and there's much for you to do. We'll want everything ready by early afternoon so we can fill ourselves with memories of this place and spend what time there is left making love. There won't be much chance of that once you go into rehearsal, so we should make the best of it now."

"I'm not afraid," Nicola assured him. "Not any more. Besides, I want to cook one last meal for us. Tomorrow I begin to starve."

He drove off at midmorning and Nicola hastened to finish her packing and begin preparing the meal she had promised. It would not be elaborate because there was only a scant supply of food left, yet she could provide him with a steak, vegetables and a rich dessert she knew how to make with what was on hand.

She set aside her cares, determined not to spoil these last few hours, sorry she'd given way to her fears last night. She heard someone outside. She rushed to the door to open it and greet David with a warm embrace. Instead, she was roughly pushed back into the lodge.

Two men came in, closed the door and approached

her as she slowly backed away from them.

"Take her!" one shouted and the other leaped forward to wind his arms around her before she could escape. She was dragged to the sofa and forced onto it with her captor seated beside her. One of his hands gripped hers behind her back.

He looked up at the other man. "Get out there and wait for him. Don't give him a chance. Cut him down the moment you see him. Do you understand?"

"Seeing that's how we planned it, of course I understand."

"I'll keep her quiet if I have to choke her half to death. But get him!"

Nicola managed to emit one short-lived scream. The arm loosened and a thick hand slapped across her mouth, smothering any chance of making another sound. She tried to calm herself, to think, to find a way to prevent this from happening. She suddenly let herself go limp, pretending to faint from lack of air. The hand was removed, but her captor still held her tightly.

She tried to estimate the time when David would return and decided he must be almost back by now. He would head straight toward the lodge, never thinking of any danger, and the other man would step out from some brush, or from the side of the lodge and David would have no chance.

She felt the arm around her relax somewhat. She estimated she had one chance to get free. If he became convinced she was completely unconscious, she might be able to surprise him. There wasn't much time left. David would drive the surrey up momentarily.

She gave one desperate attempt to leap off the sofa. The arm clamped tight again and a hand came down over her mouth so she could give no alarm. Not that it would have done much good. Suddenly she heard a

300

single shot and then silence. The hand came away from her mouth.

"You're next if you resist, *Fräulein*. We have been determined to have you and now we shall. There is nothing you can do about it. Nothing! Your man is dead and no one will come to help you. But you have a chance to live if you are nice to us. Very, very nice for a few days. I am sure you understand."

Someone was at the door. It opened and the man who held her, turned his head.

"Come, Bruno, and enjoy the fun."

Then he gave a sharp exclamation, let go of Nicola and came to his feet. The man he called Bruno was clinging to the door frame, his chest bloody, his eyes beginning to glaze as his knees gave way. He slid down and lay in a stilled heap.

Nicola, with her dancer's grace, got past the first man and almost reached the door before he seized her, his arm around her neck, bringing her head back in a choking grip.

"I will kill you, *Fräulein*," he screamed. "If you stop me, I will kill you."

He half lifted, half dragged her out of the lodge. A buggy was tied to a bush a hundred yards away. Apparently it was the means of transportation for the pair.

There was no answer to the man's shouting and no sign of anyone. Yet she knew David was out there somewhere, watching, waiting for his chance. She was being dragged to the buggy in a hold she could not break. She did reach up one hand and gouged her nails across the man's face which brought an even tighter hold at her throat until her breath was cut off and she ceased struggling. He lifted her, carried her and began a clumsy run toward the buggy.

There he could do nothing but throw her onto the seat and then try to get aboard himself, though now he was thoroughly exposed. Then there was a shot. He slowly slid down across the side of the buggy, a bullet lodged in his back.

Nicola drew in breath after breath, clearing her head and lungs as David, carrying his rifle, ran toward her. He threw aside the gun, helped her down and held her tightly.

"I shouldn't have left you for one moment," he said bitterly. "Forgive me. I thought we were safe, but I should have known better."

"We are safe now," Nicola managed. "Oh, David, when I heard that first shot, I thought they'd killed you."

"Can you walk back to the lodge?"

"Yes, yes, I can walk. How did you know they were here?"

"Like most stupid people who indulge in murder, they were too sure of themselves. They asked at the post office where we were, saying they came from the ballet with an important message. When I learned that, I whipped the horse and got back quickly. I left the carriage before it could be heard and I moved about until I saw this man hiding at the far corner of the lodge, waiting for me to come driving down the road. I got behind him, called out, and when he turned to shoot me, I fired first. I couldn't stop him from staggering to the lodge and I couldn't afford to expose myself to the man I knew was inside with you. I'm sorry, darling, I'll never forgive myself. It wouldn't have happened if I'd been as wary as I should have been."

"David, you did the right thing. I'm not hurt. If there are marks on my throat, they'll go away by the time I have to perform. Please don't berate yourself. You saved our lives. We were both at fault, but then, as it worked out, you might not have been able to do it if they had ambushed us on the way back.''

"We were lucky," David admitted. "I should have realized you had good reason to fear them. Well, it's over now."

"I wonder. The man who held me said they were not going to kill me, but were going to stay here in the lodge with me after they killed you. I believe they were not going to kill me because they had orders not to, because someone else wants to do that after Schönbrunn. When is this going to end? What can we do now?"

"We'll return in the morning. Right now we have to ride to the village and make a report of this. We have to notify Inspector Reikert when we get back. I'm sorry it had to end this way."

"I dread to think how it would have ended if you hadn't killed those men."

"True, but from here on, we must double our precautions. Before Schönbrunn we must find out who is behind it. I won't stop until I know. Meantime, if your convictions are true—and I agree with you—it's possible there is nothing to fear until after the ballet. But you will be protected, darling. Until we get aboard the clipper and it sails, you won't be left alone and only those we trust will get near you. I just hate the thought of the strain you'll be under."

"Perhaps," she said softly, "we have a chance. At least you are here. You'll be close by."

"I'm not leaving you again," he vowed. "I made that mistake once. We were overconfident. It only proves that the leader behind this is utterly ruthless.

The drive back to the city was unlike the journey to the lodge, when there'd been gaiety and happiness. Now they were mostly silent. David's mind was busy trying to solve the mystery. Nicola was filled with frustration and worry as to how and when the enemy would strike. They agreed that the moment the ballet was over and the audience cleared out from the dressing room area, she would go with him, still in costume. A carriage, protected by Inspector Reikert's men, would drive them straight to the clipper. There they'd be under heavy guard until the ship sailed. It sounded like a foolproof plan, but Nicola had long ago learned to appreciate the ingenuity of those who were scheming to kill her.

Back in Vienna, they went to her apartment. Anna called on them early in the evening. With her came two of Reikert's men, one on either side of her. Until Nicola identified her, they refused to release her.

Anna closed the apartment door. "The nerve of them," she said indignantly. "They searched me. Those men searched me. I've never been so insulted in my life." She paused and studied Nicola. "Something more happened. Something very bad. Tell me!"

"Two men found us at the lodge," Nicola explained. "But we were fortunate. Both are dead. We were not harmed."

"Anna," David said to their horrified guest, "we wrote, giving our address so you could notify us about Schönbrunn. Did you tell anyone?"

Anna hesitated. "I. . .I'm ashamed of myself. Naturally, Lapin couldn't reach you so he sent for me. I visited his studio. I. . .let it slip. I told him the name of the village. He was so afraid you'd gone so far off, you'd not get back in time. I didn't mean to, but he was angry and upset. I was trying to calm him down."

"Just so we know," David said.

Anna's discomfiture seemed to grow. "Tonio was there. He heard me."

"No one else?"

"I swear they are the only two."

"After being searched, you know the situation," David said. "Nicola is going to be protected day and night. No one will be allowed to come here, or talk to her, except the members of the ballet. Lapin will be very closely watched and so will Tonio. No one can come here without being stopped, as you were."

"David, I want Anna to come. She should know what is going on. You see, when I lost my father, she lost a prospective husband and this concerns her as much as it does me."

"Very well," David said. "I'll instruct Reikert's men to let you through, Anna. Please don't talk about what is going on, about the precautions we are taking and our suspicions."

"I will say nothing to anyone. You have my promise."

"Thank you," David said. "Now Nicky can tell you exactly what did happen up there in the country."

"Anna, before we talk about that, David and I are going to be married on shipboard. We leave for the United States immediately after Schönbrunn."

"I'll be so sorry to have you go, Nicky, but you'll be safe there in America. Perhaps someday you can come back. I hope so. I will add my prayer to yours, that you will safely reach the ship and have a good voyage. David, I offer my congratulations and I know you will care for Nicky as I have tried to do. This is a moment of sadness for me, but knowing she will be safe, dries my tears."

"Dear Anna, I'll miss you too." Nicola embraced her warmly.

Wherever Nicola went for the next ten days, there were always men accompanying her. They were posted in the theatre during rehearsals and never took their eyes off her. It was a monotonous existence for Nicola, because she went directly to the theatre and straight back to the apartment.

She was pleased to see Tonio again and to rehearse with him. She hated to suspect him, but she had promised David not to trust anyone. Lapin had greeted her with his customary enthusiasm. Tonio, she discovered, was a bit less affectionate.

"I understand you and David were looking for me," he said soberly.

"Can you blame us, Tonio? You sent David a cablegram in my name and we wanted to ask you about it. And to make sure it really was you who sent it."

"I suppose it was enough to make you suspicious of me," he conceded. "I sent it because of you—and your refusal to ask David to come back. You needed him and I thought something must be done."

"You were right, and I appreciate it," she said. "You've likely heard what happened at the hunting lodge."

"Yes."

"You're being short with me, Tonio. Is it because you think it improper that David and I stayed there? We are going to be married less than twenty-four hours after the ballet."

"I wish you every happiness," he said, and wandered off to practice his elevations.

Nicola returned to the warm-up, chagrined at Tonio's coolness. But later, when she rehearsed the *pas de deux*, he was just as skilled, just as careful of her as always. Gradually she felt their solid relationship would be restored and it was, just as she believed. The day before the Schönbrunn ballet, his manner was warm and friendly and they were the same highly capable team of dancers as ever. Perhaps a little better, so Tonio said, and it was possible.

There was some resentment in the troupe at being under the constant scrutiny of Inspector Reikert's men every moment, but they grew accustomed to it and gradually paid little attention to them.

The nights with David were not like before. She was tense, but grateful for his understanding. He made no demands on her, even though she clung to him in bed. He talked softly to her, trying to lift her spirits, but her mind was too filled with thoughts of the murder of her father, the execution of Sander and the death of the two assassins.

"It seems all I can think of is death," she complained. "I get sick thinking about it, but nothing can shut it out. I'm ashamed, darling, because I love you and you have been so patient and done everything possible to lift my spirits."

"At least when you are at rehearsal, you throw off your fears," David said. "I've watched you."

"Tonio has been very considerate," she replied. "He's himself again."

"Good for Tonio," David said, without his usual enthusiasm.

"I'm sorry, darling," she said apologetically. "I didn't mean to hurt you."

"I know you didn't." He flashed a smile that went straight to her heart. "But I've watched the two of you at rehearsal and I must confess I'm jealous. You dance beautifully together. And you seem to enjoy it."

"Not the way I enjoy this." Nicola shifted her head and kissed David's underarm. "Kiss me, darling. Let's make love as we did before."

"I won't allow you to pretend you feel passion for me when you don't."

"It won't be pretense," she argued.

"It won't be genuine. It must be—with us it must always be. I'm patient, Nicola. I love you. I intend to be

307

very protective of you."

"You have been. I didn't think I could love you more, but I do. I know how much I mean to you. You've proven it with your care, your attention and your patience. I will make it up to you soon."

"Then I won't have long to wait," he said, drawing her close to him. "The performance is the day after tomorrow. I want you to dance as you never have before."

"My performance will be for you. My eyes will seek you out whenever possible, and please be looking at me. I want to see your love for me reflected in them."

"You will, my darling. You will. And have no fear. Nothing will happen to you. Tell yourself that our love has made you strong."

Nicola looked up at him, then raised herself to touch his lips with hers. For the first time since they returned, she felt the stirrings of passion within her. His words had touched her heart.

"It has made me strong," she said after he kissed her. "Your love is coursing through my blood. I'm on fire again. Oh, my darling, my darling. I want you. Take me, my darling. Now."

The gentle movement of her body against his further assured him that, even if only for a little while, she was herself again. He was cautious at first, but once he knew she was as bestirred with the ecstasy of their emotion as he, he caressed her and rained kisses on her body until she cried out for him to take her.

# Eighteen

Nicola applied the final touches to her makeup with hands that trembled. With her in the locked dressing room was David.

"You have seen the precautions," he said. "There's little chance of anyone getting close to you. Reikert tells me he has had every member of the ballet troupe investigated and they are all cleared. Now you must perform the best *Giselle* they have ever enjoyed. The theatre is not large; the royal guests will be an appreciative audience. Many are balletomanes. There will be personages from all over the world and being here for this private performance is a tribute to you and your corps. Remember, above all other talents, you were chosen. Make it good, Nicky. For me too."

"Thank you, David." She touched his cheek and smiled. "I'd kiss you, but I'd ruin my makeup. You'd better go now and take your seat. There's not much more time."

He nodded and embraced her lightly. "Just look down at the front row and you'll see me. The Emperor himself arranged for me to have that seat. He was so pleased to do it you'd think he owed you something."

Nicola's smile was enigmatic, but inwardly she felt a glow of gratitude because she knew now, without doubt, that the Emperor had done what he could to ensure her success.

She was escorted to the wings by two policemen. The music welled, the curtain went up. Nicola waited for her cue as Tonio joined her. His arm enclosed her waist and squeezed lightly. She turned to him and smiled with more confidence.

Their *pas de deux* in the first act was excellent. Nicola, from the moment she was before the footlights, discovered once again that all fears left her. She saw David seated amidst the gaudy uniforms, the brilliant jewels and colorful gowns of the ladies. Her eyes lingered momentarily on him. He gave a barely perceptible nod of approval.

At intermission, with the house lights bright, she was able to see the theatre from the stage. It was a marvel of beauty and brilliance. The orchestra had no more than five hundred seats. The first balcony consisted of only three rows of seats that circled the theatre from one end of the stage to the other. A second balcony was equally small, but this was not a theatre meant for profit. Four enormous chandeliers hung from a ceiling painted by a master in a colorful fresco. There were more lights adorning the walls. At the far end, facing the stage, the royal purple draperies sheltered the royal box. Everything save the fresco was in gold and purple. Nicola felt that she would never again appear in a theatre as elaborate or beautiful as this.

She turned away from viewing the theatre, her heart light, her spirits soaring. Everything was going well. In another hour it would be over. There'd be no reception and while the dressing room area would be overflowing with guests, no one would be allowed in Nicola's room except David and Anna.

Before morning she would be aboard the clipper. Their luggage was already aboard. The trip from the palace to the dockside would be under heavy guard.

In the second act, she and Tonio outdid themselves,

and the entire troupe, excited in the knowledge that it was doing splendidly, cooperated until the applause began before the familiar ballet was finished.

Between taking their innumerable bows, Nicola kissed Tonio and cried a little. "I shall never again have a partner such as you. And I'll never forget you, Tonio."

"I'll try to forget you," he said good-naturedly, "but it won't be easy."

"If I dance in New York, I shall send for you. And when I come back to Vienna next year, I will pray to heaven that you'll be here to dance with me."

"I can promise I will." He was as stimulated by the applause as she. "They want us out there again." He grasped her hand and led her back to the center of the stage.

Finally it was over. Nicola felt a glow of happiness and accomplishment on her way to her dressing room. David had not yet been able to make his way from the theatre proper, but Anna was there, guarding the door. As Nicola approached she opened it, held it long enough for them to go through, and then she closed it.

Nicola hugged her, still revelling in the success of the performance. "We never did it so well, Anna. I don't think there was the slightest flaw."

"I can assure you there was not, and I can also promise you that this is one ballet at Schönbrunn that will never be forgotten for a hundred years."

Nicola sat down at the dressing table to begin removing her makeup. "I wouldn't say that, Anna. Your praise is far too extravagant."

"No," Anna contradicted matter-of-factly. She picked up a pillow from the sofa, carried it with her as she sat down in a chair just behind Nicola. She placed her handbag on her lap and set the pillow on top of it, as if to protect the handbag.

Anna said, "So many times you told me that Schönbrunn would be the peak of your career. Now that you have achieved your goal, you must be supremely happy."

"I am," Nicola smiled at Anna's reflection. "I can truthfully say I have never been happier."

"Or more successful," Anna said quietly. "Nicky, turn around."

Nicola glanced over her shoulder. "Anna, what is wrong? You look so strange. . . ."

"Turn around! I've something to tell you."

"Tell me while I'm taking off my makeup. I want to be with David."

"Forget David. Turn around, Nicky."

Nicola swung around quickly, stunned at the sharpness of Anna's tone. "Is something wrong?"

"Do you remember being told that at the peak of your happiness and success we swore you would die, as Sander died? Do you remember?"

"I've thought of nothing else. If it hadn't been for David, I'd have gone mad." She paused and regarded Anna's features. Her eyes were scornful, her mouth twisted in an ugly smile. "Anna, you said 'we'." And then, as a sudden realization came, Nicola exclaimed, "No! No! It isn't possible!"

"It is! Possible and true. Sander was my son."

"I don't believe it," Nicola said, but inwardly she knew she did. "You and my father. . ."

"Your father was an incompetent, a sad specimen of a man. I never loved him. He was useful to me, for what information I didn't pick up in the code room, I got out of him from his diplomatic travels. I have been a spy for many years and all those years I planned with my son to change history. He would have been a famous man, a member of royalty of his own making and I would have shared his success. You finished that, even after you

312

were given a chance to reconsider and temper your testimony. Why didn't you?''

"Anna, I trusted you. Papa trusted you."

"Everyone did. Everyone still does. The only one who had a chance of exposing me was that idiot of a lawyer named Kramer."

"You killed him!" Nicola exclaimed.

"He was going to ask you for money in exchange for the information he possessed, but he decided you couldn't give him enough so he came to me."

"I don't understand. You've been like a mother to me."

"You're as big a fool as your father. I have a motive for being close to you. I wanted to torture you, to see your fear."

"It didn't go as you expected it would though, did it?"

"Almost, but not quite. Kramer nearly spoiled it. He saw me behind the glass door of your apartment house. I hadn't gone upstairs for the tickets. I wanted to see my son carry out his duty as a patriot. Your back was turned. You couldn't see me, but Kramer was on the sidewalk and had a full view of me. I didn't even realize it until he came to me with his silly offer to remain silent for a fortune in florins. I put him off with a token payment and then we disposed of him."

"What did he want to tell me?"

"That he saw me behind the glass door smiling as my son gunned down your father."

Sudden realization came to Nicola. "So it was you in that room where I was taken. It was you seated in that tall chair. I couldn't identify you because of the darkness. Also, you whispered to the man at your side."

"Yes," Anna admitted boldly. "And it was I who gave instructions that you were to be violated. Watching your damned chastity taken from you gave me as much

313

pleasure as watching my son kill your father. But you got even. You killed my son.''

"Your son was a murderer. I bore witness against him and I spoke the truth. I know now he was as dangerous as you are.''

"My son was a true patriot. So am I. It has been all I could do each time I looked at you not to strangle you. But I wanted you to suffer as I have suffered.''

"I suffered when Papa was murdered.''

Anna's smile was grim. "I gloated. He was dangerous to our cause. He'd have been killed sooner if we had known how dangerous he really was. He wasn't as stupid as I believed him to be, though I fooled him for years.''

"Pretending to love him,'' Nicola said, now regarding Anna with distaste. "Do you know that outside this dressing room there are many policemen? You will never get out of here, but if you go now without harming me, I'll remain quiet.''

"Do you think I believe that? You have no more time. See this pillow resting on my lap?''

"Yes,'' Nicola said.

"I have in my handbag a small gun that shoots a big bullet. It will make no noise. The pillow will muffle the sound. I shall then merely walk out of here and tell those guards you wish a few moments to yourself. Don't you think I've planned this carefully? Everything is prepared so I can escape from Vienna. I instructed those men to harass you, to keep fear uppermost in your mind. They did well. Also, I gave orders I would kill you. I have lived only for my moment of triumph. It is here.''

Her hand dipped into her bag and frantically searched for the gun. She looked up as the dressing room door opened and David entered, holding a derringer in the palm of his hand.

"Were you looking for this, Anna?" he asked.

She gasped and half arose, but resumed her seat. Lines of fear were on her face.

"In all the excitement and the press of the crowd, Anna, one of Vienna's most skillful pickpockets removed the gun from your handbag. As a favor to the police."

Nicola was at David's side. "How did you know?" she asked. "What made you suspect?"

"I didn't suspect her until she admitted revealing the address of the hunting lodge to Lapin and Tonio. She did that to throw suspicion on them, but her timing was not very good. Neither Tonio nor Lapin could have sent those two men to kill me. Because they arrived before Anna gave that information to Lapin and Tonio."

Nicola said, "She called Papa stupid."

Anna bowed her head and said nothing.

"Inspector Reikert did suspect you, Anna," David went on. "He had no proof, but he was on the verge of getting it. You had been growing a little careless in stealing information from the code room. Of course you were certain you'd have finished your work, taken your vengeance and been gone from Austria before you were found out."

Reikert came into the room, grasped Anna's arm and lifted her from the chair. He nodded to David and Nicola. "A pleasant journey and good fortune to both of you. We are grateful for your help. Come along, Fräulein Croft, we have many questions to ask you."

He closed the door on his way out. Nicola sat down slowly on the sofa and David joined her there to put a comforting arm around her shoulders.

"I know Anna's treachery comes as a shock to you. You've nothing more to fear. Reikert has rounded up the men who worked with Anna."

"She was going to kill me," Nicola said in wonder.

"Anna was going to kill me. She said so."

"We know. Everything she said was overheard. We wanted her to tell you exactly what she was up to, so there never would be the slightest doubt in your mind that she was an ambitious spy looking for glory from the expected success of her son. All the love she professed for you, all the concern, was a sham, but so cleverly performed no one had the slightest reason to doubt her."

"I want to go to the ship, David," Nicola said. "Right now, as if the threat still existed. I'm too shocked to see anyone. I want nobody but you with me. I feel sick, but I'm also relieved that it is over, even if what finally happened was almost as bad as if she'd succeeded. All the time I thought Anna was concerned for my safety, she was plotting against me. You did right in letting her expose her hand. She was a clever woman. She fooled Papa for years."

"I know, Nicky. You'll forget all of it in time. Too many wonderful things are going to happen to let this sad business remain in your mind. Your life is ahead of you."

"Hand me my wrap, darling. Please."

"You're going in costume?"

"I want to get out of here. I want to be alone with you. I want to walk the deck of the ship and feel free. Afterward, I want you to take me to our cabin and hold me close."

"We'll be married tomorrow," David said.

He placed the wrap around her shoulders, opened the door and they walked out. No one tried to stop them, no one said anything. Lapin did raise a hand as if to touch her, but he let it drop again. Tonio reached for her hand, bent and kissed it, then stepped back.

David said, "You'll be hearing from us, Tonio."

The carriage was waiting. They no longer needed

protection. They entered the vehicle and it began to move. David drew Nicola closer.

Nicola said, "Now it begins. The shame, the violence, the treachery are over. My life will have a fresh start with you, darling. That is all I want. All I need."

He kissed her cheek and held her close. There was no longer any need for words.

# ALLEGRA
# By Rosemary Winfield

PRICE: $1.95 LB720
CATEGORY: Historical Romance (Original)

Allegra Fontana, unhappy with her guardian's choice of a husband for her, is delighted to receive an invitation to attend the wedding of a distant relative, the Prince Raimundo de Lisi, in Southern Italy. Amid the lush palazzos of the Italian aristocracy, she succumbs to a forbidden love and falls hopelessly in love with Prince Raimundo. But the Prince is soon to be married. Then Laura, who has also been in love with Raimundo, is found dead, and Allegra realizes her life may be in danger, too. When Allegra learns the secret of her birth, it promises to unlock the door to a life of boundless happiness.

# IN LOVE AND WAR
## By Lorinda Hagen

PRICE: $2.25 LB719
CATEGORY: Novel (Original)

Esther, a minister's daughter from a small town, goes to Cincinnati to seek her fortune. She is discovered singing in a night club and is signed for a national tour and an opportunity for a movie test. She meets Neil Patterson, an aspiring novelist, who sells his first book to Hollywood. Esther gets the lead in his film at Neil's insistance. Esther Eden becomes a star and marries Neil. But they are soon separated when Neil signs on as a war correspondent after the attack on Pearl Harbor. Their world is torn apart, not only by the war, but by rumors of Esther's infidelity. Esther wages a passionate battle to hold onto the only man she has ever really loved.

# TRAVELIN' WOMAN
## Katherine Gibbs

PRICE: $1.95 LB728
CATEGORY: Historical Romance (original)

Lovely young Samantha Houston lived on a small
farm in Alabama with her loving husband Josh
and their three small children. When Josh mysteriously disappeared, Samantha was forced to
flee with the children to the bustling port of
Savannah. But Samantha's struggles had only
begun. In her desperation to make a new life, she
became an uncompromising frontier business-
woman. But, when the suave, handsome Wade
McCain entered her life, Samantha wondered if
she could still be tender.